THE LOGICAL SYSTEMS OF LESNIEWSKI

STUDIES IN LOGIC

AND

THE FOUNDATIONS OF
MATHEMATICS

L. E. J. BROUWER

E. W. BETH

A. HEYTING

Editors

1962

NORTH-HOLLAND PUBLISHING COMPANY

AMSTERDAM

THE LOGICAL SYSTEMS
OF LESNIEWSKI

EUGENE C. LUSCHEI

Assistant Professor of Philosophy
University of North Carolina

1962

NORTH-HOLLAND PUBLISHING COMPANY
AMSTERDAM

112815

QA 3 STU

PRINTED IN THE NETHERLANDS

CONTENTS

1. CONVENTIONS OF EXPOSITION
AND REFERENCE

1.0 Reference to sources

Where no other source is specified, a reference numeral indicates the correspondingly numbered note (§ 9) or section of this book, according as it is without prefix or is prefixed by '§'. The abbreviation 'JSL' refers to *The Journal of Symbolic Logic*; 'PF' to the Polish philosophical review *Przeglad Filozoficzny*; and 'PM' to Russell and Whitehead's *Principia Mathematica*, and expressly to the revised first volume of the second edition, in the absence of other indications, wherever the revision is relevant. Published sources[1] are listed in the bibliography (§ 10), and may be identified by names of authors together with descriptions, abbreviated titles, or italicized dates of publication. For example, in a context referring to Lesniewski, '*1927*, § 2, p. 183, n. 1' indicates his publication (OM) on the foundations of mathematics 'O podstawach matematyki', section 2, page 183, note 1. Section numbers, being more stable throughout translations, revisions, and changes of format, are often cited in preference or in addition to page numbers. Translations are my own unless other sources are specified, and are distinguished from loose paraphrases or summaries. Dual references are sometimes given, to both an original source and a published translation.

1.1 Italics and quotation

Unabbreviated titles of articles are enclosed between single quotes, whereas titles of separate publications such as books, monographs, or journals are italicized. Other expressions are italicized to emphasize or distinguish them from homomorphs, used differently, with which they might otherwise be confused. For example, unfamiliar technical expressions are italicized for emphasis when first defined or definitively explained in English, and expressions of form 'a' or 's' used as variables, not as articles or verb endings, are italicized to differentiate them from expressions of the same form used otherwise. Signs of assertion as a definition or axiom, together with explicit binding of variables, make italics unnecessary in formalized systems. Conventional double quotes (as distinguished from iterated single quotes) serve as printed counterparts of gestures or modulations of speech, usually indicating novelty, parody, or mental reservations in momentary adoption of unfamiliar, uncharacteristic, or questionable expressions. Single quotes are used for direct quotation, to indicate that the expression quoted is of the form (or is a fairly literal translation) of the original expression. Except for translations, this is merely a special use of quotation names according to the following conventions.

1.2 Quotation names

A quotation name, formed by enclosing an expression between single quotes, serves as common name of any expression of the same form as the specimen quoted. Since the outermost quotes serve only to indicate that the enclosed expression is quoted as a sample, they may be omitted when some other device performs the same service, as when an indicated specimen stands isolated between lines or dashes or after a colon. So to say that an individual is (an expression of form) 'the' is to say that it is equiform to the expression quoted, and hence to any other homomorph such as the following expression: the. A quotation name of a quotation name is formed by enclosing it in turn between an additional pair of single quotes, and so on indefinitely, quotation always forming a common name of any expression equiform to that quoted. So to say that an individual is (an expression of form) ''the'' is to say that it is equiform to the expression quoted, and hence to any other homomorph such as the following quotation name: 'the'.

The frequent use of quotation marks may cause surprise... Pedantic as this may appear, I think it necessary. It is remarkable how an inexact manner of speaking or writing, originally perhaps used only for convenience and brevity, but with full consciousness of its inexactness, may end in confusion of thought, after that consciousness has disappeared. Numerals have even been mistaken for numbers, the name for what is named, the mere aid for the proper subject matter of arithmetic. Such experiences teach how necessary it is to demand the greatest exactness in manner of speaking and writing.... Vacillating usage occasions misunderstandings so easily that we cannot proceed carefully enough, and must not hesitate to say the obvious, to be sure of having a common starting point.

To quote an expression or even refer to it as an expression 'may seem pedantic, but is by no means superfluous', since neglect of 'what seems an insignificant trifle' has apparently been 'the source of great confusions'.[2]

A quotation name is not an extensional function of the quoted expression but a single, logically indivisible name. The quoted expression is not used in the normal, referential way but only "mentioned" or used as a specimen, like a color sample in a color chart; and the quotes are used not as a functor but as an ad hoc operator to form a common name of expressions of the same form. Expressions of form ''Oxford'' are used to name expressions of form 'Oxford', which themselves are used in the normal way to name Oxford. Not being functors, quotes are not subject to the laws of extensionality for functors, and coextensive expressions of other forms are no more logically interchangeable with the specimen quoted than with other arbitrary parts of a single name (variant spellings excepted). Even if Oxford and Oxenford are identical, 'Oxford' and 'Oxenford' are not, nor are they even equal, (§ 1.7) equiform, or equisignificant.

Derivative idiomatic uses of quotation names correspond to analogous uses of other common names, and should be clear in context. Consider for example "the" idiomatic use of the English expression 'the'. (The preceding sentence itself exemplifies but one of the many such uses of the many individual English expressions of form 'the'.) To say that the first (expression of form) 'the' in this book is black is comparable to saying that the cat on the mat here now is black. But since there are many individual English expressions of form 'the' as there are many individual cats, clearly to speak of the English expression 'the' in general, without identifying any individual 'the', is like speaking of the cat in general without identifying any individual cat. So to say idiomatically that the English expression 'the' is a word is to say that any English expression of form 'the' is a word, or that all English 'the's are words, just as to say that the cat is an animal is to say that any cat is an animal, or that all cats are animals.

1.3 Reference to individual expressions

Except for such idiomatic uses and other indicated deviations, I follow Lesniewski's example of referring strictly to individual expressions as concrete spatiotemporal objects, not to forms of expression in abstraction from their instances in context. (§ 6.1) What would commonly be called two different "occurrences or utterances of the same expression", or two different "tokens of the same type", Lesniewski called two different but *equiform* expressions: i.e., two different expressions of the same form. Expressions of the same form written at different places (resp. spoken at different times) are never the *same* expression, since they differ in spatiotemporal location.[3]

Although formalized languages are designed primarily to be written rather than spoken, remarks literally applied to printed forms of expression could be translated (*mutatis mutandis*) into analogous remarks applicable to corresponding sound or image structures, because of the essential parallelism between the written and the spoken or mentally imaged expression.

The first and the second 'the' in this book are not the same expression, but they are equiform, and each is also equiform to itself. For equiformity is an equivalence relation, transitive and symmetrical and hence reflexive, being equal to its own converse, so that its domain, converse domain, and field are all equal. Equiformity being a relation of similarity, equiformants need be only of the same form, not necessarily of the same size or height. Since I call only all equiform expressions *homomorphs* or *homomorphic*, homomorphy equals equiformity of expressions, and is also an equivalence relation, whose field equals expressions. (§ 1.7) I call *homonyms* or *homonymous* (in language L) only all expressions of the same form but of different semantic category: i.e., homomorphs differing in significance.

1.4 Definitions

No expression is defined in alternative ways, though definitions may be anticipated or supplemented by additional explanations. I distinguish my own (auxiliary) definitions and terminological explanations from Lesniewski's by some indication like 'I call' or 'I say', as in the following examples:

I call only any system *extensional* in which all expressions of each semantic category are extensional, coextensive expressions being equivalent and consequently interchangeable in any propositional context without changing truth value. (I do *not* say "a system that concerns extensions or classes as distinguished from intensions or properties".) (§ 1.8) I call *classical* only any extensional, interpreted, and two-valued system. I call *language L* only any canonic scientific language, or deductive hierarchy of interpreted axiomatic theories, based on Lesniewski's system of logic and foundations of mathematics, constructed according to directives prescribed in this book, and satisfying his canons of formalization. I call *simple* b only any b no part of which is also b; *compound* b only any b at least one part of which is also b; *dependent* b only any b merely part of another b; *independent* b only any b not merely part of another b; *organic* b only any b no part of which is logically equivalent (i.e., coextensive) to another b;[4] and b *immediately* f-*ing* A only any b f-ing A but not f-ing some b itself f-ing A. In describing parts occupying the same relative position with respect to the beginning (resp. end) of specified expressions, I call *initially* (resp. *terminally*) *homologous* b *and* c only any paired individuals that are respectively b and c preceded (resp. followed) by the same number of other individuals that are also b and c, respectively. I call *homologous* b *and* c only any paired individuals that are initially and also terminally homologous b and c, respectively, in which case, since b and c are equinumerous, only any homologous b and c are initially (resp. terminally) homologous, so that the qualifications 'initially' and 'terminally' are alike superfluous. When context makes reference clear, any and hence the sole b initially, terminally, or simply homologous to a specified c may safely be called the initial, the terminal, or simply the homolog of that c, respectively. Only any simple expression being a word, and only any word not a punctuator being a term, I call *phrase* only any term, function, or generalization.

Although the metalinguistic terminology defined or explained in this book applies strictly to expressions in canonic language L, I apply it loosely to analogous expressions in other languages, as in the illustrations below.

1.5 Nouns and names

I use different cognates of *'nomen'* technically to distinguish between expressions in language L diversely related to *nomen substantivum vel adjectivum*, or to members of the "nominal" family broadly adopted by Plato and Aristotle. Except for looser application by analogy to other languages, I call nominal only any expression belonging to the basic, non-functorial semantic category (§ 5.2) of Lesniewki's logic of predication; (§ 6.2.3) and call noun only any term that is a nominal constant. This use of the word 'noun' is narrower in certain respects and broader in others than that of traditional grammar; in particular, numerical constants such as '1', '3/2', 'π', or 'i' are not nouns in this sense but, according to Lesniewski's grammar of semantic categories, are higher-level constants in his logical reconstruction of mathematics. (See §§ 5.1.1, 6.1.6, and 6.1.8 below.) Any nominal expression, simple or compound, constant or variable, "substantive" or "attributive", is either a term or a function, and may be used grammatically as subject or predicate of predication, as adnoun or adjective in any nominal combination, or as argument of any other appropriate function, however many individual objects it may name: none, one, or more. I call *name* only any constant that names at least one individual; and *proper name* only any undefined constant term that names exactly one individual.

So only any simple name that is a term whose introductory axiom precludes its consistent application to more than one individual is axiomatically a proper name. Nominal constants that name no individual are sometimes called "fictitious names" or "empty descriptions" by writers, like Rosser, (§ 4.4) who do not hesitate to add that such "names or descriptions are not names or descriptions of anything, or name or describe nothing but the memberless empty class or unexemplified null property", unless they are arbitrarily assigned a denotation. But, to avoid verbal snares and misleading suggestions, (§ 4) I call such expressions simply nouns or nominal constants, not names, adding that to be significant an expression need not be a name, and that in language L any constant has unique significance whether it names an individual or not. For example, the constant significance of 'nonentity' (§ 1.7) by definition precludes its naming or describing an individual. Woodger[5] calls names of just one individual (whether proper names or "definite nominal descriptions") unshared names; and names applicable to more than one individual (whether "common names" or "indefinite nominal descriptions") shared names. I avoid using traditional terminology to subclassify names into (1) names of just one and (2) names of more than one individual. For, this dichotomy depends on uncertain factual questions of extralinguistic reference; simple nouns in canonic language L are grammatically neither singular nor plural; and I wish to avoid attendant ambiguities, suggested by the following remarks: All names ("individual and particular" or "general and universal") alike are unique and hence individual; indeed, the noun 'individual' itself is not a proper name of some one individual but rather a "general and universal" name of any individual whatever; a name common to several individuals may be not common but rare and "singular" in certain respects; and all names in language L (whether "definite" or "indefinite" in extralinguistic reference) are definite in the sense of having univocal significance.

Whether unshared or proper names of just one individual, shared names applicable to more than one individual, or not names at all, simple nouns in canonic language L, which is strictly isolating and analytic, are *grammatically* genderless, impersonal, and neither "singular nor plural but numerically indeterminate", like 'sheep', 'deer', 'swine', etc. They resemble adnominal or "nominal-adjectival" stems such as the following in English: individual, criminal, suspect, Siamese, feline, light, cold, fluid, iron, adhesive. Numerically definite or indefinite functors, analogous to articles, affixes, inflections, or grammatical changes, may be defined to form compound expressions indicating number, as suggested by the following counterparts in English: the philosopher (not the historian) Socrates; a but not the sole Pekingese; one of the n or more Japanese; one of the at least m, at most n Chinese. But in canonic language L nouns may be used simply yet grammatically, such formal accessories being optional, as if in German one or more knives, forks, or spoons could (but need not) be described grammatically without embellishments converting the stems—*Messer, Gabel, Löffel*—into singulars or plurals respectively neuter, feminine, and masculine in gender. For binding of variables, together with use of various logical verbs, makes it unnecessary to rely on grammatical agreement, use of articles, and other colloquial devices in order to preclude ambiguities in crossreference.[6]

6.1 Verbs

Similarly, except for application by analogy to other languages, I call verbial (not verbal, for obvious reasons, if ambiguity is to be avoided) only any expression belonging to the semantic category of a functor of a propositional function having exclusively nominal arguments; and call verb only any term that is a verbial constant. Any verbial expression, simple or compound, constant or variable, logical or extralogical, attributive or relational, "copulative" (resp. "predicative") or not, is either a term or a function; and, whatever its semantic category, may be used grammatically as functor of a function having the appropriate number of nominal arguments or as argument of any suitable higher-level functor, such as '-ing is (logically) symmetrical'. (§ 6.1.8)

Not to confuse the logical "theory of relations" with the grammar of verbs, I avoid using 'intransitive' and 'transitive' as grammatical terms. For in terms of the *logic* of verbs or "theory of relations", some f are transitive, others non-transitive, and some even intransitive, for 'f' of the semantic category of binary (grammatically "transitive") verbs; whereas the foregoing remarks would not even make sense for 'f' of the category of singulary (grammatically "intransitive") verbs.

Simple verbs in canonic language L are grammatically impersonal and tenseless, like the copula or other logical verbs in logical or mathematical texts. They resemble not tensed compounds of specified "person" but rather the indeterminate verbial stems from which these are formed by conjugation in inflected Indo-European languages such as English. Although in language L temporal indications and relations might perhaps be expressible by tensed compound verbial phrases formed from verbs by extensional tense functors, Lesniewski himself, for precision, used dated compound nominal phrases together with tenseless verbs instead.[7]

1.7 Technical use of English expressions

For clarity in technical contexts I use English expressions according to technical conventions like those implicit in classical logical and mathematical texts, approximately paraphrasing in English corresponding expressions in canonic language L. Thus inflected expressions used technically, to express or paraphrase idiomatically in English what in language L is expressed by numerically indeterminate, tenseless, genderless, and impersonal expressions, need not convey the usual grammatical implications of number, time, etc.

In particular, idiomatic use of English plurals need not imply plurality or multi-plicity. For example 'an individual' and 'individuals' alike technically have the significance of 'individual', 'an or the sole individual', or 'one of the one or more individuals'; 'exists' and 'exist' alike have that of 'at least one…exists sometime' or 'one or more…exist sometime'; 'is' and 'are' alike have that of 'is or are eternally' (*not* "sempiternally, always, or everlastingly"); and 'all…are' has that of 'any… is'. Only their awkwardness prevents my always using the more accurate circum-locutions.

Propositional connections are intended as classical truth functions of their arguments, context sometimes indicating that they para-phrase theses of language L.

Accordingly, alternations in particular are nonexclusive, even without the explicit indication 'or both', unless disjunction (§ 11) is explicitly indicated by adding to 'or' some exclusive qualification such as 'but not both'. The nucleus (§ 11) of any conditional proposition is intended as a "material" implication, false if and only if its antecedent is true but its consequent false. Implications expressed merely by 'if' are weaker than coimplications or "material equivalences" expressed by 'if and only if', 'only if' having the force of 'if…then'.

Certain idiomatic exceptions to these technical conventions should be clear in context: for instance, non-standard uses of definite and indefinite articles, (§ 1.2) parenthetical use of the nonexclusive 'or' with the suggestion of 'i.e.—or, alternatively and equivalently, in other words', and analogous parenthetical uses of other logical constants such as 'if', 'if not', or 'unless'. Stylistic variants, such as 'but' for 'and' or 'when' for 'if', logically have the same force as the standard expressions. In particular, where it is unidiomatic simply to prefix 'not' to a propositional expression, I use variants such as 'it is false that', 'it is not true that', or 'it is not the case that' as logically indivisible signs of negation, in which the parts 'true' and 'false' are not independent metalinguistic expressions.

Letters used as variables but not explicitly bound are treated as if bound throughout any one context by a tacitly prefixed universal quantifier. Capitalization of variables, or a qualification such as 'the sole' or 'individual', parenthetically or openly placed wherever convenient, indicates no distinction of semantic category but only implication of uniqueness. In connection with 'is', for example, such aids serve only to eliminate the ambiguity of the English copula by indicating its use as functor of singular predication, corresponding to Lesniewski's epsilon, in contexts where its status might not otherwise be sufficiently clear. So capitalizing or uncapitalizing variables in 'A is b' would not alter their semantic category, since subject and predicate of predication alike belong to the category of nouns; and definite or indefinite articles, inserted parenthetically where required by English idiom in paraphrases, but having no counterparts in canonic language L, may be omitted when not needed to prevent ambiguity.

My technical use of certain other expressions should be clarified by the following table and appended comments. After each sample homomorph of a constant in Lesniewski's system, I list a few alternative, logically interchangeable paraphrases or corresponding expressions in English.

$\varepsilon\{Ab\}$ *Singular predication* or *inclusion* (*"relation of being"*): A is b; (the sole) A is (a or the sole) b; (individual) A is (one of the one or more) b; A is (an individual that is) b; A is (one of the one or more individuals that are) b; being b characterizes (individual) A; there is exactly (i.e., at least and at most) one A, and (any) A is b.

ex$\{b\}$ For at least one A, (the sole) A is b; (at least one) b exists; (one or more) b exist; at least one (resp. some, a certain) individual is (a or the sole) b; one or more (resp. some, certain) individuals are b; there is at least one (individual which is) b; there are one or more (individuals which are) b.

sol$\{b\}$ For every C and D, if (the sole) C is b and (the sole) D is b then C is D; at most one individual is b; at most one b exists; there is at most one b; any b is the sole b.

ob$\{A\}$ For at least one b, (the sole) A is b; (the sole) A is A; exactly (i.e., at least and at most) one A exists; exactly one individual is A; there is exactly one A; A is unique (resp. individual, an object).

$\varepsilon\{AV\}$ A is individual (resp. unique, an object).

Id(B) the (sole individual which is) B; (individual) identical with B; the same individual as B; what is identical with (resp. is the same individual as) B.

$\sim$ (b) *Nominal negation*: non-b; (individual) not-b; (individual but) not b.

$\varepsilon\{A\Lambda\}$ A is (a or the sole) nonentity (individual but not individual; individual not identical with itself); A is (individual but) not A.

$\cap$(bc) *Nominal conjunction*: (individual both) b and c.

$\cup$(bc) *Nominal alternation*: (individual either) b or c (or both).

$\triangle\{bc\}$ *Partial predication* (or *inclusion*): For at least one A (the sole) A is b and A is c; at least one (resp. some, a certain) individual is (both) b and c; at least one (resp. some, a certain) b is (an individual which is) c; one or more (resp. some, certain) b are (individuals which are) c.

$\subset\{bc\}$ *Weak* (not necessarily existential) *predication* or Boolean *inclusion*: For every A, (the sole) A is b only if A is c; any (individual which is) b is c; all (individuals, if any, which are) b are c; whatever is b is c; c include(s) b; only c (is or) are b.

⊏{bc}   *Strong, existential* (quasi-Aristotelian) *predication* or *inclusion*: Any and at least one (resp. some, a certain) b is c; every (resp. each) b is c; b (is or) are comprised in c; c comprise(s) b; the only b are c.

={AB}   *Identification (singular equality, individual identity,* or *mutual being)*: (The sole) A is B and (the sole) B is A; A is the same individual as B; A is identical with (individual) B; (the sole) A is the sole B; (individual) A is B, and conversely; only the sole A is B.

≡{bc}   *Equation (weak,* not necessarily existential *equality* or *mutual inclusion)*: For every A, (the sole) A is b if and only if (the sole) A is c; any individual is b if and only if it is c; any b is c, and conversely; only any b is c; only whatever is b is c; all b are c, and conversely; only all b are c; b include(s) c, and conversely; b and c are equal.

▢{bc}   *Coincidence (strong, existential equality* or *mutual comprehension)*: Every (resp. each) b is c, and conversely; only every (resp. each) b is c; only any b is c and at least one b exists (resp. is c); b and c are equal and exist; b comprise(s) c, and conversely; b and c coincide.

ingr(B),   or for brevity: in(B), el(B) (§ 6.3) *Ingredience* or *elementhood*: (individual) ingredient, resp. contained, incorporated in (individual) B; (individual) ingredient (resp. element, constituent, component, part or whole) of (individual) B; "collective individual subset" of (individual) B.

pt(B)   (individual) part (not whole) of (individual) B; (individual) contained (resp. incorporated) as part in (individual) B; (individual) piece (resp. segment, section, sub-section, "proper part", "part less than the whole") of individual B.

cl(b)   (individual) collection of (at least one individual which is) b; (individual) collection of (one or more individuals which are) b; (collective) composite (resp. aggregate, set, manifold) of (one or more) b.

Kl(b)   (individual) totality (resp. entirety, whole, collective class) of (the one or more individuals which are) b; (collective) composite (resp. aggregate, set, manifold) of all the (one or more individuals which are) b; collection of all (the one or more) b.

extr(B)   (individual) outside (resp. external, exterior, extraneous to individual) B.

ov(B)   (individual) overlapping (resp. overlapper of individual) B.

dscr{b}   (Any individuals which are) b are discrete (i.e., outside each other).

∞{bc}   There are exactly as many b as c; (individuals which are) b are equinumerous to (the *zero* or more individuals which are) c.

⌵{bc}   There are fewer b than c; (individuals which are) b are less numerous than (the *one* or more individuals which are) c.

To paraphrase constants that may be differently defined but logically have the same force in language L, I use expressions such as 'unique', 'individual', and 'object' interchangeably, as also 'nonentity' and 'non-individual', 'element of' and 'ingredient of', (§ 6.3) selecting whichever seems least likely to mislead readers not acquainted with Lesniewski's systems. Sometimes in critical contexts I even use logically redundant combinations, such as 'unique individual object', to avoid suggesting that "only material bodies are objects", or to reinforce the indication that these *nouns* can grammatically be used to say for example that numerals are unique individual objects, but not to say that "numbers are individuals or objects". (§ 1.5)

I use the stylistic variants 'any' and 'all' without existential import, and 'every' and 'each' with existential import, as for example in paraphrasing predicative or "copulative" verbs, such as Lesniewski's singular (epsilon), partial, weak, and strong (existential) predicators. 'Any' never carries the existential import of 'some'. To avoid awkwardness or ambiguity as between *non-equivalent* interpretations, where idiom dictates or scope would otherwise be unclear,[8] I use 'all' instead of 'any' with the significance of 'all (if any)', and 'each' instead of 'every' with the significance of 'all and at least one'.

Whereas expressions of coincidence or strong equality have import of existence, but not necessarily of uniqueness, and expressions of individual identity or singular equality have import of both existence and uniqueness, expressions merely of equality have neither. Similarly, whereas existential or singular predications of negative predicates, such as 'every king of France is non-bald' or 'Scott is (individual but) not author of *Waverley*', have the existential or singular import of the corresponding affirmative predications, negations of predication, such as 'not every king of France is bald' or 'it is not true that Scott is author of *Waverley*', have neither. (§ 6.2.3) In certain contexts I use 'non-' instead of 'not', or prefix a parenthetical qualification such as 'individual', in order to make quite clear that the nominal rather than the propositional expression is negated, and to maintain Lesniewski's Aristotelian[9] and Russellian[10] distinction between denial of predication and affirmation of a negative predicate.

The following examples illustrate these points: Since only any nonentity is non-individual, and no individual is non-individual, it follows that no individual is a nonentity, and so it is not true that at least one nonentity exists. Suppose that there are at least two horses but no horse is winged; and that in language L, by definition, only any winged horse beloved by all the Muses of Mt. Helicon, who with his moon-shaped hoof stamped out the well Hippocrene, is Pegasus. Then it is true (*a fortiori* meaningful to say) that at least one horse exists, every horse is individual, any nonentity is individual and a nonentity, only every horse is a horse, Pegasus equals Pegasus, and only any winged horse and nonentity is Pegasus. It is false (though equally meaningful to say) that there is just one horse, the sole horse is a horse, only every winged horse and nonentity is Pegasus, Pegasus exists, or that Pegasus is an individual identical with Pegasus, is winged, is a horse, is individual, or even is non-individual or a nonentity.

Since translations can hardly be both literal and idiomatic, I do not strive for unattainable word-for-word accuracy, but try to find natural, representative, idiomatically flexible English paraphrases.

For it would be inadvisable to neglect context and translate, say, Lesniewski's singular predicator epsilon inflexibly into languages such as English, which idiomatically requires use of definite or indefinite articles even where they have no counterparts in the paraphrased notation of canonic language L. Invariable use of 'the sole...is a', for example, might obscure essential distinctions in paraphrasing compounds formed by defined functors analogous to English articles, and foster awkward redundancies, as suggested by the following unidiomatic stammerings: the sole the sole feline is a the sole Siamese; the sole the sole feline is a a Siamese; the sole a feline is a the sole Siamese; the sole a feline is a a Siamese.

Loose formulation is unavoidable at the beginning, in linear discourse, since essential qualifications cannot be intelligibly expressed all at once. One cannot write everything in one line, nor say everything in one breath. A presentation of too many fine points at once would, like a hedgehog, be too well-armed to be grasped. But I try to formulate even initial explanations clearly enough to permit their reformulation, at a later stage in the spiral way of successive approximation to clarity, in the precise language L that they serve to explain.

So questions concerning technical use of English expressions or concerning paraphrases in terms of informal logic should be referred to the corresponding notations in canonic language L, not taken out of context regardless of technical conventions. The formalized notation 'illumines the meaning of the expression in words. It is the finer instrument for determining the meaning. If you want to know what the verbal expression means, look at' the notation; 'not the other way about. The verbal expression casts only a dim general glow' over the notation; 'but the notation casts 'a brilliant light on the verbal expression.'[11]

In the language of mathematical logic it is much easier to say what I want to say, but much harder to induce people to understand what I mean when I say it.[12]

1.8 Material mode of expression[13]

The foregoing remarks pertain especially to the dangerous but convenient material mode of expressing concepts of formal logic in terms of informal logic, such as the following and their logical relatives: fact, substance, class, property, attribute, relation.

On occasions Carnap[13] misused his much-abused distinction between the formal and the material mode of expression, in pursuit of oversimplification, as when for example he translated the statement that yesterday's lecture was about Babylon into the statement that yesterday's lecture contained the word 'Babylon'. But, though misuse or abuse may be a reason for hesitation, it does not lessen the usefulness of the terms nor the importance of the distinction.

Expressions of this family have been called "formal, categorial, transcendental, universal, or metaphysical". Used unreflectively, without clarification by what Quine[13] calls "semantic ascent" into the formal mode of expression, they may appear to project the shadows of words or verbal categories into the world, and generate ontologies of "universals or abstract entities" suggesting that in the beginning was, not even the individual word, but the abstracted form of the word. Yet one has only to stop using words for a moment to recognize that reality does not arrive neatly tailored and dressed in words or verbal categories. If reality cannot be described without suiting words of various linguistic categories, this awareness can at least help one to avoid being misled, and to appreciate what is so without saying so. I do not presuppose or imply that such expressions are "names" at all, much less "names of universals or abstract entities". Nor do I intend this disclaimer as a denial that "abstract entities exist", since the denial would provoke as many misleading questions as the affirmation. I use such terms only to express in English, without undue use of variables or category indices, what in canonic language L is expressible solely by use of quantifiers, variables, punctuators, and logical constants; only to help make clear in English what in language L is clear enough without such terms. (§ 3.3) Even this informal paraphrastic use has its dangers, but I hope that in context it is clear enough not to invite mis-interpretation.

I employ the "class" and "property" vocabularies of the material mode *extensionally* and *interchangeably*, using whichever in context seems idiomatically preferable to express or paraphrase what in canonic language L is expressible without using words such as 'class' and 'property' at all. (§ 3.3) So these interchangeable idioms here below are to lead a restricted, purely extensional, intramural life.

Suppose for example I say that Socrates is a member of (resp. belongs to) the class of individuals; is an instance (or example) of (resp. instances, exemplifies, has, possesses) the property of being individual; or is characterized by being individual. I mean only to say that Socrates is individual (and perhaps parenthetically to in-dicate something about semantic category of the expressions themselves). If I say that Socrates and Xanthippe are respectively members of the class of x and y such that x is husband of y, or that Socrates stands in (resp. is linked by, bears) the relation of being husband to Xanthippe, I mean only that Socrates is husband of Xanthippe.

The material mode of expression, often used habitually but need-lessly even where it is more cumbersome than the corresponding simple distributive predications, (§ 3.3) facilitates informal expres-sion in complicated examples such as the following, which explain what I mean by expressions not used in one standard way by all logicians:[14, 15]

I call c *closed with respect to* f if and only if, for all A and B, if A f-s B and B is c then A is c. So any f-er of an instance of a class (resp. property) closed with respect to the relation of f-ing is itself an instance. Since any homomorph of an expression is itself an expression, the class of expressions (resp. property of being an expression) is closed with respect to homomorphy. I call *hereditary with respect to* a relation only any property (resp. class) closed with respect to the converse relation. So whatever is f-ed by any possessor of a property (resp. member of a class) hereditary with respect to the relation of f-ing itself has or "inherits" that property (resp. member-ship in that class). Since whatever an individual is equiform to is itself individual, individuality or the property of being individual (resp. the class of individuals) is hereditary with respect to equiformity. Since any equivalence relation equals its own converse, whatever is either closed or hereditary is both closed and hereditary with respect to equiformity or homomorphy.

I call b *an equivalence class* (or *property*) *with respect to* f if and only if, for at least one individual, only every f-er of that individual is b. So, with respect to an equiva-lence relation, only any closed class whose one or more members[14] are all related by that relation is an equivalence class. Since only all equiformants (resp. homo-morphs) are individuals (resp. expressions) of the same form, and any equiformant of an individual is an individual of the same form, equiformants (resp. homomorphs) of any individual (resp. expression) are an equivalence class with respect to equiformity (resp. homomorphy), and forms of individuals (resp. expressions) are also. Equivalence classes with respect to any equivalence relation being mutually exclusive and jointly exhaustive of its field, no individual or expression is of two different forms, and all equiform individuals or expressions are of one and the same form.

I say that individual A *is an ancestor of* B, or individual B *is a descendant of* A, *with respect to* base relation f, if and only if B inherits (i.e., has) all properties of A hereditary with respect to f, and individual A belongs to the field of f. Hence individual B does also, since belonging to the field of f is one such hereditary property. Another is that of being a descendant of any member of its field. An equivalent set of necessary and sufficient conditions is obtained by tracing the genealogy backward to the ancestor instead of forward to the descendant: A belongs to all classes of which B is member and which are closed with respect to f, and individual B is a member of the field of f.[15] Hence A is also, since the field of f is such a class. Another is the class of ancestors of any member of its field. This technical use deviates from colloquial idiom, not only in being generalized for any relation whatever, but in the anomaly that any member of the field of f counts as an f-ancestor of itself. What is sometimes called the "proper ancestral", though less useful, corresponds more closely to colloquial idiom as used to express the ordinary ancestral relation (with respect to parenthood), though as the parenthesis indicates it too is generalized for any relation whatever. It equals the relative product of the base relation and its ancestral in either direction: i.e., A is a proper f-ancestor of B if and only if individual A is an f-er of an f-ancestor of B; or, equivalently, is an f-ancestor of an individual f-er of B. It may be independently defined as follows: A *precedes* (resp. *is a predecessor* or *proper ancestor of*) B, or B *succeeds* (resp. *is a successor* or *proper descendant of*) A, *with respect to* base relation f, if and only if individual B inherits (i.e., has) all properties hereditary with respect to f and possessed by all individuals f-ed by individual A; in which case individuals A and B both belong to the field of f.

Only any f-predecessor of B or any member of the field of f indentical with B is an f-ancestor of B. Any f-er of an individual is both an f-ancestor and f-predecessor of that individual. Any ancestral or proper ancestral relation being transitive, any f-predecessor of an individual is also f-ancestor of that individual, though an f-ancestor need not be an f-predecessor of the same individual, since it may be that individual itself. Individuals A and B are related by the *zero power of* relation f if and only if they are the same individual member of its field; and by the $n + 1$th *power of* f if and only if A is f-er of an individual related to B by the nth power of f. So the zero power of a relation equals identity of individual members of its field; the first power equals the relation itself; and its $n + 1$th power equals the relative product of itself and its nth power. To be related by the ancestral (resp. proper ancestral) of f is the same as to be related by zero (resp. one) or more intermediary links. Consider a relation of immediate precedence, for example: Its ancestral is a reflexive relation of preceding or being the same individual member of its field; its proper ancestral is the corresponding irreflexive relation of precedence. With respect to the relation of parenthood, one's ancestors begin with oneself (the anomaly mentioned above), one's predecessors or proper ancestors begin with one's parents, and both further include one's grandparents, great-grandparents, etc.; one's descendants begin with oneself, one's successors begin with one's children, and both further include one's grandchildren, great-grandchildren, and so on indefinitely. To be related by the ancestral (resp. proper ancestral) relation is thus to be linked by some finite (resp. finite positive) number of generations, as in the genealogy: Abraham, Isaac,..., Eleazar, Matthan. In terms of the ancestral, however, it is possible to define 'finite' and make explicit what is only loosely suggested by dots of ellipsis or 'etc.'s in such representative schemes.[62]

2. LESNIEWSKI'S DEVELOPMENT

2.0 Background and associates

Stanislaw Lesniewski was born in Serpukhov on 30 March 1886[16] and died in Warsaw on 13 May 1939. Between the two wars, from 1919 to his death, he was professor of the philosophy of mathematics at the University of Warsaw, where he and the senior Polish logician Jan Lukasiewicz (1878–1956), supported by the philosopher Tadeusz Kotarbinski, created a center of logical research active until its disruption by the second world war. Of Lesniewski's pupils, Mordchaj Wajsberg was killed, Adolf Lindenbaum disappeared after arrest by the Gestapo, and the survivors were dispersed: Lesniewski's work in logic, semantics, and the foundations of mathematics is carried on by Czeslaw Lejewski in England, Jerzy Slupecki in Poland, and Boleslaw Sobocinski in the United States, where Alfred Tarski has concentrated on research in mathematics and metamathematics.[1]

Lesniewski studied at several Continental universities, and in 1912, following Lukasiewicz and Kotarbinski, took his doctorate in philosophy under Professor Kazimierz Twardowski at Jan Kazimierz University in Lwow. Twardowski, who has been called "the father of Polish philosophy" because he taught or influenced so many leading Polish philosophers, was like Husserl a pupil in Vienna of the Aristotelian and scholastic empiricist Franz Brentano. Lukasiewicz, Kotarbinski, and Lesniewski were deeply influenced, not so much by Twardowski's philosophical opinions as by his insistence on rigor and clarity, solidly grounded in history of philosophy and logical traditions, and based on precise definition and analysis, which he inherited from Brentano and passed on to them. Maintaining this common inheritance in their divergent ways, they were early influenced by Frege's and Husserl's attack on psychologism in logic and by the pioneer work of Frege, Whitehead, and Russell. Except for Boolean algebra, Twardowski knew no mathematical logic, a subject introduced into Poland chiefly by Lukasiewicz, who was largely self-taught. Lukasiewicz later called attention to *Principia Mathematica*, which in turn pointed out the importance of Frege's earlier work. But Lukasiewicz was not yet familiar in detail with these works when in *1910* he published his book on the principle of contradiction in Aristotle, which introduced many Polish thinkers to mathematical logic, and which Lesniewski later said was a 'revelation' to him when it 'fell into' his hands in 1911. Among other things it revealed the paradoxes which preoccupied him for the next eleven years. In time its influence loosened his attachment to the philosophy of his former teacher Cornelius and to the psychological theories of Petrazycki, and channeled Lesniewski's research into logic, semantics, and the foundations of mathematics.

But Lesniewski's initial reaction to mathematical logic was extremely ambivalent. The encounter produced an aversion which lasted for years. At first, 'steeped in the influence of John Stuart Mill, preoccupied with logical and semantical problems of philosophical grammar in the tradition of Husserl and the Austrian school', and baffled by 'nebulous and equivocal commentaries', he found logistics too foreign to assimilate. Later, criticizing ambiguous exposition of mathematical logic, he nearly exhausted the letters of the alphabet in listing different interpretations of a single thesis, apparently permitted or suggested by the commentaries in *Principia Mathematica*. He emphasized that equivocal use of terms such as 'true', 'false', and 'implies' both to express and to describe propositions or connections of propositional arguments makes it unclear whether theses are *in* or *about* the system in question, and remarked that such ambiguities discourage those who do not derive the same delight as 'devotees of meaningless mathematics' from manipulating formal patterns but want to know what they are doing and why, and what the formations and transformations mean.[17]

2.1 Early work and publications[18]

Lesniewski's doctoral thesis (*1911*) was a contribution to the analysis of existential propositions. Between 1911 and 1913, reacting to the influence of Lukasiewicz and Kotarbinski, he also published an attempt to prove the ontological principle of contradiction (*1912*), a discussion of whether truth is only eternal or both eternal and sempiternal (*1913*), and a critique of the logical principle of excluded middle (*1913*). He later described his *1914* article on whether the class of classes not subordinate to themselves is subordinate to itself as a 'sorry discussion', in which he aired his views on Russell's "antinomy", yet, not having developed his own deductive theory of "classes", had to call at need on various theses he believed to be true, like set-theoreticians who do not base their work on explicit axiomatic foundations. In these early articles, which Lesniewski later repudiated, Jordan[19] sees a certain affinity with the colloquial linguistic analyses of recent British philosophy. But already in 1915 Lesniewski developed and axiomatized what, in his *1916* treatise of its foundations, he called his general theory of "manifolds" or "collective sets", but later rechristened mereology, or theory of parts, (§ 6.3) in order to distinguish it from divergent mathematical theories of "sets" and logical theories of "classes". (§ 3.3)

Thus in time Lesniewski lost his distrust of technical notation and his 'yearning to return to nature'. Between 1915 and 1923 he gradually transformed his style of presentation and abandoned his 'stubborn effort logically to subjugate colloquial language and bend it to theoretical ends for which it was never created'. For colloquial languages are historical and practical compromise formations, which have to serve many divergent or even competitive purposes, and so remain flexible and universal in tendency. Since they must be sufficiently plastic approximately to express what is expressible in any other language, they must contain terms to express their own semantics. But study of semantic antinomies convinced Lesniewski that in any "universal" language, semantically closed wholly to incorporate its own semantics, the laws of classical logic cannot consistently hold. (§ 3.3) Philosophers unaccustomed to deductive methods tend to disparage formalized languages as artificial, in contrast to the natural languages of everyday speech. But Lesniewski believed that rigorous application of classical laws to the semantics of colloquial languages would inevitably lead to confusions and contradictions, which could be overcome only by resolving the ambiguities of colloquial languages and reconstructing them in hierarchical strata, each stage enriched by metalinguistic semantical terms introduced to describe preceding stages of construction (§ 5.2)—in short, only by defining their structures and approximating them to formalized languages. And such a logical reform of colloquial languages would be an undertaking not only thankless but doomed to frustration. For rigor of definition and investigation depends on precise specification of structure, whereas colloquial languages are too vague and ambiguous closely to approximate any structurally determinate model. Colloquial languages and exact logic, both useful, are made incompatible by attempting to subjugate either to the other's purposes instead of treating them as complementary. For the useful vagueness and ambiguity that make colloquial languages versatile, practical, and associatively rich all-purpose media of expression unfit them for rigorous deductive investigation and analysis.

So, after talking with Leon Chwistek in 1920, Lesniewski decided to use logical symbolism in his future theoretical work, having concluded that as a scientific instrument it is simpler, more exact, and less conducive to misinterpretation. At first he merely translated theses and proofs as exactly as he could from ordinary language into technical symbolism, but continued to carry out his deductions in an intuitive way not strictly codified in any system of mathematical logic. But, by semantic analyses based on his linguistic insight and study of various logical traditions, he had already overcome ambiguities and tensions arising from divergent usages in colloquial language, and developed a universally valid, logically consequent treatment of singular and existential propositions, universal and particular (§ 6.1.3) generalizations, etc., which enabled him to make fine distinctions without having repeatedly to 'rend his "symbolic" garments'. For example, long before he represented such distinctions in technical notation, he consistently distinguished between predication respectively with or without import of existence or uniqueness, such as between negation of nominal and of propositional arguments, between affirming that the king of France is non-bald and denying that the king of France is bald. (§ 1.7) So, by analyzing and axiomatizing his technical usage, he codified his intuitive logic into exact formalized systems. Although he later criticized some of his earlier formulations as not sufficiently clear to preclude alternative interpretations, his use of colloquial expressions such as 'element of' or 'subordinate to' harmonized with his later use of corresponding mereological constants, (§ 1.7) and his use of expressions such as 'for every (resp. some) significance of expressions 'x'...' corresponded exactly to his later use of universal (resp. particular) quantifiers paraphrasable simply by 'for every (resp. some) x...'. (§ 6.1.3) So his earlier deductions could easily be translated into the precise canonic language L of the systems he derived by axiomatization, symbolization, and formalization. For his transition to use of technical symbolism was but a notational innovation unaccompanied by any comparable change in his intuitive logic.

Lesniewski never lost his respect for Twardowski, nor quite lost the Husserlian style. But already in his *1913* critique he had proved to his own satisfaction that no "general object represents" (i.e., has just those properties common to all) the several individuals Twardowski supposed it to represent. This early essay to refute a representative "platonist" theory on strict logical grounds was characteristic of the rigorous approach to philosophical problems that Lesniewski inherited from Twardowski himself. In *1927*, after dedicating his first mature publication to his 'esteemed and beloved teacher' from a 'philosophical apostate but grateful pupil', Lesniewski recapitulated his refutation of such theories of "representation". In 1913, assuming that "properties" and "relations" were two of the varieties of objects existing in the universe, he had not scrupled to call them by their presumptive proper names. But by 1927, no longer inclined to this belief, he hesitated even to use such expressions of the material mode as 'property' and 'relation' in delicate contexts without extensive precautions; (§ 1.8) and, in view of the danger of misinterpretation, to contribute further to the discussion of "general objects", except to cite Kotarbinski's account of *1920*[13] and to demonstrate again that no "general object" thus "represents" more than one individual object.[21] Although he disregarded arguments for the "universals" of ancient and medieval "realism", the "general ideas" of Locke, the "representative general objects" of Twardowski, the "eternal, irreal, ideal objects" of Husserl, and the like, Lesniewski pointed out that deductions according to the same scheme would remain valid even if expressions of the form 'general object representing objects such-and-such' were replaced throughout by expressions, used analogously, of the form 'general object such-and-such', 'object of the concept such-and-such', 'general conceptual object such-and-such', 'Idea of such-and-such', or the like. He considered his thesis the result of careful formulation of reasoning more or less explicit in traditional arguments against "universals",[21] which he regarded in certain respects as "much ado about nothing". His refutation of course applies only to interpretations or varieties of "platonism" literally assuming that whatever characterizes any "Platonic Idea" characterizes, in the same sense, whatever individual objects it represents; for instance, that whatever characterizes any such "Ideal Bed" characterizes all beds.[21] But, Lesniewski said, if his thesis were dismissed as banal, his rejoinder would be that, unfortunately, philosophers all too often defend positions incompatible with banal truisms.

Looking back in *1927*, Lesniewski wrote that in the darkest days of their common philosophical past he and his friend Kotarbinski had 'strayed amidst the misleading ridges of semantics and theories of "truth", sometimes unexpectedly' glimpsing a way out of antinomies, sometimes taking 'disorganized flight before the menacing shadows of the Epimenides-Liar and other dreadful creatures breathing contradictions'. Within range of the 'scientific attainments' of mathematical logic, but under the 'pernicious influence of one-sided preoccupation with philosophical grammar', he had grappled with problems beyond his strength at the time, on occasion only to 'discover that America had already been discovered'. Regretting that his earlier publications remained in print, he 'solemnly repudiated' them and 'confirmed the bankruptcy' of his initial enterprises in philosophical grammar. This disavowal marks the turn foreshadowed by his refutation of "representative general objects" in *1913*, analysis of Russell's contradiction in *1914*, and axiomatic development of mereology in *1916*. These deductions he recapitulated in his first mature publication on the foundations of mathematics, (§ 2.3) since he wished to be judged solely by his later works.

2.2 Research in Warsaw

At the University of Warsaw, reopened in 1915, Lukasiewicz concentrated increasingly on Aristotle, history of logic, and deductive problems in syllogistic, modal, many-valued, and propositional logic. Kotarbinski expressed his broad philosophical interests in his *1929* treatise of elements of epistemology, formal logic, and scientific methodology, and in a wide range of other publications. Lesniewski was less interested in purely formal and historical problems, and in general philosophical issues, than in rigorous investigation of logical and semantical problems in formalized but interpreted languages. He left the elaboration of certain of his fundamental semantic and metalogical insights to Tarski, (§ 3.4) who shared the conviction that the semantics of formalized languages alone can be rigorously treated, despite a divergent inclination to investigate problems of meaning and truth in abstraction from context, and to "postulate" what he needed to simplify formal deductions, which detracts from the philosophical value of Tarski's in many respects original and mathematically brilliant research. (§ 4.6, § 4.7) For, although an acute critic of formalism, Lesniewski was more interested in logic than in metalogic. His ambition was not to add one more calculus to the variety already invented, nor even to prove general metatheorems about alternative formal calculi, in the interests of "comparative logic"; it was instead to perfect a universally valid classical system of logic and foundations of mathematics, in which he could rigorously formulate generalizations expressible only in the metalanguages of systems poorer in means of expression, (§ 4.12, § 6) and on which he could rely as a true instrument of deduction and scientific investigation. (§ 4)

2.3 Mature publications

By the end of 1922 Lesniewski had already developed his foundations to a stage requiring further refinements only in detail. By 1927 he had in his drawer the unpublished results of more than a decade's research. The longer he hesitated, the more material accumulated and the more difficult publication became. His embarrassment was heightened by the loyalty of associates who held back related contributions of their own. In this 'painful situation' he felt constrained to publish some account of his results, however premature. Since to expound his systems comprehensively on the model of PM would be a work of many years, he decided to anticipate by sketching their evolution and foundations instead. So in *1927* he published in PF (§ 1.0) the first instalment of a long series on the foundations of mathematics, in which he redeveloped and elaborated mereology, and incorporated other "hard" deductive results he thought worth salvaging from his earlier publications. (§ 2.1) In *1931* the eleventh instalment closed with the misleading indication 'to be continued'. For, although this was a preliminary discussion of his logic of singular propositions, he intended to return to mereology in further instalments (never published).[18] Detailed accounts of his basic logic were to follow, but since publication might be long delayed, he decided to anticipate and epitomize these elsewhere. So in *1929* (NS) and *1930* he published complete architectural blueprints of the axiomatic foundations and structural design of his logical systems, without elaborating their deductive superstructure. In *1929* and *1931* respectively he also published treatments, independent of his own systems, of the theory of groups and Abelian groups and of definitions in the theory of deduction.

The twelfth section of his *1929* outlines of a new system of foundations of mathematics was to have followed the first eleven sections in *Fundamenta Mathematicae* but, after Lesniewski withdrew his manuscript in 1930, (§ 3.10) did not appear until, nearly a decade later, an opportunity for its publication, preceded by new introductory remarks, was afforded by the founding of *Collectanea Logica*, edited by Lukasiewicz and Sobocinski. The inaugural volume of *Collectanea Logica* contained eight contributions on Lesniewski's

logic—three by Lesniewski, four by Sobocinski, and one by Slupecki. But only a few offprints distributed in advance, including a
few of Lesniewski's first two papers which he sent out before his
death, survived the war. The several hundred pages of *Collectanea
Logica* already printed or in proof were completely destroyed:[20] The
Warsaw printing house was burned down in the siege of 1939, and
what then escaped destruction in Sobocinski's flat was destroyed in
the uprising of 1944, together with Lesniewski's lecture notes and
unpublished manuscripts, the results of more than two decades of
intensive research in logic, semantics, and the foundations of
mathematics. (§ 3.10)

3. LESNIEWSKI'S ACHIEVEMENTS

Lesniewski integrated his central contributions in the classical system of logic and foundations of mathematics which was his fundamental achievement. His peripheral contributions mainly represent steps toward or incidental by-products of its construction.

3.1 Refutation of a "platonist" theory of "representation" (§ 2.1)

In his *1913* critique Lesniewski logically refuted a "platonist" conception of "general objects", supposed to represent certain individual objects and characterized as having just those properties common to them all. He demonstrated that no "general object represents" (in this sense) more than one individual object. So any (§ 1.7) "Platonic Ideal Bed", for instance, represents only itself, being the sole bed in the universe.[21] Together with related arguments, this deduction made Lesniewski hesitate to use traditional "class-property-relation" terminology in critical contexts without careful preliminary explanations, and motivated his "constructively nominalist" formalizations.

Fearing misinterpretation, I use this loose and slippery label (§ 4.12) with hesitation and only as a convenient caption, to indicate no more than is explained in § 6.1.7 below. What certain other writers may take the label to suggest is not quite clear to me.

3.2 Formalization of logic and foundations
of mathematics (§ 6)

Prescribing rules of definition as comprehensive and rigorous as his other directives, Lesniewski formalized his system completely, combinatorially on a finite basis, and in extensional terms. It is further distinguished by its "constructively nominalist" and "contextualist" character; its basic grammar of semantic categories; its rigor, generality, and power of expression; its demonstrable relative consistency; its universal validity; and its logical purity, economy, and elegance. It consists of three axiomatic deductive systems in hierarchic order: *protothetic*, *ontology*, and *mereology*— etymologically, proto-theses, theory of being, and theory of parts, respectively. Protothetic and ontology together form a unified system of logic comparable in scope and power to *Principia Mathematica* as a foundation for classical mathematics and for any further axiomatic theory, such as mereology, in a deductive hierarchy.

I rely on context to distinguish Lesniewski's ontology from the homonymous branch of metaphysics. The names stem from the same root, the genitive case of the participle of the Greek copula, whose initial letter provides the epsilon of singular predication in Lesniewski's ontology. Lesniewski chose the name advisedly: (§ 6.2.3) 'The medieval conception of a purely metaphysical proposition, as a statement which is true for anything whatsoever insofar as it is anything at all, is the analogue of the modern conception of a logically true sentence...of the object language.... For Buridan, the "first principle" of *logic* is the metatheorem, "For any proposition '*p*', either '*p*' is true or '*p*' is not true". But the "first principle" of *metaphysics* is the analogous *theorem*, "*p* v -*p*".' [22]

Mereology is an extremely general extralogical theory based on the two logical systems. Together with them, it provides a mathematical basis for spatiotemporal theories of topology, for geometries such as Tarski's axiomatic geometry of solids,[23] as distinguished from arithmetical representations in analytic geometry, and for scientific description of reality in canonic language L.

Lesniewski developed mereology from 1914 onwards, publishing his original axiomatization in *1916*; codified his intuitive logic in ontology as basis for mereology between 1919 and 1921; completed his foundations by constructing protothetic as basis for ontology and mereology in 1922; and in the same year prescribed directives for protothetic and ontology incorporating his grammar of semantic categories. Thus the evolutionary order of his systems was converse to their hierarchic deductive order. After refining their details, he redeveloped and elaborated mereology in publications between *1927* and *1931*, and published his complete formal directives for constructing standard systems of protothetic and ontology in *1929* (NS) and *1930* respectively. So he developed a "constructively nominalist" (§ 3.1) formalization of classical logic and foundations of mathematics more than a decade before Russell wrote in *1937*:

How far it is possible to go in the direction of nominalism remains, to my mind, an unsolved question, but one which, whether completely soluble or not, can only be adequately investigated by means of mathematical logic.

Lesniewski developed his logical syntax and grammar of semantic categories three decades before Goodman and Quine's 'Steps toward a constructive nominalism' and Martin and Woodger's 'Toward an inscriptional semantics'.[24]

3.3 Resolution of paradoxes[25]

Lesniewski's directives, designed to ensure consistent determinacy of meaning (and thereby to preclude antinomies) at every stage of construction, even beyond the purely logical or mathematical, represented the conclusion of eleven years' study of paradoxes, begun in 1911 with Russell's paradigm.

3.3.1 Investigation of Russell's paradigm. In a deep analysis of Russell's contradiction, Lesniewski resolved ambiguities and conflicting uses of "class or set" terminology underlying and giving it the paradoxical appearance of an antinomy. (§ 4.8) His initial analysis in *1914* (§ 4.9) led him to develop mereology, ontology, and his comprehensive rules of definition (§ 7) and grammar of semantic categories. (§ 5, § 7.1) In a later investigation, publicized by Sobocinski in *1949–50*, he demonstrated Frege's set-theoretic "way out" to be a blind alley. (§ 3.9)

3.3.2 Analysis of collective and distributive conceptions. Lesniewski attributed these logical paradoxes to faulty definition

together with confusion of collective and distributive conceptions, characteristic of naive theories of "sets or classes as collections not actually composed of their elements". (§ 4.10) Having pointed out the fallacy in Frege's argument for the necessity of distinguishing between an individual and the corresponding "unit set" or "singular class", Lesniewski did not require an unintuitive distinction between an *individual* and the totality (i.e., "collective class") of itself, the totality of individuals identical with itself, any (§ 1.7) totality of which that individual is sole ingredient element, or ("the distributive class" of) individuals identical with itself. (See §§ 4.10, 5.2, 6.2.3, and 6.3 below, together with § 1.8 above.) Nor did he resort to distinctions between "proper and improper objects, membership-eligible elements and ineligible non-elements, ordinary and extra-ordinary sets or classes, or sets representing classes and classes un-represented by sets." (See §§ 4.10, 4.12, and 6.1.6 below.) Instead, without in any way departing from his intuitive criteria of meaning, he resolved the confusions and attendant paradoxes by formulating adequate rules of definition, extensionality, substitution, etc., and by analyzing use of "class or set" terminology. He concluded that its use to describe totalities, or collections of all individuals "having a specified property", which like "social sets or classes" literally consist of their ingredient elements, must be clearly distinguished from its distributive use to "predicate a definitive property of any member element of the corresponding distributive class". (§ 1.8) In distributive use it is dispensable, whereas in collective use it is not. For in distributive predication "class" terminology serves only to express what in canonic language L (or any other system having adequate principles of definition and extensionality) is expressible without abstraction operators by means of the copula together with other functors and defined constants. (§ 1.8) But a collective functor is essential to describe any collection or totality as a "concrete" individual literally composed of one or more individuals (which, if it has more than one, is diversely analyzable into and so has no unique number of ingredient elements). For not only is any individual the same individual as the totality (i.e., "collective class") of itself, and hence as the totality of the totality of itself, etc., but any ingredient (element) of an ingredient, or any collection of ingredients, is itself an ingredient of that individual, regardless whether it is a continuous whole or certain of its individual ingredients are spatiotemporally separated.

For example, only individual planets (such as Earth, Mars, or Lunik I) are (as expressed in the material mode, "member elements of the distributive class of") planets. Whereas not only individual planets, but also arbitrary parts of planets (such as Australia, the marks on Mars, the nose cone of Lunik I), arbitrary collections of planets or their parts, and even the totality of planets itself are ingredient elements of the totality (i.e., "collective class") of planets, which consequently has no uniquely determinate number of ingredient elements. The totality (i.e., "collective class") of planets is the same individual as the totality of itself, of parts of planets, and of collections of either planets or parts of planets. Yet clearly ("the distributive class of") planets need not coincide with ("the distributive classes of") the totality of planets, parts of planets, and collections of either planets or parts of planets.[25]

3.3.3 Conception of mereology and of ontology.

So Lesniewski axiomatically characterized collective and distributive uses in mereology and ontology, respectively; and incorporated his grammar for canonic language L in universally valid directives which enabled him to define constants by whatever conditions satisfied his criteria of meaning, and to use them in all the ways in which abstractions or "distributive class symbols" can be used in PM. (§ 6.1.6) In mereology he axiomatized ordinary collective use in a way that he thought consistently realized Cantor's intentions, without restricting Cantor's original use of 'set' or requiring unintuitive distinctions. (§ 4.10) In ontology Lesniewski axiomatized ordinary distributive use of the copula in singular predication in a way that I think consistently realizes what I consider the fundamental aims of Russell's logic of descriptions and abstractions, or "theory of individuals, classes, relations, and functions",[10] without requiring special abstraction or description operators, (§ 6.1.6) unintuitive distinctions of category or "type" between subject and predicate of predication, (§§ 1.5, 5.2, 6.2.3) ad hoc conventions and restrictions, apparent violations of logical laws, and other logical defects.[26] Unlike the "theory of events" that Whitehead informally expounded in *1919*, mereology is rigorously axiomatized and deductively developed. (§ 3.9) Unlike the reformulation of mereology that Leonard and Goodman call the "calculus of individuals" (§ 6.5) and, instead of *adding to*, try to *substitute for* a distributive "theory of properties or classes", it *presupposes* the basic logic and grammar of protothetic and ontology. This, although it requires no distinction of category between the nominal subject and predicate of predication, joined by a copula or verbial functor such as 'is', does require a distinction of semantic category between a nominal argument of a function and its higher-level, verbial functor such as 'is so-and-so' (§ 6.2.3)—a distinction that prevents logical paradoxes as effectively as the analogous distinction in a simple grammar of types.

3.3.4 Resolution of Russell's paradox.[25] The original formulation of Russell's paradox (or a prototethical analog) violates Lesniewski's grammar and rules of definition. (§ 7) Translated into the distributive idiom by use of legitimate definitions and meaningful propositions of ontology, Russell's derivation is no paradox but simply contradicts the supposition in question. (See terminological explanation XLIV of § 7.1 and LVI° of § 7.3 below.) Translated into the collective idiom by use of legitimate definitions and meaningful propositions of mereology, it likewise loses the paradoxical appearance of an antinomy (§ 4.8) and simply contradicts the supposition that the "collective class" or totality in question exists. For since any individual is the collective class of itself, and is an ingredient element of itself, no individual is a collective class (of individuals) that is not an element of itself, nor *a fortiori* a collective class of such collective classes. So it is simply false (but meaningful to say) that the "Russellian collective class" is anything at all, even itself, or an element of itself. (§ 1.7) (For details see § 4.9 and § 6.3 below, together with Sobocinski, *1949—50*.)

3.3.5 Generalization for other paradoxes.[25] By generalizing his diagnosis and treatment of Russell's paradigm, Lesniewski resolved, in his ontology, all contradictions represented by the yet more general scheme of a paradoxical b f-ing just those b not f-ing themselves; for instance: (1) an entity characterizing just those entities not characterizing themselves ("Russellian entity"); (2) a villager supporting just those villagers not supporting themselves ("paradoxical village subsidizer"); (3) an expression describing just those expressions not describing themselves (Grelling-Nelson "heterological" expression). Now if the definiendum of any definition in canonic language L implies uniqueness then, to maintain the definitional equivalence, so too must its definiens, according to Lesniewski's directives, which require such a definition to exemplify the following scheme: For every A, (the sole) A is such-and-such if and only if (the sole) A is so-and-so.... (See § 6.1.9 and T.E. LVI° in § 7.3 below.) So, even if the "paradox" is formulated in language L with the aid of a definition, it follows that any such paradoxical being must both f and not f itself, and hence cannot exist. In short, the consequences by Lesniewski's logic simply and consistently contradict the supposition that any such paradoxical being exists. Lesniewski's diagnosis of Grelling and Nelson's paradox, in particular, helped persuade him to stratify language L (§ 3.4.2) and relativize semantic concepts to stages of its construction, (§ 5.2) so as to dispense with Russell's order restrictions and to use what, by certain criteria, might be judged "impredicative" definitions[27] without generating "vicious circles" or antinomies in language L. (§ 5.3)

3.4 Contributions to semantics

Lesniewski pioneered the scientific development of semantics through his lectures and discussions in Warsaw from 1919 onward. Although his unpublished lectures were destroyed during the war, (§ 3.10) certain of his fundamental insights have been made known by others whom he influenced.[28] Tarski, discussing semantic antinomies and the difficulties of defining semantic concepts such as that of truth, especially in colloquial languages, expresses in his own words certain insights that stimulated his own, more extensive investigation of the concept of truth in formalized languages, and his project to establish a scientific semantics. He attributes to Lesniewski the first formulation of an exact criterion for an adequate definition of truth,[29] and mentions that Lesniewski pointed out that pseudo-definitions, such as axioms of "reducibility, definability, class abstraction, or set existence", are partial substitutes for adequate rules of definition, (§ 6.1.9) and that quotation names of expressions are not extensional functions of the specimens quoted.

(§ 1.2) Kotarbinski in his *1929* preface acknowledges his own treatment of problems in epistemology, formal logic, and scientific methodology—indeed his whole thought—to be pervaded by Lesniewski's influence. He corroborates that Lesniewski constructed a general method for eliminating nonextensional functions from canonic language L (in fact 'from all known arguments' according to Tarski), though neither Tarski nor Kotarbinski specifies details or conditions, which probably only Sobocinski could still explain. I have already mentioned (§ 2.1) Lesniewski's published criticism of failure to distinguish clearly between (1) propositions, or connections of propositional arguments, and (2) their metalinguistic descriptions.

3.4.1 Grammar of semantic categories.[30] Lesniewski's logical grammar, whose foundations Jordan[19] traces back to Lesniewski's prelogistic essays of *1912* to *1914*, evolved from Lesniewski's simplification and generalization in 1921 of Russell's ramified theory of types, after talking with Chwistek, (§ 2.1) who was investigating the consequences of dispensing with Russell's order restrictions. Lesniewski's initial "simple theory of types", coeval with Chwistek's, anticipated Ramsey's by several years. But, even at the time, Lesniewski considered it at best an 'inadequate palliative', which enabled him at will to use functor variables of any type, without fear of antinomies, in expounding ontology, mereology, and foundations of mathematics, and to formulate directives of definition to fill conspicuous gaps in formalization, where others prescribed inadequate rules or none at all. So in 1922 he designed his grammar of semantic categories to replace hierarchies of types that he could not intuitively justify.

3.4.2 Fundamental semantic insights.[28] In his seminal lectures from 1919 onward, Lesniewski was the first (at least in modern times, to Tarski's knowledge) to attain, express clearly, and appreciate the consequences of certain fundamental insights, anticipating Russell, Ramsey, and Gödel. Recognizing that semantic concepts are relative to the "object" language or theory discussed, which may not coincide with though it may be part of the "metalanguage" in which it is discussed, Lesniewski stressed the distinction

between these correlatives. Recognizing the extralogical, metalinguistic character of semantic antinomies formulated in referential terms, he distinguished these from logical paradoxes expressible within formal systems in purely logical or mathematical terms. He concluded that in a language not constructively stratified and relativized but supposed to be universal, ideally completed, and semantically closed to incorporate *all* its own semantics, the laws of classical logic cannot consistently hold. Grelling and Nelson's paradox of "heterological" expressions, in particular, demonstrates that no expression in a two-valued language at any stage of development can consistently describe just those expressions of the same language-stage that cannot truly describe themselves. (§ 3.3.5) But, relative to a different language, or earlier stage of the same language, an expression may consistently be "heterological", itself belonging to a richer semantic metalanguage, or metalinguistic extension of that stage, enriched by introducing names of expressions of preceding stages. (§ 5.2, § 5.4)

3.4.3   Relativity, stratification, and design.

Lesniewski designed his grammar to ensure consistent determinacy of meaning throughout language L, and thereby preclude both logical contradictions within and semantic antinomies in descriptions of his systems, even in metalinguistic extensions sufficiently developed to describe preceding stages of language L itself. But, having recognized the relativity of semantic concepts and the need for hierarchical stratification years before these were underlined by Gödel's demonstrations, he sought to attain the ends of Russell's order restrictions by simpler, more intuitive, mathematically less restrictive means, and to impede vicious circles but not the crucial deductions of classical mathematics impaired by ramified but not by simple type restrictions.[31]

Except for its principle of hierarchical stratification, constructive relativity, and other salient characteristics (§ 5.2), Lesniewski's grammar of semantic categories formally resembles simple theories of types devised ad hoc to preclude familiar paradoxes. But, in grammatical conception and scope, it has greater intuitive affinity with the tradition of Aristotle's categories, Husserl's *Bedeutungs-*

kategorien, and the grammar of parts of speech in Indo-European languages. Whereas type theory was devised chiefly as a prophylactic, Lesniewski's grammar, wrote Tarski[32] (investigating truth in languages formalized on such a grammatical basis), is so deeply rooted in intuitive criteria of meaning that any conceivable scientific language whose propositions had a clear intuitive meaning could be constructed in harmony with it.

3.5 Principles of formalization (§ 6.1)

In constructing his logical systems, Lesniewski developed rigorous canons of formalization. Perhaps his most important methodological contributions are his rules for introducing new expressions by axiom or definition, for using variables of any semantic category, and for deriving consequences by substitution. His directives are universally valid, for all expressions of any appropriate semantic category, and do not prescribe specific forms of definitions or defined constants in advance but are designed to be easily adaptable to alternative systems and developments (§ 6.1.5), the better to serve as a framework for general theory.[33]

3.5.1 Directives for definition. I know of no other rules comparable in adequacy and rigor of formalization to Lesniewski's directives of definition, more comprehensive and exact even than Frege's,[34] which Lesniewski took as his model, adapted to his own system, and strove to perfect by designing grammatical requirements to preclude the inconsistencies of Frege's foundations of arithmetic. Lesniewski's rules for definition too are among his most important scientific contributions, and need to be rescued from comparative oblivion. Remarking that, despite their importance in exact disciplines, definitions had received stepmotherly treatment even in systems otherwise carefully formalized,[78] Lesniewski also published, in *1931*, directives independent of his own systems and incorporating exact rules of definition for the classical theory of deduction, as based on Lukasiewicz's thirty-three word single implication-negation axiom of 1930[35]—a bracketless system that contains expressions of only a few semantic categories, and so

presents a simpler problem than Lesniewski's own indefinitely extensible and grammatically exhaustive system. (§ 5.2)

It is symptomatic of the neglect of definitions[78] remarked by Lesniewski in *1931* (p. 290) that, despite the famous contradiction Russell himself derived from a definition permitted by even Frege's careful rules, Russell devoted only two paragraphs (p. 19) of the informal introduction to the first of the three large volumes of PM to specifying a solitary rule of definition, though he and Whitehead observed other rules in practice. And later logicians have usually followed this careless example instead of the more rigorous example of Frege. It is true that Carnap in *1937* (§§ 8, 22, 29) treated definitions at some length, prescribing rules like Frege's but adapted to a simple grammar of logical types. But even Carnap in later writings gives definitions short shrift, remarking in *1942* (pp. 57–58) that 'For the sake of simplicity, we will leave aside definitions as parts of calculi in the following discussions.' Reichenbach in *1948* (pp. 123–124) first misquoted one of the rules he took from Carnap, and then added that 'little work has been done in this field, and the author feels unable to present a more satisfactory set of rules'—a remark indicating ignorance of the contributions published decades earlier by Frege[34] and Lesniewski. Nor are these contributions mentioned in Bochenski's *1956* history of logic. Characteristically, Rosser specifies no rules of definition in his otherwise unusually comprehensive *Logic for Mathematicians;* formulates many definitions carelessly, without even schematically indicating suppressed variables, though instinctive restraint appears to inhibit him from deducing contradictions; and by a symptomatic oversight does not even list the term 'definition' separately in his index. Quine in his *Mathematical Logic* (*1951*, § 24) does warn that 'caution is needed in adopting definitions which impose like abbreviations upon primitively unlike formulae', since this might lead to the fallacious conclusion that a non-theorem, definitionally abbreviated in the same way as a theorem, is itself a theorem. But he does not remark that the non-theorem might even contradict the theorem; nor does he implement this informal warning by any formal rule effectively barring contradictory definitions even of the most flagrant kind. Such gaps in formalization would permit defectively formalized systems to be undermined at will by contradictions admitted through these loopholes, were absence of effective prohibitions taken as license to adopt faulty definitions. (§ 3.9, § 3.10)

3.5.2 Directives for substitution and extensionality.

Anticipating Russell and Whitehead, Lesniewski recognized in 1920 that free variables are logically superfluous, and used only bound variables, so that one may speak simply of *the* variables of a generalization in canonic language L, and need not discriminate in the usual way nor use distinctive predetermined forms of variables and constants. (§ 6.1.8)

Five years later, in *1925* (pp. xiii, xviii), Russell eliminated a logically redundant "primitive proposition" by stipulating that variables free in theses as printed in the first edition of PM were to be considered bound by a tacitly prefixed universal quantifier. See Lesniewski, *1929* (NS, § 4, p. 31).

Consequently he formulated directives of substitution valid for any expression—propositional, nominal, or functorial—of any semantic category, independent of questions of existence or extralinguistic reference. (§ 6.1) Published in *1929* (NS) and *1930* and translated in § 7 below, these universally valid directives antedate by several years the formulations cited by Church (*1956*, pp. 157–158, 289–290) and Kleene (p. 179) as the first faultless rules of substitution for "predicate" or functor variables of any category, and make it possible to state rigorously within his system generalizations expressible only in the metalanguages of systems permitting variables of fewer categories to be bound, and accordingly weaker in means of expression. At the same time Lesniewski formulated universally valid directives of extensionality, also published in *1929* and *1930* and translated in § 7 below.

3.5.3 Canons of axiomatization.

Lesniewski established comprehensive methodological principles for well-constructed axiom systems, published for the first time by Sobocinski in *1955–56*. As heuristic guides and stylistic canons these principles serve a need stressed in *1954* by Church, to whose knowledge

not even the slightest suggestion has ever been made (and the reviewer has none) towards a general theory... Yet it seems worth while to ask whether such theory, or at least partial theory, might not be found.

Lesniewski's ideal was to reduce a theory to a primitive basis consisting of a minimal number of universally valid directives, together with a single, relatively short and simple axiom satisfying his principles of formalization. Each such axiom is an organic thesis of the theory, (§ 1.4) not a mere translation into primitive notation of the conjoined axioms of some set. Being a universal generalization whose nucleus (§ 11) is a coimplication, it neither presupposes the extralinguistic reference of expressions nor implies the existence, number, or kind of individual objects in the universe. (§ 6.1) So it is a canonic introductory thesis like a definition, except that it does not define and make eliminable but only introduces, determines the semantic category and significance, and characterizes the use of a single basic form of undefined constant. (§ 6.1.9)

Cf. Wittgenstein's remark in *1922* (5.451, 5.4541) that, since a constant must be introduced not surreptitiously but explicitly and for all propositional contexts, what Frege[34] required of definitions must hold (*mutatis mutandis*) for introduction of new constants by axioms too: 'Die Lösungen der logischen Probleme müssen einfach sein, denn sie setzen den Standard der Einfachheit.' Frege himself made this requirement in *1903*, § 65.

Just as any other principle is derivable from the primitive basis, so any other constant of the theory is explicitly definable in terms of such an undefined constant, which takes a minimal number of arguments all of basic, non-functorial category.

3.6 Axiomatic reductions

Once Tarski (in his doctoral research, published in *1923)* had demonstrated Lesniewski's project to be feasible, Lesniewski constructed protothetic, the first indefinitely extensible logic of propositions (and other expressions of the unbounded hierarchies beginning with propositional expressions) to be based on the coimplicator (§ 11) as sole undefined constant. Reducing the logic of coimplication or "material equivalence" to axioms A1 and A2 below,[36] he initially based protothetic on three axioms represented as follows in familiar notation:

A1. $[p\,q\,r] \therefore p \equiv r . \equiv . q \equiv p : \equiv . r \equiv q$

A2. $[p\,q\,r] \therefore p \equiv . q \equiv r : \equiv : p \equiv q . \equiv r$

A3. $[g\,p] :: [f] \therefore g(p,p) \equiv . [r] . f(r,r) \equiv g(p,p) . \equiv . \lfloor r \rfloor . f(r,r) \equiv$
$g(p \equiv . [q] . q, p) \therefore \equiv . [q] . g(q,p)$ [36]

From the beginning he was able to base ontology on a single axiom satisfying his principles, except for its subsequent reduction to a yet shorter axiom. (§ 6.2.3) He and his associates constructed, and in time reduced to satisfactory single axioms, not only his standard but many alternative systems of protothetic, ontology, and mereology, together with various other logical and mathematical theories. In particular, Lesniewski developed "tautological" or "computative" systems of protothetic, relative to which his other systems of protothetic, ontology, and mereology are demonstrably consistent by classical elementary logic. (§ 6.4) Into his primitive logical basis, consisting of the axiom of protothetic, the axiom of ontology, and his directives for definition, substitution, extensionality, detachment, and distribution of the universal quantifier, he condensed all universally valid classical logical principles and rules for deducing propositions, (§ 6.0) including in particular the following: (1) his exhaustive (§ 5.2) grammar of semantic categories; (2) his axiomatization (as a method for proving theses of protothetic) and generalization (for expressions of any semantic category of protothetic) of the case-analysis decision procedure, exemplified by the principle of bivalence for expressions belonging to the basic category of propositions, and ordinarily implemented by use of "truth" tables or value matrices;[37] (3) his universally valid classical principles for using quantifiers and (bound) variables of any semantic category; and (4) his universally valid principles of predication, which represent a synthesis of Aristotelian[9] and Russellian[10] logic, freed from specialized conventions and restrictions.[26] Lesniewski also constructed systems of geometry proper (§ 3.2) on the basis of mereology, and in *1929* reduced the mathematical theory of groups and that of Abelian groups, which theoretically belong to ontology, each to an adequate single axiom, indepedent of his own system and introducing a single basic form of undefined constant.

3.7 Natural deduction by the suppositional method

From *1916* onward Lesniewski used the intuitive technique of natural deduction, or derivation from unasserted premises, exemplified in his development of mereology in *1916*, in Tarski's publication of *1923*, and in Sobocinski's and Lejewski's postwar publications. Any deduction by Lesniewski's method is, distinctively, represented at every stage by a complete proposition, conditional in form, incorporating and summing up what has so far been proved. Thus it involves no use of indeterminates as "dummy names (or constants)". Lesniewski never published technical directives for his method, as Gentzen and Jaskowski did for theirs in 1934–35, since he presented his intuitive deductions only as outlines demonstrating how to construct rigorous proofs according to his official directives.

To derive explicit rules for Lesniewski's method from his official directives would require a development of his system beyond the scope of this survey and exposition of its foundations. But for sake of illustration I use the method to carry out deductions connected with his refutation of "representative general objects".[21]

3.8 Ideographic notation for propositional logic (§ 8)

Lesniewski invented an ideographic notation for constant connectors of one or two propositional arguments. Though not obligatory even in protothetic, since forms of defined constants are not predetermined by his directives, his notation has two advantages to offset its unfamiliarity: (1) Like Lukasiewicz's and Parry's,[38] it can be easily typewritten, since basically all constants are formed from "hubs and spokes"; i.e., from signs of the following forms: o, –, '. (2) More important, it is designed to a uniform ideographic and mnemonic scheme, according to which these constants reflect in their notational forms and interrelations their logical characteristics and interrelations. Because of its schematic form, Lesniewski's symbolism has been called a "hub-and-spoke, wheel, or clock" notation; but, because of its ideographic design, it might equally accurately and more suggestively be called an ideographic dial, matrix, or semaphore notation, to indicate that the constants represent their own value matrices and Boolean expansions in a simple, inbuilt semaphore code easy to learn, remember, and interpret. Since their logical characteristics and interrelations can be inferred from their forms alone, by simple ideographic principles of notational correspondence, it becomes feasible to use whichever constants are most convenient and economical to express a propositional connection, not just combinations of the standard few commonly used in other systems, and to develop within protothetic a general theory of combinators, (§ 7.1) in which logical laws can be stated in abbreviated forms containing fewer or no lower-level variables.[39] In Lesniewski's ideographic notation it is easy to ascertain whether a connection is tautologous, contradictory, or contingent; whether it implies, is implied by, is equivalent, is consistent, or is inconsistent with another; what are its Boolean expansions or canonic normal forms; to what simpler logical equivalents it can be reduced, in solving Quine's (*1952*) problem of simplifying "truth functions";

and so on. As generalized by Standley[38] for connectors of any finite number of propositional arguments, Lesniewski's basic ideographic scheme makes it possible to solve any problem solvable by matrices or "truth tables", and facilitates an unusually simple mechanical decision procedure for propositional logic, which does not require special tables of truth-value or case analysis, since the constants themselves take the place of their own matrices. So too the method of abbreviating truth tables suggested by Ivo Thomas in *1951* (§ 3, § 5) becomes even more intuitive if based on ideographic matrix notation, and the logical interrelations he points out between constant connectors can then be explained in terms of simple mechanical transformations and rotations. (§ 8)

3.9 Other peripheral contributions

In constructing protothetic Lesniewski proved the following metatheorem concerning any "purely equivalential" proposition P (i.e., any proposition P whose nucleus, together with any coimplicant in its nucleus, is either a coimplication or a propositional variable): *P is a classical tautology if and only if related variables* (§ 11) *of each form* (§ 1.3) *occuring in P are even in number*. (*1929*, NS, § 3) To use the familiar manner of speaking, any "iterated material equivalence" is tautologous if and only if "each variable in it occurs an even number of times". Ironically, this metatheorem, which provides a derivative method for deciding whether any two purely equivalential propositions are logically equivalent, by simply checking the result of connecting them by a coimplicator (i.e., functor of "material equivalence"), seems to be more widely known than Lesniewski's less marginal contributions, perhaps because independent of the unfamiliar details of his own systems.

Lesniewski's peripheral contributions include his negative results and criticisms concerning other systems. His study of various contradictions led him not only to formalize his own systems with exceptional rigor but also to look for, discover, and point out faults in formalization of other systems, especially defective formalization of rules for introducing new expressions. He proved contradictions in Chwistek's propositional calculus of *1924–25*, and in both versions of the system Von Neumann presented in *1927* and revised in *1931*. (§ 3.10)

In *1938* (EB, VI) Lesniewski extended the criticisms and inconsistency proofs he had published in *1929* (NS, § 11, pp. 80–81), by demonstrating that Von Neumann's *1931* revision remained inconsistent even if Von Neumann did not suppress but retained brackets, as Lindenbaum in *1931* had suggested Von Neumann should. See Lesniewski on "complexes" in *1929* (NS, § 11, T.E. VII and p. 77, remarks C and D, explained in § 6.1 and § 7.1 below) and in *1931* (UD, T.E. I).

By means of an interpretation Lesniewski proved in 1926 (as Tarski had conjectured earlier in the same year) that, provided a standard arithmetical theory is consistent, neither of the following two theses of the informal "theory of events" expounded by Whitehead (in *1919*) are derivable from the six postulates listed by Whitehead:[40]

If every intersector of *b* also intersects *a*, then either *aKb* or *a* and *b* are identical.... It follows that if *b* is part of *a*, there are always events separated from *b* which are also parts of *a*.

In 1938 Lesniewski demonstrated, in the analysis published by Sobocinski in *1949–50*, that Frege's set-theoretic repair is inadequate, since even as revised in *1903* Frege's foundations of arithmetic are inconsistent with there being more than one or two individual objects in the universe.[41]

3.10 Why is Lesniewski's work relatively unknown?

Certain reasons are obvious; others are suggested by parallels in the fate of Frege and Peirce.

Lesniewski died prematurely, and shortly before the disruption of war, which dispersed the few who survived to continue his work. (§ 2.0) Even during his lifetime only a few close associates were sufficiently familiar with its details to be able to appreciate at first hand its originality and importance. By others it has often been misinterpreted and misrepresented, though more often it has simply been overlooked or ignored. According to Jordan (p. 24) 'The most thorough, original, and philosophically significant attempt to provide a logically secure foundation for the whole of mathematics comes from Lesniewski.' Yet, two decades after Lesniewski's death, his work seems less widely known than that of

Lukasiewicz and Tarski, who survived the war to publish in English. No history of logic yet published even sums up Lesniewski's original contributions and major achievements. (§ 3.5.1)

The technical and fragmentary character of his publications, together with their unfamiliar expressions and relative inaccessibility, also fosters their comparative oblivion or neglect. Lesniewski was a perfectionist and hesitated to publish his results in less than definitive form. He did not live to publish a systematic synthesis of his work, or even complete a conspectus. His anticipatory publications and related contributions by others are fragments scattered over several decades in different journals in various languages. None appeared in English, the main international vehicle of communication in mathematical logic. To the confusion of librarians, two of his major publications appeared in German, with Polish over German titles, in a Polish journal with variously abbreviated French and Polish titles. Several were delayed for years by editorial difficulties, and outside Poland all but one (*1929*, NS) are difficult to obtain.

Lesniewski's most comprehensive publication, his long series (OM) on the foundations of mathematics, appeared in Polish and mainly concerned mereology. His published accounts of his logical systems are mere epitomes, in which he sketched their evolution, explained his technical terminology, and prescribed directives for constructing standard systems of protothetic and ontology. These exact terminological explanations and directives provide a solid foundation for reconstruction. But not only are they based on unfamiliar notation, and embedded in German articles in Polish journals; they are themselves condensed into twenty-four pages of logical symbols and Latin abbreviations of unfamiliar technical terms. (§ 7.0)

These lapidary inscriptions, mostly without commentary, have not hitherto been expanded and explained in detail. Few not already convinced of their value would make the effort to decipher this Rosetta stone, the cornerstone of Lesniewski's foundation; and it is hardly surprising if only his immediate collaborators have done so. Yet his achievements cannot fairly be assessed without mastering these explanations and directives, nor by those 'anxious to spare themselves' what Jordan (p. 44) calls 'the valuable though somewhat excruciating experience of going through Lesniewski's writings', since Lesniewski's most important contributions are integrated in the monolithic structure to which these are the key.

Like Peirce, Lesniewski died with a drawer full of unpublished manuscripts and lecture notes, which were to have been edited for publication by Sobocinski. Instead they were all destroyed during the war, (§ 2.3) together with all but a few copies of certain of Lesniewski's and related contributions to *Collectanea Logica*,[20] Slupecki's current survey being based on whatever incomplete and sometimes inaccurate students' lecture notes Kotarbinski was able to collect after the war.[42] Throughout the war Sobocinski worked to reconstruct Lesniewski's systems, only to lose his manuscript on ontology, nearly a thousand pages long, in an air raid, after saving it from the destruction of Warsaw earlier in 1944. Only in recent years has the work of salvage, reconstruction, and development issued in Woodger's English translation of Tarski's prewar articles, and in the postwar publications of Lejewski, Slupecki, and Sobocinski. (§ 10.0) In this book I can at most provide an introductory survey of Lesniewski's work and a basis for evaluation and reconstruction of standard systems of protothetic and ontology.

But disruption by death and war, dispersion, unfamiliarity, language barriers, and relative inaccessibility are not the only reasons for neglect: another is divergence of motivation. Lesniewski pursued aims fundamentally philosophical as well as mathematical or metamathematical, like Peirce and Frege, who in his *1893* foreword predicted that his work would be neglected by philosophers for whom it was too mathematical and by mathematicians for whom it was too philosophical. From a purely formalist point of view, preoccupation with meaning and truth, interpretation, and philosophical clarification may seem mere "quibbling over subjective trivialities or philosophical subtleties", resulting in needless inhibitions and complications. Would any pure formalist hesitate to simplify formal arithmetic by postulating an axiom of infinity just because, in a system interpreted as basis for counting, measuring, and scientific description of reality, it might not be true? (§ 4) Would he complicate his formalism with grammatical criteria of meaning, and restrict himself to using expressions he could intuitively interpret and understand? Would he suppose that such "mathematically primitive and self-explanatory entities as natural numbers" need explanations more basic and clear than Peano's axioms or their set-theoretic correlates? These rhetorical questions are intended only to suggest a fundamental divergence of attitude. This divergence may be illustrated by a critique (§ 6.5) of Grzegorczyk's *1955* evaluation of Lesniewski's systems in relation to current research, whose outlines will stand out more clearly against the contrasting background I sketch in the intervening pages. Even those who do not share Grzegorczyk's formalist and historicist bias may appreciate why those who do tend to depreciate Lesniewski's work.

But it would be strange if there were no other reasons. Not all Lesniewski's critics have been so fairly disposed as Grzegorczyk, and it would be surprising if they had. For Lesniewski was a true heir of Frege, and his incisive criticism of what he considered careless formalism can hardly have endeared him to its authors. It apparently antagonized some and alienated others. According to Jordan (p. 25),

His extremely high demands of precision (for which he was famous among some people, notorious among others), combined with deep philosophical intuitions, which he tried to symbolize and express in mathematical language, made him a formidable personality and a mind to be admired and dreaded at the same time. There was hardly anybody of distinction who escaped his influence, and no one able to stand the ground against his combined power of criticism and of invention.

Lesniewski had been on friendly terms with Chwistek in the 1920s. But after Lesniewski criticized the directives for Chwistek's propositional calculus of *1924–25*, (§ 4.11) and backed up his criticism by proving a contradiction in the calculus, (§ 3.9) Chwistek (*1948*, pp. 125–126, 136–137) retorted that 'one could hardly agree' with Kotarbinski's[22] judgment that of all systems he knew ontology is the most mature, natural, and practical in its applications. (§ 6.2.3) To the contrary he, Chwistek, regarded it as artificial and yielding nothing essentially new. He agreed that it is closely related to traditional Aristotelian formal logic, but this he considered no great recommendation. Drastically misrepresenting Lesniewski's system, he concluded that it is clearly metaphysical and consequently cannot be employed as a constituent element of the system of the mathematical sciences.

Overlooking or unaware of Lesniewski's consistent distinction between collective and distributive uses of "class" terminology, and between expressions, their uses and meanings, and what they are used to describe, Chwistek charged blindly that Lesniewski did not 'like the concept of the null class'. To Lesniewski's citing Frege's critique of Schröder, Chwistek rejoined that 'one could tell that', as 'Lesniewski boasted',

throughout Lesniewski's life there was, on the whole, no time when he understood the concept of a class.... However, a critique...based upon common misunderstandings...imposed on the reader by the use of powerful dialectical devices...must lead to confusion of concepts.

Chwistek asserted that 'Lesniewski spoke as if it were a common mistake to employ null classes', and proceeded to set Lesniewski right:

Logic and mathematics can deal only with certain expressions. Obviously therefore classes are certain expressions. Null classes are equally good expressions as universal classes. Nothing further need be said.

Lesniewski's argument that in daily life null classes are not handled cannot be sustained. It can be confirmed repeatedly that certain classes which are regarded as universal classes are in fact null classes. Progress could not be made if discussion were limited to non-null classes... Artificial language like that of Lesniewski would have to be employed.

Thus Chwistek demonstrated chiefly that he was too pure a formalist to appreciate the force of Frege's and Lesniewski's arguments, and too unfamiliar with Lesniewski's work to realize that Lesniewski did not mean only expressions by 'classes', consistently distinguished between collective and distributive uses, and himself defined and used the noun 'Λ' which I translate by 'nonentity', and which Chwistek would presumably call not just the "expression for but the null class itself". Indeed, Lesniewski used this constant, whose significance by definition precludes its being a name, to prove it false that a "null class" or nonentity exists. (See §§ 1.5, 1.7, 1.8, 3.3, 4.10, 6.1.)

To Lesniewski's proof that the system Von Neumann had expounded in *1927* is inconsistent, (§ 3.9) Von Neumann retorted in *1931* that to prove contradiction Lesniewski had violated the law

that compound expressions of any symbolic "language" be univocally resoluble into the intended constituents—a law that he,
Von Neumann, had thought too elementary to mention, since it
belonged to an earlier, pre-mathematical stage of formalism having
nothing to do with his aim to prove the consistency of mathematics,
and in no way affected his treatment of mathematical formalism as
in principle meaningless (*prinzipiell sinnlos*).[17] Whereupon Lesniewski proved two more contradictions, in quite different ways, in Von
Neumann's system as revised in *1931*. (§ 3.9) It was after publication
of Lesniewski's technical criticisms of Sierpinski and Von Neumann,
in *1928* (OM, § 3) and *1929* (NS, § 11), that Lesniewski, 'for reasons
of a personal nature', withdrew from the Polish mathematical
journal *Fundamenta Mathematicae* the sequel (NS, § 12) that remained unpublished for nearly a decade, until the founding of a
new, logical journal under the editorship of Lukasiewicz and
Sobocinski. (§ 2.3) In *1958* (LO, p. 150) Lejewski remarks that it is
significant that the Warsaw center of logical research, dominated
by philosophers rather than mathematicians, influenced the development of philosophy in Poland more than it ever influenced
that of mathematics.

4. LESNIEWSKI'S CRITIQUE
OF PURE FORMALISM[43]

Like Frege, Whitehead,[44] and Russell, Lesniewski was a philosophical as well as mathematical logician; and, like Leibniz, De Morgan, and Peirce, he respected the foundations established by Aristotle and other great ancient and medieval logicians. Following these forbears, he sought to generalize truly, and thought logic should set an example of rigor, not merely imitate current fashion and codify common practice, however careless.[45] So he carried on the work of systematizing and formalizing results from complementary traditions.

The construction of his systems reflects both his philosophical motivation and his mathematical proficiency: It attests that he too was a logician who did not evade but concentrated on philosophical problems that he could investigate rigorously, and a philosopher who did not twist and turn to bypass but instead worked through mathematical problems that he had to solve before he could go on.[45] For his systems evolved from his analysis of antinomies which, like Russell, he attributed to faulty grammar and logic. Lesniewski too worked toward a comprehensive solution, as distinguished from 'so-called solutions' which Ramsey (*1925*, p. 21) called 'merely inadequate excuses for not giving a solution', such as the opposite professional evasions—(1) that since antinomies "involve concepts of a scholastic nature", mathematicians are not responsible and can leave their solution to philosophers; or (2) that since antinomies involve technical kinks in the calculating mechanism, philosophers are not responsible and can leave their solution to mathematicians—

which together dump antinomies into no-man's land. And Lesniewski's systems are designed as foundations, not just for the
superstructure of pure mathematics, but also for canonic scientific
description of reality: not just as duplicators of familiar theorems
formally consistent relative to models in abstract "domains of sets
or numbers", but as logistic systems that he could intuitively interpret and apply; systems that he could use to define mathematical
constants in logical terms basic to all propositional expression, and
so explain what he meant by such constants not just in calculating
but also in counting, measuring, and describing individual objects.
(§ 4.6, § 4.7)

Lesniewski entered logic from philosophy rather than from mathematics; intuitive interpretation, meaning, and truth concerned him
more than mere formal consistency and technique; and his formal
systems themselves represent the codification of his intuitive logic
developed, systematized, axiomatized, symbolized, and formalized
over the years. (§ 2.1) He always considered interpretation first and
formalization second: Formalization served him but as a precision
instrument of rigor and clarity, an effective technique in the service
of meaning and truth. He formalized his terminological explanations
and directives with great care—but not because he favored formalization for its own sake.[17] He was too concerned with interpretation
to enjoy even formally consistent

"mathematical games" in which, according to this or that conventional rule, one
paints various more or less picturesque formulas, not necessarily meaningful or even,
as some "mathematics players" prefer, necessarily meaningless. So I should not have
taken the pains to systematize and scrupulously control the directives of my
system, checking them again and again, had I not sought to assign to its theses a
certain quite definite sense, precisely this and no other, in which I cannot intuitively
deny the validity of the axioms and methods of inference and definition codified
in its directives. I should see no contradiction in asserting that I construct my
system in a radically "formalist" fashion just because I am a confirmed "intuitionist". For in formulating deductive theories I try to express a series of thoughts
on this or that subject in a series of meaningful propositions, and to deduce the
individual propositions from others according to principles of inference I take as
"intuitively" binding. And I know of no more effective method to acquaint the
reader with my "logical intuitions" than to "formalize" the deductive theory
presented which, "formalized", in no way ceases to consist solely of meaningful
propositions that are for me intuitively valid. The method of carrying out mathematical deductions on the "intuitionist" basis of various logical mysteries seems to
me a decidedly less expedient method. (*1929*, NS, § 11, p. 78)

Like Frege, Husserl, and Russell, Lesniewski saw more point in criticizing the pure formalist's game than in playing it himself, and took pains to prove contradictions in Von Neumann's[17] attempt to replace classical mathematics and logic by a formal calculus constructed from nothing but meaningless marks and treated as merely (what someone has called) a *"spielgerecht zu spielenden Spiele"*. (§ 3.10)

Lesniewski[43] sharply distinguished between interpreted 'mathematical sciences as deductive theories conceived to comprehend the diverse reality of the world in ideally exact laws' and uninterpreted formal calculi 'free from contradiction and prolific in generating theorems but lacking any intuitive scientific connection with reality'. He acknowledged that certain theorems of mereology (§ 4.10, § 6.3) might shock thinkers 'subtle enough' to admire 'elegant theoretical constructions' without enquiring whether they contributed to scientific comprehension of reality or only paid tribute to the 'inertia' of current formalist fashion. But, he continued, he was more concerned that his systems should conform to the 'common sense of lay minds investigating realities they had not created' than to the "creative spirit" of 'professional theoreticians, equipped with all the centrifugal apparatus of "free creation" to invent abstractions, and demoralized by speculative constructions "in abstraction, detached from" reality'. He insisted, to quote Russell (*1919*, pp. 169–170), that 'a robust sense of reality is very necessary':

feeling for reality...ought to be preserved even in the most abstract studies. Logic...is concerned with the real world just as truly as zoology, though with its more abstract and general features.... The sense of reality is vital in logic, and whoever juggles with it...is doing a disservice to thought.

Since he interpreted expressions of language L as he used them in describing individual objects, not just in terms of any abstract isomorph, Lesniewski refused to make assumptions of whose truth he was not certain. Instead of postulating that individual objects are infinite in number, he agreed with Russell (*1937*, p. viii) that the extralinguistic reference of expressions and the population of the universe, or even its existence, is not to be decided by logic:

for logic aims at independence of empirical fact, and the existence of the universe is an empirical fact. It is true that if the world did not exist, logic-books would not exist; but the existence of logic-books is not one of the premises of logic, nor can it be inferred from any proposition that has a right to be in a logic-book.

Russell (*1919*, p. 203) saw no logical necessity 'why there should be even one individual—why, in fact, there should be any world at all', and came to consider any such implication a defect in logical purity. Existence or number of individuals is expressible but should not be provable in pure logic. The consequences of existential hypotheses and of their negations alike should (as in PM, despite the mis-nomers "axiom of infinity" and "multiplicative axiom") be investi-gated without assuming their truth or their falsity. For they are not necessarily true and Russell[46] saw no conclusive empirical evidence of their truth, nor of their falsity, though in PM as in language L they are meaningful hypotheses, not just uninterpreted formulas conventionally asserted or rejected but no more true or false than moves in a game of anagrams.

The question how many individuals there are in the universe, or even whether the number is finite or infinite, seems to me unanswerable, not only because of practical difficulties but also because of inevitable vagueness. Even in language L, though the noun 'V' which I translate by 'unique' or 'individual' is theoretically unequivocal, this is a limiting question concerning an extremal case. For how many individual drops of unspecified volume and duration are there in the ocean? how many in-dividual circles of unspecified radius in a given plane, overlapping and concentricity not being excluded? how many individual phenomenal aspects and spatiotemporal slices, sections, or stretches are to be counted in addition to the material object throughout its existence? For surely momentary phenomenal aspects, visual, tac-tual, auditory, olfactory, and gustatory—or, to use a different metaphysical idiom, the ways it looks, feels, sounds, smells, and tastes—are as unique and individual as the material object itself. And whether or not "theoretical entities", such as atoms and electrons, are also to be counted depends on whether or not theoretical constants are introduced as nouns or as higher-level functors. Lesniewski himself did not prejudge but (in *1928*, § 3) left it an open question whether or not some individual is a spatiotemporally indivisible point.

Lesniewski's directives are universal logical rules that he took as "intuitively" valid; and his axioms are universal generali-zations that he believed to be true, since he believed all their sub-stitution instances to be true, though in language L instances could be derived by substituting extralogical as well as logical constants. So Lesniewski did not consider only extralogical propositions "descriptive", and consequently interpreted his systems as true though abstract logical (categorial and structural) descriptions of reality, of maximum generality.[22]

For reasons discussed elsewhere,[47] I find it difficult clearly to distinguish this from the verbally contrasted or "opposed" view that the rules of a formalized system of logic are valid and its theses "true" by convention or definition, being prescribed or asserted in order to establish the grammatical and inferential rules and the categorial and structural framework of any language based on the logical system in question.

Discussing a logical proposition about which he was doubtful, he would consider extralogical instances as well as formal relations of symbols; dissatisfied with a formally unexceptionable proof, he would take it home to ponder until he discovered a false presupposition or resolved his perplexity. He avoided announcing results until he had rigorous written deductions he believed to be valid from theses he believed to be true, and published full proofs when space permitted. He was a thinker less facile than penetrating and thorough, distinguished by the length to which he was willing to go in pursuit of truth—or, as a more thorough pragmatist[48] put it, 'notable for the degree of prolixity which he was willing to admit in the interest of complete rigor and precision' (Quine, *1940*, p. 83).

4.1 "Thorough pragmatism"[48]

Lesniewski did not, like Quine (in *1953*, p. 46), 'espouse a more thorough pragmatism', stress a moral of utility graced by symmetry, and develop a succession of experimental models, each elegantly streamlined in a different way and incorporating a novel automatic paradox-preventer, to compete freely on the logical market as smooth-running utility vehicles of scientific myth. He did not even aim at an ideal of maximum 'liberality' and 'manipulative convenience' paid for 'at bargain rates': a 'device' or 'expedient' or 'milder and technically much more convenient sort of restriction', permitting him to "postulate classes" determined by arbitrary formulas, provided only they survive a mechanical test of hierarchical stratification, and their bound variables be restricted to elements able to survive conditions that emerged from the trial and error of natural selection, after yet more liberal predecessors had failed to suppress class contradiction. He did not feel he had to compromise or suppress his would-be nominalist scruples and philosophical misgivings, in order to "postulate, presuppose, or assume abstract entities" which he would rather "avoid" than "recognize, countenance, or admit"—though there is little danger of meeting anything but the expressions said to be their "names" or the variables said to "designate such entities ambiguously or take them as values". He did not uneasily postulate and pragmatically justify "classes and derivative abstract entities as idealizations, useful posits, or convenient fictions in a scientific myth", a coherent scheme that somehow hangs together as a whole, but that blends fact and fancy too smoothly and indissolubly to permit their separate justification, indulging a 'vaguely pragmatic inclination to adjust one strand of the fabric of science rather than another' in 'warping his scientific heritage to fit his continuing sensory promptings'. Lesniewski was never satisfied with ingenious "devices or expedients" just because they somehow "seemed to work" and smoothly duplicated formulas of familiar or desirable shapes. So he voluntarily renounced his right to manipulate formulas arbitrarily and assert nonsense at will, and restricted his "creative freedom to posit, postulate, assume, generate, or determine arbitrary and even infinite classes" by arbitrary conditions, intuitively meaningful or not. Nor did he elaborate a rationale of 'definitions and the double life'.[78] Instead he only defined constants by conditions meaningful according to the criteria of his grammar, and investigated the consequences of existential hypotheses for infinite cases. Doubtless he was a pragmatist to the extent one must be to survive, but he took into account what a deeper pragmatism acknowledges and stresses but a shallow pragmatism neglects: the philosophical need for clarity as well as the practical need for utility, and the basic recognition that the two need not compete where the meaningless is useless.

4.2 "Useful nonsense"

Lesniewski's model deviated widely from the current fashions displayed by the following lines,[49] which fail to explain just how formulas are to be useful without being meaningful:

complete lack of any reference to the meanings of statements in symbolic logic indicates that there is no need for them to have meanings. This allows us to introduce formulas whenever they are useful without reference to whether they are meaningful. In fact, there is a type of formula about whose meaning (if any) there is great disagreement. It happens to be a useful type of formula, and we use it frequently, not being the least bit inconvenienced by its possible lack of meaning... This lack of reference to meanings also enables us to evade quite a number of difficult philosophical questions. This situation is quite in line with current mathematical practice. Consider the positive integers, which are at the basis of most of mathematics. Mathematicians do not care in the least what the meanings of the positive integers are, or even if they have meanings...any information as to the meanings of the integers is wholly irrelevant for mathematical purposes. The same applies to...any other of the paraphernalia of mathematics.... Any attempt to be precise and pay attention to meanings would involve us with...problems...really quite irrelevant for mathematics. For mathematics, it is the form that must be considered, and the meaning can be dispensed with. Our symbolic logic will accord with this doctrine.

Even if all mathematicians *were* pure formalists, surely some would agree with Frege that to "abstract from" is not to "dispense with":

Inattention is a very strong lye; it must be applied at not too great a concentration, so that everything does not dissolve, and likewise not too dilute, so that it effects a sufficient change in the things. Thus it is a question of getting the right degree of dilution; this is difficult to manage, and I at any rate have never succeeded.... We attend less to a property, and it disappears. By making one characteristic after another disappear, we get more and more abstract concepts.... Inattention is a most efficacious logical faculty; presumably this accounts for the absentmindedness of professors. Suppose there are a black and a white cat sitting side by side before us. We stop attending to their colour, and they become colourless, but are still sitting side by side. We stop attending to their posture, and they are no longer sitting (though they have not assumed another posture), but each one is still in its place. We stop attending to position; they cease to have place, but still remain different.... By continued application of this procedure, we obtain from each object a more and more bloodless phantom.... Different things cannot be made to coincide by abstraction, and to regard them as the same is simply to make a mistake. If, abstracting from the difference between my house and my neighbour's, I were to regard both houses as mine, the defect of my abstraction would soon be made clear. (*1884* and *1903*, § 99, as translated in *1952*, pp. 84–85, 194.)

No more than Frege or Russell did Lesniewski claim it as an advantage 'of a symbolic logic over a simple intuitive notion of logical correctness' that 'because of this lack of reference to meanings, many difficult philosophical problems can be evaded'.[49] Details not affecting interpretation, validity, or truth may be of primarily esthetic significance and hence relatively arbitrary, philosophically, as between alternative inferentially equivalent and grammatically comparable systems. But Lesniewski did not agree that in general 'our choice of a system of symbolic logic is arbitrary', nor consider his 'a formal system divorced from intuition…an artificial representation' whose 'advantages outweigh its obvious artificiality'.[49]

4.3 Convenient carelessness

Rosser[50] continues:

it is generally agreed about statements that a statement about something must contain a name of that thing, rather than the thing itself. We shall conform with this usage….to talk about a name of a statement or of a word, one must use a name of this name. This becomes rather awkward…. Failure to comprehend this point is one of the major causes of difficulty in comprehending the proof of Gödel's theorem. For the greater part of logic, no such difficulties arise. Thus for the greater part of logic one can be rather careless about the use of quotations marks without getting into any difficulty. Such carelessness is usual, and in the future we shall indulge in such carelessness ourselves…. Be it understood that we are not admitting such omission of quotation marks to be correct; we are merely condoning it as convenient. This is in line with current mathematical practice….confusion occasionally arises from a failure to preserve a careful distinction between an object and its name…in connection with fractions…. As we said once before, failure to observe such distinctions carefully can seldom lead to confusion in logic and still less seldom in mathematics, and so in much of our text we shall omit the quotation marks that should appear. In so doing, we follow accepted mathematical practice.

Of course it is not only in connection with Gödel's theorem and fractions that such carelessness leads to confusion: the literature is full of examples, pointed out by Frege, Lesniewski, Carnap, and Quine;[50] and indeed Rosser appears to provide further examples himself, though a fair reader, acknowledging Rosser's[49] statement that much of his discussion is 'not particularly precise', will admit that Rosser himself may know whether he means numerals or "numbers", abstractions or "classes" in the following lines.

4.4 "Names" which name nothing

There is no requirement that a statement of symbolic logic have meaning. Consequently the names which occur in such statements need not be names of anything. This is very convenient, since we are thus entitled to use names without first (or ever) being assured that they are the names of something….[50] If we were attaching meanings to our statements, the meaning of $x = y$ would be that x and y are names of the same identical object. We…shall have equality…between numbers (names of numbers, really),…or indeed between the names of any logical object…. In other words, one is to put '=' between two names if and only if they are names of the same object. The resulting statement about the object, that it does not differ from itself in any way, is of an excessive degree of triviality. Nevertheless the statement does call our attention to the fact of the two names being names of the same object, and hence justifies our using the names interchangeably in statements about the object.... "Things equal to the same thing are equal to each other." However, this is not quite an accurate rendering of the meaning of the theorem. A more accurate version would be "If x and y are names of the same object, and y and z are names of the same object, then x and z are names of the same object." (Rosser, pp. 163–165)

It is not our intention to pursue further the distinction between definitions and more ordinary names, or to analyze the mechanism by which a name can be associated with an object if the name is not a description of the object. We proceed now to a formal treatment of descriptions.

Since 'we have not committed ourselves to using only formulas which have meaning..., we shall simply consider' a "definite description" which describes nothing definite 'as a meaningless formula. In fact we shall not even require' that it contain any variable bound by the description operator. The resulting "description"

is to be a name and may properly occur as a constituent of statements, even though it may fail to be a name of anything. If the reader is unhappy about using formulas without meaning, he can arrange for...a meaning, regardless..., by adopting the following convention. Choose some arbitrary, fixed object, say the number π (Rosser, pp. 181–182, 185)

—though it might be easier to fix some simpler "object". Similarly for "class abstraction":

$\hat{x}P$ is the class determined by P. Clearly $\hat{x}P$ can function as this class only in case there is such a class. If there is no class determined by P, then we may consider $\hat{x}P$ as meaningless. Actually, if P determines no class, then...$\hat{x}P$ would have whatever meaning we have agreed to give...under such a circumstance. One possibility is that no meaning at all is assigned, but this does not prevent us from making formal use of $\hat{x}P$. Note that P need not contain any occurrences of x in order to give a meaning to $\hat{x}P$.... More generally, given an arbitrary x and P, there may or may not exist the class which we would like to denote by $\hat{x}P$. Note that we are entitled to use $\hat{x}P$ in our symbolic logic even if there is no class which it denotes, since we do not require that our formulas have meaning. (Rosser, pp. 219–220)

4.5 "Identification" of discernibles

Nor did Lesniewski invoke the convenient methodological principle of "identifying suspect entities" with others supposed to lead an innocent existence, in order to simplify formal calculations, resolve philosophical perplexities, or convert semantic confusions into technical problems to be passed to any expert willing to accept them. He did not, like Rosenbloom, a former chemist (*1950* Preface), first refuse (p. 101) to 'digress at this point and enter into the dangerous quicksand of philosophical controversy' and then go on to remark (p. 201), concerning "abstract entities", that

One can, however, consider these entities as "existing in space-time" by identifying them, for example, with certain chemical reactions in men's brains. This is not the only possible interpretation, but the existence of at least one such interpretation shows that we can work with these entities without assuming any metaphysics like Platonic idealism.

Lesniewski did not thus tempt Plato's shade (or its chemical representative) to enquire whether the chemist could assure the existence, in men's brains, of an infinite chemical reaction of chemical reactions of chemical reactions of chemical reactions, in order to guarantee that the number series be endless. Not he but Fraenkel (*1953*, p. 19) pointed with pride to an enviable method, by which police departments might increase overnight their efficiency records in the identification of suspects: 'precisely the act of *equating logically different objects* is one of the most powerful and efficient methods in mathematics.' Rosser, here (p. 342) more cautious, puts in at least the qualifications I italicize in quoting: 'By dealing with...equivalence classes...rather than elements..., we have *the effect of* identifying any two equivalent elements', simplified by the "elimination" of any (?) distinction between equivalent elements. 'We find this idea' of "using equivalence classes" to 'produce *the effect of* identification of elements...a standard device in many parts of mathematics'.

4.6 Convenient fictions and possible interpretations

Lesniewski did not attempt to solve existent problems by appealing to nonexistent but convenient fictions or "idealizations" such as "expressions (resp. classes or forms of expressions) infinite in number or length", whose missing members in "infinite conjunctions, alternations, proof sequences", or the like are indicated by convenient 'etc.'s or dots of ellipsis,[62] suggesting the infinite number of expressions not actually written down for lack of space and time.

(§ 4.10) Indeed, he said he would not consider a "collection consisting of an infinite number of words" an expression at all. (§ 6.1.7) He did not conceive his systems as platonic forms: ideal universal repositories of disembodied truth, completely developed, finished, and static, fixed in some eternal realm. Not pursuing metamathematical investigations based on "platonist idealizations", Lesniewski did not share Tarski's[32] complaint that, although only protothetic and ontology were formalized with sufficient rigor, unfortunately, because of their "constructively nominalist" (§ 3.1) and relative design, (§ 5.2) they seemed extremely unrewarding objects for Tarski's metatheoretic investigations, and indeed hardly fitted Tarski's conception of a deductive system at all.

Nor did Lesniewski attempt to clarify the "semantic concept of truth" by a purely structural definition[29] (adequate to establish any instance of the same scheme as the following: 'It is snowing' is a true sentence if and only if it is snowing);[47] yet at the same time 'simplify' formal calculations by committing what Tarski[51] himself calls the 'common error' of "identifying" equiform expressions. But, Tarski continues, in order to avoid 'objections' and 'superfluous complications', it is 'convenient' to investigate semantic problems in terms of forms of expression in abstraction from context, and 'useful' from a metamathematical point of view to postulate that "expressions" be denumerably infinite. 'From an intuitive point of view', Tarski[51] admits, this seems 'dubious' and 'far from evident', but 'I do not intend to examine more closely this difficult question', which involves the following 'subtlety':

Normally expressions are conceived as products of human activity (resp. classes of such products); thus the supposition that infinitely many expressions exist appears manifestly absurd. But the possibility of another interpretation presents itself: it would be possible to take for expressions all physical bodies of definite form and size. The center of gravity of the problem is then shifted to physics; the assertion of their infinite number ceases to be absurd and even represents a special consequence of assumptions normally admitted in physics or in geometry.

Tarski[51] adds that to eliminate or weaken postulates which "guarantee"

existence of all possible expressions would make construction of the metatheory extremely difficult, make a series of the most natural arguments impossible, and so entail considerable complications in formulation of definitions and theorems.

For example, that something is so does not alone "guarantee" existence of a corresponding description,[52] for individual expressions themselves are part of the universe, and doubtless even certain snowfalls will be among the things in heaven and earth never specifically described by any expression, nor accidentally "expressed" by any other physical facsimile. From an ideal "platonist" viewpoint this may be unfortunate; but from a common-sense viewpoint so is the fact that, if what Tarski calls "expressions" must be infinite in number, they can hardly be (what we call) individual expressions, (§ 1.3) so that the consequences of his postulates need not be true of individual expressions, nor even of physical configurations such as the 'W' of Cassiopeia. It may seem 'cruel to bring down so high a flight of the spirit by such a homely objection', but expressions as physical configurations 'must be subject to all the limitations of such a material existence.'[52] What is actually gained by trying to shift the burden, by appealing to cosmology to convert absurdity into plausibility?—especially if one's colleagues decline the burden with thanks, so that it falls into a no-man's land of professional irresponsibility.[52] Such faith in physics is moving: If it does not move mountains, at least it may "technically reduce" them to molehills of "possible interpretation" in the eyes of the faithful. But a faithful pragmatist will not commit himself to faith in an infinite universe prematurely, before scientific mythmakers are agreed, and current speculation seems divided.[48] For procedures too obviously arbitrary and artificial make even thorough pragmatists suspect they are 'lost in a world of make-believe' (Goodman and Quine, *1947*, p. 105). Such solutions are a little too facile, since it is "possible to interpret" practically anything as something quite different. We could interpret good intentions as payments in sterling, but could not in reality solve financial problems thereby, even were the will a model of the deed, unless banks accepted the same possible interpretation, or some other institution afforded support. For "identifying" discernibles does not make them identical, even if they are equiform or isomorphic, and so seem practically identical to possible interpreters concerned only with form or structure.

4.7 Formal simplification and philosophical clarification

Lesniewski did not overlook the distinction between formal simplification and philosophical clarification in the illusion that they necessarily coincide. So he did not "technically reduce relations to classes" by an 'expedient' like that by which Wiener, in Quine's estimation,[48] 'resolved' some of the complexity of the 'jungle' of Russell's grammar of types. For, by replacing binary verbs by higher-level expressions and mixing different categories, this 'device' would violate Lesniewski's logical grammar in several more ways at once than the substitution of verbs for nouns violated Russell's. (§ 5.1) By requiring not only the notation of "functional application" but also a constant operator of "ordered pairing", it would violate Lesniewski's (and Frege's[34]) principles of complete definition and simplicity of the expression defined. By converting simple relational propositions into "mere abbreviations for notational convenience" of formulas containing hundreds of billions of symbols (see below), it would make them difficult to interpret and verify outside pure mathematics if, say, they described thunderclaps following lightning flashes. Even apart from grammatical inhibitions against, Lesniewski had no motive for "reducing" relational propositions to abbreviations of the same length, since he did not suppose he could thus reduce "ontic commitments".[48] So he did not need to introduce his treatment of "relational" formulas by remarks like Rosser's (pp. 280–281, 285):

It would be a bit hard to say just what the ordered pair...of the two objects x and y consists of from an intuitive point of view. All that is really necessary is that it be uniquely determined by x and y, and that conversely it shall uniquely determine x and y and specify their order. Any object which does this can serve for us as the ordered pair.... We shall exhibit such an object and use it as the ordered pair.... The definition which we give will seem extremely artificial and will certainly provoke the reaction that this is definitely not what one thinks of as the ordered pair.... It is not our claim that what we shall use as the ordered pair...is what one would think of intuitively as an ordered pair. We merely claim that it does the things that an ordered pair should do. Hence we can and will do with it all the things that one could do with a more congenial kind of ordered pair. Moreover, we know no way to construct a less artificial ordered pair, and until someone shows how to construct a less artificial one, we shall use ours to do all the things that an ordered pair is expected to do.... The sort of ordered pair which we are using was invented by Quine (see Quine, 1945).

But even a formalist with no grammatical scruples about replacing one part of speech by another, mixing up semantic categories, and ordering and pairing ink marks at will inside a grammarless calculus might not be able to use such up-to-date, newly invented mixtures to make intelligible and true descriptions as well as formal calculations. And even those like Tarski[32] or Quine,[53] who favors 'a single unpartitioned universe of values of bound variables, and a simple grammar of predication which admits general terms all on an equal footing', make no attempt to substitute their "nouns" for verbs such as their epsilons of "elementhood or membership". Quine even speaks of "defective nouns"[53]—whose chief defect as "nouns", according to Lesniewski's grammar, is that they are not nouns at all. (§ 1.5)

In *1951* (§ 36; also in *1960*, § 53) Quine adopts the similar but less arithmetical 'expedient' that he invented earlier and patterned more closely on Wiener's original model, finding it 'convenient to think of' relations as classes, since 'any notion of pair which meets' the purely formal demands expressed by Rosser above 'will serve our purpose'. So the "class" formula corresponding to its six-word "relational abbreviation" of form 'R(x, y)' in Quine's book is always to be 'imagined' or 'thought of, theoretically,' as written out in full primitive notation without definitional abbreviations.[78] The unabbreviated expansion really in Quine's system is not actually printed in his book, nor have I taken time and space to write it down and count the symbols. But, if my calculations are correct, it would contain 266, 506, 344, 873 words. A single example of a corresponding description of a thunderclap following a lightning flash would be difficult to publish, understand, and remember. Lack of perspicuity might be more troublesome in extramathematical descriptions than in purely formal calculation. Yet Tarski too (in *1933* and *1936*, § 5) "reduces relations to classes" as a preliminary to defining "the semantic concept of truth" for, among other things, "relational" formulas.

Lesniewski kept in mind the extramathematical applications of logic and mathematics, and sought to clarify what he meant by his constants and how he used them outside the realm of purely formal calculation, unlike Russell's[54] formalist 'watchmaker who is so absorbed in making his watches look pretty that he has forgotten their purpose of telling the time, and has therefore omitted to insert any works'. So instead of presenting an empty case and hoping for its conversion by other hands into a ticking timepiece, Lesniewski made sure he could use his watches to tell time by inserting his works himself. No more than Russell did he aim at a 'liberalization' which, according to Quine's 1940 preface to his inconsistent system

of *Mathematical Logic*, 'besides making for algorithmic facility,...
turns out to render the existence of infinite classes demonstrable
without special postulation'—though one might ask whether the
members of Quine's "counter sets" are sufficiently "homogeneous
and concrete" to be intuitively correlated with and used to count
individual objects. Russell[55] considered only to reject 'various technical devices' of mixing types:

It would be natural to suppose—as I supposed myself in former days—that, by
means of constructions such as we have been considering, the axiom of infinity
could be *proved*....taking all kinds of objects together, and not confining ourselves
to objects of any one type, we shall certainly obtain an infinite class, and shall
therefore not need the axiom of infinity. So it might be said.

Now, before going into this argument, the first thing to observe is that there is an
air of hocus-pocus about it: something reminds one of the conjuror who brings things
out of a hat. The man who has lent his hat is quite sure there wasn't a live rabbit
in it before, but he is at a loss to say how the rabbit got there. So the reader, if he
has a robust sense of reality, will feel convinced that it is impossible to manufacture
an infinite collection out of a finite collection of individuals, though he may be
unable to say where the flaw is in the above construction. It would be a mistake to
lay too much stress on such feelings of hocus-pocus.... But...when the above argument is scrutinised it will, in my opinion, be found to be fallacious.... The fallacy
involved is..."confusion of types."

No more than Frege, Whitehead, or Russell did Lesniewski claim
for his system Quine's[48] 'virtue of involving no complications in the
matter of meaningfulness of formulae', so that 'we can compose
formulae in simple manner', uninhibited by grammatical restrictions, replace meaningful relational propositions by mixtures of
nonverbial expressions of higher levels and different categories,
substitute the results for variables at will, 'without fear of meaninglessness', and even prove as "theorems" lines which might be taken
from the poetical (not the logical) works of Lewis Carroll, and which
presumably are "true" in whatever Pickwickian sense their equally
poetic negations must be "true", in a "two-valued" system, if they
are not.[53] Nor did Lesniewski agree with Tarski,[32] as opposed to
Russell,[55] that there is 'obviously no obstacle' to introducing variables of transfinite level which 'so to speak run through all possible'
levels, and which can be used as functors or arguments of propositional functions (or even as both functors and arguments of the
same functions), regardless of the categories of other expressions in

the same context. (Tarski adds that 'we must proceed with the greatest caution if we are not to become entangled in antinomies.... But we cannot go into details here.') At least, conventions being relative to aim, Lesniewski did not agree if the relevant aim is to construct, not just an uninterpreted calculus mechanically reproducing meaningless duplicates of familiar or desirable forms, but an interpreted and true system; indeed, as Tarski[32] hoped, to obtain "languages" actually superior 'in abundance of expressible concepts', from which it is 'but a step' to practically grammarless set-theoretic calculi, 'much more convenient and actually much more frequently applied' as an 'apparatus for the development of logic and mathematics', and of 'very simple structure', since 'all their variables belong to one and the same semantic category'—even though all their constants do not, since the epsilon of set theory is not treated as a noun even by set-theoreticians. For, even if the game turned out to be formally consistent, Lesniewski had no wish to facilitate arbitrary manipulation of formulas by mutilating grammar, abolishing grammatical distinctions between different parts of speech, and making expressions he classified into different categories interchangeable and substitutable for the same variables. His own aim was to know and be able to explain what he meant by the abundance of "concepts he expressed" in canonic language L. So he prescribed a basic logical grammar that no more permits replacing one part of speech by another of different category than does the grammar of English or of any other Indo-European language. (§ 5)

4.8 Treatment of antinomies[43]

Just as he distinguished true mathematical sciences from uninterpreted formal calculi, Lesniewski distinguished genuine antinomies from mere formal contradictions. He thought it not at all surprising, but only natural, that contradictions should result from ambiguity, confusion, faulty definition or axiomatic characterization, and dubious presuppositions arbitrarily manipulated according to unintuitive rules. If such artifacts were antinomies, then antinomies could be invented and eliminated at will. But to Lesniewski a contradiction represented an antinomy if and only if he believed it, paradoxically, to be validly deduced from true propositions. The technical kink in a calculating mechanism signalized by formal contradiction can be artificially eliminated by various experimental devices.[56] But the conflict of belief latent in an antinomy, of which contradiction is merely an overt symptom, is not a technical fault to be repaired by trial-and-error tinkering, without understanding what is wrong and why the repair "seems to work": it is a malady to be remedied by investigating and detecting its sources; making conscious, analyzing, and resolving unconscious ambivalence; and intuitively undermining, freeing oneself from, and substituting sound for mistaken beliefs. Only by diagnosing the general case can one prescribe a remedy that is not merely a palliative of recurrent symptoms but is an effective prophylactic.

Lesniewski believed that attempts to avoid antinomies by ways remote from their historical and intuitive sources could not resolve them but would only blur the vital distinction between true mathematical sciences and uninterpreted formal calculi. His prognosis is confirmed by pragmatic advertisements of the latest models in artificial paradox-preventers as 'arbitrary, unintuitive expedients', and invocations of the goddess of success to bless adoption of '*ad hoc* devices justified only in that, or in so far as, they seem to work' as parts of a convenient and coherent scientific myth, and are 'unavoidable except at the cost of other no less artificial expedients'.[48] Such confirmatory symptoms are a natural expression of reactions like Quine's:

Whatever the inconveniences of type theory, contradictions...show clearly enough that the previous naive logic needed reforming.... There have been other proposals.... But...none of these proposals, type theory included, has any intuitive foundation. None has the backing of common sense. Common sense is bankrupt, for it wound up in contradiction. Deprived of his tradition, the logician has had to resort to myth-making. That myth will be best that engenders a form of logic most convenient for mathematics and the sciences; and perhaps it will become the common sense of another generation. (Quine, *1941*, p. 153)

But no more than Russell (§ 5.1) did Lesniewski consider his intuitive logical common sense 'bankrupt' or 'of no avail'[48] simply because well-deserved and symptomatic contradictions had dealt a salutary shock to naive illusions or abuses of "creative freedom". He did not avow that 'all that can be expected is the exclusion of the logical and semantical antinomies known at present' (Bernays-Fraenkel, *1958*, p. 5); nor that 'the best we can do is to seek some testable condition' presumably including as many 'harmless statements...as is conveniently possible, while excluding any actually refutable ones', weakening a powerful but self-contradictory notion of class 'enough but not too much for future service'.[48] He did not practice pragmatic brinkmanship, calculating risks, devising and testing one experimental deterrent after another, hoping in the end to find one just strong enough effectively to prevent disastrous surprises without boomeranging or proving too costly for logistic economy. Instead, reacting to antinomies as alarm signals to awake from dogmatic slumbers, treating them as outbreaks of latent conflicts and misunderstandings, as the following example illustrates, Lesniewski spent more years even than Russell in analyzing strategic situations and designing positive security measures against unforeseen incidents.

4.9 Initial analysis of Russell's contradiction

In 1911 Lesniewski encountered Russell's paradox, as formulated by Lukasiewicz in *1910* (pp. 129–131) somewhat as follows:

Most classes are not elements of themselves but, as collections, possess properties quite different from the properties characterizing their own elements. The collection of men is not a man, nor the collection of triangles a triangle, etc. Certain classes, however, such as the class of classes, apparently are exceptions to the rule. Since there are non-empty classes, having at least one element, the class of non-empty classes for example is non-empty, and consequently is an element of itself. Now consider the class K of classes not elements of themselves: Since a class is an element of class K if and only if not an element of itself, class K is an element of itself if and only if not an element of itself. Is or is not K an element of itself? If it is, then it also is not. So it is not. Yet if it is not, then it also is. Either of the possible alternatives leads to the contradiction that it both is and is not. What is to be done about it?

For the next eleven years Lesniewski was preoccupied with problems such as this. He wished to "do something about it", but could not at first justify rejecting the assumptions or reasoning that together entailed contradiction. He began by analyzing his actual usage, considering various instances which he did or did not regard as classes, using 'class of' *in the sense of* 'collection of *all*', and consequently disregarding the notion of an "empty class", which he regarded as "mythological".

In *1914* he reasoned as follows: (1) Some object is class of objects (that are) b only if some object is b. (2) An object may be class of such and such objects and at the same time class of other, quite different objects (as illustrated in connection with steps 13 and 14 below). (3) If one and only one object is P, then P is class of P. For example, in Figure I below, segment AB is class of segment AB. By analyzing his usage, Lesniewski arrived at the following definition: (4) P is an element of class K if and only if, for some b, K is class of objects b, and P is b.

In these paraphrases I follow Lesniewski's later mode of expression. (§ 2.1) In *1914* and its recapitulation in *1927* (OM, § 2) he actually used (Polish equivalents of) 'for some significance of expression 'b'' just as he later used particular quantifiers which I paraphrase simply by 'for some b'; and, following Lukasiewicz, used 'subordinate to' just as he later used 'element of' in mereology. (§ 2.1) Here as elsewhere, English idiom sometimes requires insertion of logically gratuitous definite or indefinite articles where none correspond in the Polish translated. (§ 1.7)

Lesniewski's use of 'is' (i.e., '*jest*') in singular predication, corresponding to his later use of '*ε*' in ontology, let him assert that (5) if P is b then one and only one object is P; and (6) if P is b then P is P. Steps 5, 3, and 6 entail that (7–8) if P is a class, then P is class of P and P is P. It follows that (9) if P is a class then, for some b, P is class of b and P is b; in other words, according to definition 4, that (10) if P is a class then P is an element of class P. Since it follows that (11) no object is a class not an element of itself, Lesniewski concluded, on the basis of steps 1 and 11, that (12) no object is class of classes not elements of themselves.

Thus having reached the conclusion that there is no such class, Lesniewski no longer saw 'even a shadow of antinomy' in the contradiction entailed by supposing that the class of classes not elements of themselves either is or is not an element of itself; just as, believing no square to be round, he saw no antinomy in the contradiction entailed by supposing that the round square either is or is not round. He had rid himself of one of the conflicting beliefs that had made Russell's contradiction appear to him paradoxical. (§ 4.8)

Using 'class' in the same, *collective* sense, and interpreting Russell accordingly, (§ 4.10) Lesniewski further convinced himself that

Russell's construction was faulty on the basis of an example like Figure I here.

$$(I) \quad A \underset{\longmapsto\,|\,\longmapsto\,|}{C|D} B$$

It is an instance of step 2 above that (13) AB is class of segments that are either segment AC or segment CB; and at the same time (14) AB is class of segments that are either segment AD or segment DB. Since (15) AC is a segment that is either segment AC or segment CB, steps 13 and 15 together entail that (16) for some b, AB is class of b, and AC is b; in other words, according to definition 4, that (17) AC is an element of class AB. Yet (18) AC is not a segment that is either segment AD or segment DB. Steps 14, 17, and 18 together show that an ingredient element of (the collective) class of b is not necessarily b. On the basis of this counterexample, Lesniewski rejected the assumption that if K is (the collective) class of b, and P is an ingredient element of K, then P is b—an assumption that, if accepted, would lead to a collective version of Russell's contradiction.

For substituting 'the class of classes not elements of themselves' for 'K' and also for 'P', and 'classes not elements of themselves' for 'b', would yield the following instance: If the class of classes not elements of themselves is the class of classes not elements of themselves, and the class of classes not elements of themselves is an element of the class of classes not elements of themselves, then the class of classes not elements of themselves is a class not an element of itself. And this consequence, together with an instance of step 6 derived by substituting 'the class of classes not elements of themselves' for 'P', and 'an element of the class of classes not elements of themselves' for 'b', would yield the following simpler result: If the class of classes not elements of themselves is an element of the class of classes not elements of themselves, then the class of classes not elements of themselves is a class not an element of itself. Consequently the supposition that the class of classes not elements of themselves is an element of itself leads to self-contradiction; and so does the alternative supposition that it is not.

But, having rejected on intuitive grounds the crucial assumption that any ingredient element of the collective class of certain objects is necessarily one of those objects, Lesniewski avoided the contradiction and, in a way consonant with the theories he axiomatized later, reinforced his conclusion that it represented no antinomy. (§ 4.8)

Lesniewski later returned to Russell's contradiction and, in a deeper investigation, revealed the underlying confusion between collective and distributive conceptions, concealed by ambiguous use of "class" or "set" terminology. But since the analysis and deductions by which he then resolved the confusion, and demonstrated Frege's set-theoretic "way out" to be a blind alley, (§ 3.3, § 3.9) are fully presented by Sobocinski in his French exposition of *1949–50*, which is more widely accessible than Lesniewski's Polish accounts of his initial analysis of 1914, I omit this further example of Lesniewski's treatment of antinomies. Here I only comment that nothing more clearly reveals the philosophical rationale of Lesniewski's system than his investigations of the contradiction which was his point of departure; that his own formulation of the contradiction had for him the paradoxical character of a genuine antinomy, unlike more familiar formulations that seemed to him merely the natural but formally contradictory or absurd consequences of faulty definition[41] together with ambiguous or meaningless usage; (§ 4.8) and that to re-create the paradox it is necessary to "forget" or "dis-remember" the distinction between collective and distributive conceptions which emerged from the analysis by which he resolved the antinomy, and return to the uncritical and—as it turned out—ambiguous usage of "class" or "set" terminology that made Russell's contradiction so baffling.

4.10 "Collections not actually composed of their elements"

The need for critical analysis of traditional notions and principles of "naive set theory" was demonstrated by Russell's contradiction, which through analysis lost the paradoxical appearance of an antinomy but stimulated the development of mereology and ontology, in the way retraced by Sobocinski in *1949–50*. Lesniewski was not the first to make casual distinctions between (1) collective use of "set" or "class" terminology, indispensable to describe collections or totalities literally composed of their ingredient elements, and (2) distributive use of the same terminology, convenient in the material mode of expression of informal logic (§ 1.8) but not needed in formal logic. (§ 3.3.2) Such distinctions are made, incidentally, in earlier writings,[57] such as Frege's critique of Mill, Husserl, Dedekind, and Schröder, or the analyses that led Russell to what has been called his "no-class theory of classes",[10] in which Lesniewski detected the 'aura of mythical specimens from a copious gallery of "invented" objects' concerning whose existence Russell himself had doubts. But so far as I know Lesniewski, in mereology and ontology respectively, was the first to base two complementary deductive theories on exact axiomatic characterizations of these two distinct uses. Whereas ontology needs no operators of "class abstraction", though distributive "class" terminology may be used to paraphrase its theses into the material mode of expression, (§ 1.8) Lesniewski stressed that mereology and his related investigations are based on the conception of a class (or set) of such-and-such as a totality of individuals that are such-and-such, a collection literally composed of all those individuals as ingredients, which are not necessarily discrete. This conception he considered firmly based in popular usage and in the theoretical tradition of Cantor.

For example, according to one of Cantor's[58] characterizations, 'Any set of distinct things can *itself* be regarded *as a unity, a thing* in which those things are ingredients or constituent elements', as a musical composition is composed of sounds, or a picture of matching parts, which together constitute it and of which it is the collection.[59] But, though Lesniewski felt that, on the whole, his conception agreed with Cantor's, he demurred at Cantor's[60] suggestion that a musical composition, as a collection of sounds, is related to the Platonic εἶδος or ἰδέα, and to what in the dialog *Philebus* Plato called μικτόν. Lesniewski remarked that to pass judgment here would exceed his qualifications as an interpreter. Nor was he sure how far his conception harmonized with Cantor's characterization of a "manifold" or "set" as "any multiplicity that can be conceived as a unity; i.e., any *Inbegriff* of definite elements that can be bound into a whole by means of a rule";[60] "any collection into a whole of definite, distinct objects of our intuition or of our thought".[61]

It is true that, in much of "set" or "class theory", the words 'set' or 'class' are used informally more or less interchangeably with such expressions as 'assemblage', 'aggregate', 'totality', or 'collection (of all)'. But do Cantor, many later set-theoreticians, and the untutored layman distinguish this *prima facie* collective use from distributive use clearly and consistently enough to permit unequivocal judgment of their intentions? As several quotations in this section illustrate, many theoreticians seem to confound the distinction by beginning with concrete aggregates of material objects, and then proceeding to speak of "sets" or "numbers" as "abstract mathematical individuals" or "logical objects of thought", citing "collections of sets, numbers, etc., finite or infinite", as further, "abstract examples", without marking the transition; and meanwhile, despite the efforts of Frege, persist in confusing numerals with numbers, the sign with what it signifies, by speaking of "actually infinite sets of numbers" while pointing to finite sets of numerals chalked on the blackboard, or inked on paper, and ending in suggestive 'et cetera's or trailing off into enigmatic dots of infinite ellipsis.[62] (§ 4.6)

For example, in *1953* (ch. 1, § 1) Fraenkel illustrates and explains as follows what he calls Cantor's "definition" (the last characterization quoted above):

Imagine a certain number of concrete objects. From a fruit bowl, for example, take five apples, two oranges and one banana. The collection of this fruit is a certain aggregate, and each individual fruit is an element of the aggregate. Even in this obvious example, collecting the fruit into an aggregate is an intellectual act.... Instead of fruits we can collect abstracts. Thus we may form aggregates whose elements are certain qualities, certain laws of nature, or certain triangles. In particular, we can collect numbers.... If we compare these numbers with the set of fruits..., we see that there is no difference between them...except for the particular nature of their elements.... Now consider the set of all possible books.... Be the print as small and the paper as thin as can be imagined, the space up to the farthest visible stars holds only a tiny part of our collection of books.

We may use this gigantic set to point out the unspannable abyss between the finite and the infinite.... Until now, we have considered *finite aggregates*, i.e. aggregates containing a finite number of elements only. Since the formation of an aggregate is a purely abstract act of thinking, we can drop the restriction to finite sets and form *infinite aggregates*, containing an infinite number of elements. For the present we use the terms *finite* and *infinite* in the simple sense intelligible to every reader.... It is true that instances of infinite sets can hardly be indicated as long as the elements are confined to objects of our possible sensual perceptions.... As a matter of fact, the recent research in physics has in increasing measure convinced us that the exploration of nature cannot lead to either infinitely large or infinitely small magnitudes. The assumption of a finite extent of the physical space, as well as the assumption of an only finite divisibility of matter and energy...completely harmonize with experience. It thus seems that the external world can afford us nothing but finite sets.

'Therefore in order to reach infinite sets, we have to consider the *creations of our thinking....* In sharp contrast' to 'the improper or *potential infinite*, or…the infinite as a limit', 'the set of all natural numbers…is a proper, definite *actual infinite*'.

And popular usage likewise seems to me to shift, metaphorically and unconsciously, from collective to distributive use and back again, by means of the verbal bridge of a common word and its associated metaphors; or to employ the word not so much ambiguously as vaguely and indeterminately, without conscious distinction or transition. *Practically*, the distinction does not matter, where no choice is necessary: Individual persons belong to educational classes and to social sets or classes, individual volumes belong to sets of volumes, and pieces of furniture belong to sets of furniture in *either* sense. So only further interrogation would reveal whether an individual speaker (1) would admit arbitrary parts of such elements, and arbitrary collections of either elements or parts of elements, as elements in turn, thus committing himself to the collective as distinguished from the distributive interpretation, (2) hesitated to decide, or (3) had in mind some yet more specific sense requiring special analysis. Such "intermediate" or "mixed" uses may be explicable only in terms of some combination of distributive and collective uses, and thus require the combined resources of ontology and mereology: for example, (1) certain "statistical" uses exemplified in speaking of "the average or representative member, or the majority, minority, or specified fraction of a class"; (2) sociological talk of "conflict, dispersal, or decline of classes"—parlance which, depending on context, might refer to the behavior of a totality, of certain of its elements, or of "members having a certain property" implicitly understood but not explicitly mentioned; (3) or advertisement of "sets whose elements are not detachable for separate sale", with a tacit restriction to elements or parts of a specific kind. Judging by Cantor's famous "definition", I am not sure that his usage was not such a mixture, too vague or ambiguous to be considered either consistently distributive or unequivocally collective.

Certainly, to use the material mode of expression, (§ 1.8) the mereological relation of ingredience is all too easily confused with the "logical relations of being or singular inclusion, weak (not necessarily existential, Boolean) inclusion, and strong (existential, quasi-Aristotelian) inclusion", symbolized in canonic language L by 'ε', '$\subset$', and '$\sqsubseteq$', respectively. (§ 1.7) For up to a point these relations are parallel, each being transitive, antisymmetrical, and "quasi-reflexive" in the sense that any member of the field (as defined in D91 of terminological explanation LVI° in § 7.3 below) bears that relation to itself. So, as Frege remarked in his *1895* criticism of Schröder for confusing ingredient of elements in a totality or "collective class" with logical inclusion, logical relations can be consistently and intuitively represented by Euler diagrams—up to a point: the point where the analogy supporting the use of diagrams goes lame, and the different relations must be sharply distinguished, for reasons made evident by examples such as those in § 3.3.2 above.

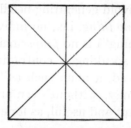

For example, only the five squares in Illustration A here are (as expressed in the material mode, "member elements of the distributive class" of) squares in Illustration A; whereas the one comprehensive square, the four smaller square subsections, the triangles into which the five squares are subdivided, and any other arbitrary parts of Illustration A, discrete or overlapping, are alike ingredient elements of the totality (i.e., "collective class") of Illustration A, none of which need be indivisible. Similarly, only individual soldiers are ("member elements of the distributive class" of) soldiers in an army; whereas soldiers, platoons, companies, battalions, regiments, divisions, the army itself, and arbitrary collections of any of these or of their parts are ingredient elements of the totality (i.e., "collective class") of soldiers in the army.

Thus the analogy between mereological ingredience and logical inclusion breaks down at the point, remarked by Frege, where Schröder tries to make a distinction between ingredience as an individual and ingredience as a collective class. For in mereology there is no ground for such a distinction, since any totality (i.e., "collective class") of individuals is itself an individual, and any individual is the same individual as the totality of itself; whereas in logic, to use the material mode of expression, "singular inclusion" of individuals not only can but must be distinguished from weak, not necessarily existential, Boolean inclusion of "distributive subclasses". Furthermore, a collective class as a totality ("aggregate, assemblage, whole, or collective unity"), literally and not just metaphorically composed of its ingredient elements, vanishes with its ingredients, as the wood vanishes with its trees. No class in *this* sense can be "empty", despite vain efforts to generate by "creative definition" (§ 6.1.9) a nonentity to be christened "the empty class". As Frege remarked, if an oval figure or zero-sign inked on paper could be magically endowed with any requisite new property (of more than purely formal character) merely by verbal fiat, then it might not be hard to make diamonds. A so-called "proper name that names nothing" (to be explicit, and to avoid generating needless existential anguish, a "name" that names *no thing*, i.e., no individual—*not* that names "the Nothing or No-Thing") is no *proper* name, nor even literally a name, but is strictly speaking a contradiction in terms. (§ 1.5, § 4.4) On the other hand, a noun such as 'nonentity' (§ 1.7) that names no individual may, without even pretending to be a name, (§ 1.5) be both significant and useful, as for example in the following remarks:

No individual is a nonentity, and so too no individual is a totality of a nonentity; (§ 6.3) consequently any (§ 1.7) nonentity or any totality of a nonentity is (*vacuously*) anything whatever; whereas it is false (but meaningful to say) that the nonentity or the totality of a nonentity is ingredient in itself or in anything else. In other words, as expressed in the material mode of informal logic, it is false (but meaningful to say) that ("the empty distributive class of") a nonentity exists, and so too that the ("empty") collective class of a nonentity exists; consequently ("the empty distributive class of") a nonentity or the ("empty") collective class of a nonentity is (vacuously) *logically included* in anything whatever; whereas it is false (but meaningful to say) that the ("empty distributive class of a") nonentity or the ("empty") collective class of a nonentity is *mereologically ingredient* in itself or in anything else.

The italics directly above indicate another point of contrast remarked by Frege (who habitually expressed himself in the material mode) (§ 6.1.6) where the analogy between logical inclusion and mereological ingredience breaks down.

Since "elements" are the real constituents of Schröder's "collective classes", as of Dedekind's "systems", Frege points out in his Introduction of *1893*, an "empty class" ought to be no more possible for

Schröder than an "empty system" for Dedekind. But Dedekind, though 'for certain reasons' he excludes "the empty system", remarks in *1888* (pp. 2–3) that 'for other investigations it may be convenient to invent such a fiction.' Frege comments that apparently such a fabrication would be quite permissible, only Dedekind renounces it 'for certain reasons', whereas Schröder dares to "invent" an "empty class". Though both appear to agree with many others that one may invent at will, not only nonentities, but even inconceivabilities, Frege continues, it is less likely to be agreed just where arbitrary invention is to be limited, if at all.

In *1927* (OM, § 3) Lesniewski painstakingly demonstrated, by proofs and examples, that his mereology is immune from Frege's criticisms. He showed, in particular, that two suppositions which Frege throughout *1895* apparently treated as interchangeable are not equivalent, as interpreted collectively in mereology, even in the sense of having the same truth value. But I pass over his detailed examination of Frege's argument, and of Frege's, Zermelo's, and Russell's remarks concerning "classes as extensions", because to do justice to the issues involved would require going far beyond the scope of the present discussion. In any case, Frege's argument invalidates neither (1) the thesis of mereology that any individual is the same individual as the totality (i.e., "collective class") of itself, as the totality (i.e., "collective unit set") of individuals identical with itself, and as any (§ 1.7) totality (i.e., "collective singular class") of which that individual is the sole element, (§ 6.3) nor (2) the thesis of ontology that any individual is the same individual as itself, and as (expressed in the material mode, "the distributive unit class" of) individuals identical with itself. So, as Quine writes in *1951* (§ 25; cf. *1937*, p. 82), whether Frege's and Quine's words be taken in the collective or in the distributive sense, Frege's arguments 'do not militate against the identification, in particular, of individuals with their unit classes (and hence with the unit classes of their unit classes and so on). Within the domain of individuals, retention of the pre-Fregean attitude leads to no trouble.' Using illustrations similar to those of Lesniewski, Quine adds characteristically (italics mine) that 'Though I have been led to this course by considerations *only of technical efficiency*, a certain naturalness may be argued for it on the basis of such illustrations as the following. Let us think of points as individuals, and of lines and planes as classes of points. Then the intersection or logical product...of two planes is a line; but, if we distinguish individuals from their unit classes, the intersection of two lines is only the unit class of a point and not a point. Again, whereas a line in a given plane is related to the plane by inclusion..., a point in a given line is not related to the line by inclusion if we distinguish individuals from their unit classes; the point is rather a member of the line, while the unit class of the point is included in the line. Under the proposed theory, on the other hand, intersections of lines are points, and points bear to lines the same inclusion relation which lines bear to planes.' Cf. Carnap, *1937*, § 71e.

Lesniewski commented in *1927* (OM, § 3) that, unfortunately,

Frege's criticism of the addiction to inventing nonentities was still all too opportune. According to Hausdorff (in *1927*, pp. 11–12),

A set arises through collection of individual things into a whole. A set is a multiplicity conceived as a unity. These or similar propositions, as definitions, would be justly criticized as defining something in terms of itself, or even the obscure by the still more obscure. But they may stand as pointers, indicating a primitive act of thought, familiar to all men, which perhaps neither can nor need be resolved into yet more primitive acts. We content ourselves with this conception, and assume as fundamental that a thing *M* determines, in a peculiar, indefinable way, certain other things *a*, *b*, *c*,..., and conversely—a relation that we express by the words: the set *M* consists of things *a*, *b*, *c*,...

called its elements. Hausdorff goes on to say that a set may be finite or infinite, and cites as examples the finite sets of inhabitants of a city, of hydrogen atoms in the sun, of integers from 1 to 1000, and the infinite sets of all integers, of all points on a line, and of all circles in a plane. In this way, Lesniewski remarked, Hausdorff prepares for the "admission" (Dedekind and Schröder would say "invention") of a "collection containing no element" and therefore hardly composed of "elements collected into a whole": 'On grounds of expediency we admit also a set 0, the *null* or *empty set*, which contains no element.'

According to Sierpinski's definition (in *1923*, pp. 4–5) of the product of two collections as 'the collection composed of all and only those elements' common to them both, any such product must be composed of at least one such common element, Lesniewski commented; and since in our world, as distinguished from that of mythology, nothing can well be composed of nonentities, there can be no product of collections having no common element. Yet, just as Hausdorff "admits", Sierpinski "invents" an "empty collection" to be the desired product of collections having no common element.

Lesniewski was tempted to caricature Fraenkel's invention of an "improper set" in Fraenkel's own words as a "set that, although a set, is properly speaking not really a set at all". For in *1923* (p. 55) Fraenkel points out that the intersection of certain sets containing no common element equals the 'so-called *null set*', an 'improper set' introduced 'on purely formal grounds, to facilitate simpler and more convenient expression of certain facts', and 'defined as the set containing no element at all. The null set is therefore not really a set at all, but is to be taken as such and designated by 0.' Lesniewski qualified his criticism by remarking that Fraenkel's use of the expression 'improper set' may be modeled on colloquial use of expressions such as 'dead man', 'false diamond', or 'painted fish' [63] (the modifier 'improper' being not a "co-ordinate adjective"— i.e., conjunct in a nominal combination—but rather, like 'non-', the functor of a nominal combination whose argument is 'set'). But such an escape clause would avoid introducing the contradiction of a "set that is not a set" only at the price of admitting that the "improper set" is not a set that is improper but, rather, is something that is not a set at all, yet is to be "taken for" and "treated as a set".

More than six decades ago Frege criticized confusion of collective and distributive conceptions, and questioned the "creative freedom of invention" cherished in theory; more than three decades ago Lesniewski axiomatically characterized the two distinct conceptions, and reinforced Frege's attack on over-free creations. Yet, were he still living, Lesniewski might add the following current examples: In *1953* (ch. 1, § 1) Fraenkel, without answering Frege's and Lesniewski's objections, persists in freely creating illustrative mixtures of the two conceptions; continues to defend 'that possibility of *free creation* in mathematics which is not equalled in any other science'; declares that 'it is no accident that at the birth of the theory of sets...was coined the sentence: the very essence of mathematics is its freedom'; and then proceeds with the illustrations already quoted above. In *1958* Fraenkel remarks significantly that 'one cannot expect to determine the *number* of...subsets...before it is unambiguously settled *what they are*' (Bernays-Fraenkel, p. 26); and, after speaking of 'the paradise into which Cantor has led the mathematician', proceeds freely to "re-create the object" of Lesniewski's unanswered criticism of *1927*, stipulating that his

universe of discourse is to encompass...objects that are not sets, in the ordinary sense of 'set', and *ipso facto* contain no members.... Now, at least for mathematical purposes there seems to be no real need to deal with individuals or rather to countenance more than one individual. For such purposes we may therefore treat all objects as sets, with the exception of just one object, the one and only memberless object whose existence is needed for obvious technical reasons. (We should like, for instance, that the intersection of any two sets should belong to the universe even when these sets have no member in common.) We also decide at present not to admit non-elements (though systems encompassing non-elements may be, in a certain important sense, more adequate...). Altogether, we want all objects to be elements and all but one to be sets... we finally decide to use the term 'set' from now on...for any object belonging to the universe of discourse....*the one and only member-less object will also be regarded as a set* and called '*null-set*', as customary. (Fraenkel and Bar-Hillel, pp. 13, 29–31)

And in *1953* Rosser,[56] after discussing 'various proposals for elimi-nating Russell's paradox' and finally opting for 'the possibility of denying step 7, which appeals to us as the most natural of all', thus adopting Quine's expedients at the price of a condition restricting Cantor's theorem, (§ 6.2.3) remarks of 'classes of this sort, which, from an intuitive point of view, are not at all sharply defined', that 'For such large, vague classes on the frontier of our comprehension, it is not really surprising that some properties,...extrapolated from finite classes, should fail to hold.'

4.11 Lesniewski's assessment of other systems[43]

As his model of systematic development Lesniewski took *Prin-cipia Mathematica*, whose general outlines he intended to follow in elaborating his own system. But as his model of deductive rigor he took Frege's *Grundgesetze der Arithmetik*, which impressed him as the most valuable 'deductive consolidation of foundations of mathe-matics' since the work of classic Greece. Yet even before demonstrat-ing the inadequacy of Frege's repair, Lesniewski concluded from the tenor of Frege's appendix of *1903* that Frege himself could not intuitively justify the set-theoretic revision by which he proposed to repair his foundations of arithmetic, undermined by Russell's contradiction. Zermelo, in his investigations of *1908* (p. 124), con-cluded that 'not every arbitrary extension of a concept may be treated as a set'; and consequently, in what Lesniewski called Zer-melo's 'architectonically refined construction' of foundations of set theory, also relied on what Lesniewski considered unintuitive re-strictions to rule out contradictions. Therefore Lesniewski regarded the consistency or inconsistency of Frege's and Zermelo's systems 'quite irrelevant' to the 'reality-directed intellectual torment' of intuitive compulsion to believe presuppositions "true" and infer-ences "correct" that together lead to contradiction, thus representing antinomies which can be resolved only by intuitively under-mining their sources. For 'Mathematics without intuition cannot effectually remedy the maladies of intuition.'

Though he drew attention to Chwistek's criticisms of the first edition of PM, neither was Lesniewski satisfied with the more scrupulously formalized system of Chwistek's "theory of construc-tive types", in which he proved a contradiction. In formulating his own terminological explanations and directives, Lesniewski had often recognized how careless oversight of certain conditions or provisions would admit contradiction. So he looked for and dis-covered analogous defects in formalization of other systems. In *1929*, introducing his outlines of a system of foundations of mathe-matics 'new in certain respects', he presented his formalization 'with all modesty' as 'but one of numerous attempts' since Frege, 'one of the possible foundations of the totality of the system of mathematical sciences'. But although he suspended final judgment of the work of Hilbert and his collaborators pending its completion, he added that he knew of no formalization (other than his own, which 'at the moment' satisfied him in both respects) that both met his requirements for deductive systems and resolved familiar antin-omies in what he considered an adequate way. In his last publica-tion, nearly a decade later, he did not qualify his earlier statement that he knew of no other foundation of mathematics whose direc-tives were adequate to establish all theses, effectively admitted (*anerkannt*) in the system, without either arousing doubt as to interpretation or at the same time admitting contradiction in some way unforeseen by its author.

4.12 Avoidance of misconceptions (§ 6.1)

Lesniewski had little sympathy with ideological catchwords, and rarely used stereotyped labels without double quotes. He never printed "nominalist" labels for himself or his systems. (§ 3.1) But his thinking might be called "nominalist" in tendency—though more in the spirit of medieval "nominalists" and thinkers like Hobbes (writing of names, propositions, truth and falsity) than of latter-day would-be "nominalists" willing to compromise and "countenance or admit entities too abstract to recognize as proper individuals", provided only favorable references seem to occur in the material-mode testimonials of accredited physicists. (§ 4.6)

Lesniewski expressed his "nominalist" tendencies linguistically and constructively, not by denying "existence of abstract entities", (§ 1.8) but by constructing a logical basis for canonic language L, in which language individual aspects of reality can be described without "referring to abstract entities" at all. (§ 6.1.7) If he had to be labeled, at risk of misinterpretation, he might perhaps be called an intuitive logician or "Lesniewskian intuitionist", who rigorously formalized his intuitive logic in universally valid classical and "linguistically or constructively nominalist" systems. This criss-cross classification helps explain why he avoided capitalized exclusive alternatives and chose individual names for his systems, which despite their "nominalist" linguistic construction are "logically pure and metaphysically neutral", in a sense yet to be explained, (§ 6.1) and might even be judged "platonistic" by the obscuring half-light of oversimplified formal criteria of "ontic commitment".[48]

For Lesniewski did not suppose that, to be meaningful, constants must name and variables "ambiguously designate or take as values entities which, if not concrete, must perforce be abstract". He did not speak of "ontic commitments", nor imagine these (whatever they are) could be formally assessed—say, by inspecting quantifiers and variables written on paper—without understanding the intended interpretation of quantifiers and use of the system in question. (See Russell, *1959*, pp. 235–237, and Hall, *1960*, ch. 2.) He treated with care the equivocal family of "existential" expressions,[64] ambiguous relations and confusions of whose different members proliferate misconceptions dismaying those who, from a logical point of view, prefer desert landscapes and deplore overpopulation of the world by "classes" or "sets" that they would rather not "countenance, recognize, or admit", if unwanted generations could only be "avoided" without sterilizing classical mathematics.[48] So Lesniewski saw no ground to discriminate between innocuous bound variables and inconstant bounders from the concrete to the abstract.

Quine[48] for example admits in his *Mathematical Logic* only one type of variable, uses the material mode of expression, speaks of the "existential" quantifier, which he reads as "there exists...", and, under the influence of his syntactical criterion of "ontic commitment", associated in his mind with this "existential" reading, fixed in the slogan 'to be is to be the value of a variable', hesitates to bind other variables, lest he have to "recognize their values". Instead he prefers to use corresponding "schemata" or "schematic dummies" in his metalanguage. These "dummies" serve approximately the same purpose as variables in Lesniewski's system itself. But Quine does not doubt their innocence because 'Schemata are to sentences not as names to their objects, but as slugs to nickels', and Greek variables bound within quasi-quotes "take as values" not "abstract entities such as classes" but (presumably concrete, not abstract forms of) expressions in his system. Bernays,[65] also expressing himself in the material mode, cites Quine's interpretations in connection with Frege's suggestion that contradictions might perhaps be avoided by distinguishing "proper from improper objects". Bernays then uses a terminology deviating from Von Neumann's and Quine's to make such a distinction between (1) "a fixed domain of sets as collections, which are proper individuals or mathematical things representing classes", and (2) "an open universe of classes as extensions of predicates, which have in comparison the character of ideal objects not always represented by sets". (§ 5.0) He decides that 'From this point of view we shall not tend to bring formally together classes and sets in one domain of individuals and even we might refrain at all from handling with a domain of classes to which bound variables refer.... Thus we are induced to employ class variables only as free variables, what in fact is sufficient for giving our formal language a suitable flexibility, so that we are not obliged to employ continually syntactical variables in the formulations. At the same time this formally stronger separation of the classes from sets conforms to the view that the universe of mathematical objects (sets) is not itself a mathematical object', and lets each of the 'axiomatic statements of class existence' (except the 'axiom of choice...the only axiom stated in existential form') be equivalent to 'explicit introduction of a class formation' replaceable 'for the usual mathematical purposes... by an assertion of mere set existence'.

Consequently Lesniewski could admit variables of every semantic category without having to "admit extralinguistic counterparts, however abstract". He opened no Pandora's box of ontological monsters; neither did he unlock Quine's[48] dam sluices and precipitate 'a torrent of universals against which intuition is powerless', in which we 'can no longer see what we are doing, nor where the flood is carrying us'. His logical foundation of classical mathematics is not 'up to its neck in ontological commitments' just because he bound variables of high levels. To import existence of "extralinguistic values" to Lesniewski's variables and assimilate all variables, regardless of category, might commit Lesniewski against his will to an ontological asylum housing "beings" of every species, a Noah's ark pairing linguistic representatives of every category with extralinguistic mates. But quantification in language L is a logical device innocent of existential import, not a potential delinquent spawning illegitimate entities and liable to paternity suits whenever its guardian relaxes control. To say this is not to "explain away apparent ontic commitments". For none appear unless they are imported. Quantification in language L need not be proved innocent; it may be presumed innocent unless found guilty. And implications of "platonism" would be difficult to substantiate without implanting extraneous evidence of unrecognized offspring.

How did Lesniewski find his way through a maze of antinomies without following hard-beaten tracks and misleading verbal bridges to end in ambivalent abstraction and desperate pragmatism? — Partly by not stirring up a dust in which he could not see, through careless use of the material mode (§ 1.8) of expression and through assimilation of different categories; especially by not confusing his logic of "existence" with "existential" reading of particular quantification; and above all by not taking steps requiring pragmatic absolution in lieu of intuitive justification. Certain key steps and verbal bridges he avoided may be summarily indicated without attempting to trace all the complications of a bewildering maze: Instead of asking in the material mode whether or how "classes or sets" are discovered in reality or conceived in mind, whether principles holding for finite can validly be extrapolated to infinite "classes", (§ 4.10) and other such questions, he carefully analyzed distinct but easily confused uses of "class" or "set" terminology. (§ 3.3) Habitually *not* calling particular quantification "existential", (§ 6.1.3) Lesniewski did not read into it import of existence (in the sense in which "only any exemplified class, set, or property exists"), (§ 1.7) nor cast suspicion on innocent theses by material-mode paraphrases such as the following: "Since the null class has no member, it does not exist; so, by existential generalization, there exists a class that does not exist." (§ 6.1.9) No more than Frege did Lesniewski imagine that he had the creative freedom or power to call extralinguistic entities into existence by verbal fiat. He merely assumed he could define significant constants by meaningful definitions and investigate the consequences. Recognizing their indispensability in practice, he never pretended to dispense with definitions, nor rationalized neglect and the 'double life'[78] by calling them "mere abbreviations, notationally convenient but theoretically dispensable". Rather, he formulated comprehensive directives making it possible to derive particular corollaries from explicit definitions. So he had no need to assert particular generalizations, without proof, as axioms, interpreted as "existential postulates" expedient in pragmatic myth, and controlled by artificial devices to prevent their engendering contradictions (not just "arbitrary classes" and misconceptions). Lesniewski himself interpreted such postulates as pseudo-definitions which, if used at all, as partial substitutes for definition, should likewise be controlled by intuitive semantic principles of logical grammar. But in canonic language L, corollaries of the same form being derivable from explicit definitions, except in "infinite cases" investigated hypothetically, pseudo-definitions are dispensable, and pragmatic rationalization is not necessary. (§ 6.1.9)

5. LESNIEWSKI'S GRAMMAR OF SEMANTIC
CATEGORIES

No more than Russell[66] did Lesniewski agree with Quine[48] that 'all the various reformulations of logic...proposed for avoiding the contradictions' implicit in 'the inferential methods of uncritical common sense' are 'artificial and foreign to common sense', 'naturalness, for whatever it is worth', having been 'of course lost', so that one can only choose from 'a multitude of mutually alternative, mutually incompatible systems..., each with only the most bleakly pragmatic claims to attention'. Nor did he, like Quine,[48] regard grammatical 'precautions against contradictions' merely as 'one of various alternative devices, and, perhaps, indeed the least convenient of known devices for avoiding the paradoxes': at best necessary nuisances endurable only for lack of smoother expedients; annoying obstructions to mass production of replicas along the streamlines of least resistance.

Rosser, opting (p. 206) for Quine's stratagem after considering various maneuvers to avoid Russell's contradiction, expresses this common attitude as follows: 'All the present suggestions for avoiding the paradoxes retain a tinge of artificiality. Certainly the theory of types is artificial. In the Zermelo set theory, the distinction between sets and nonsets is irksome, and the various criteria for deciding between sets and nonsets are not intuitively very natural. In the system of the present text, Quine's New Foundations, it is irksome that not all conditions determine classes, and the criterion of stratification for deciding which conditions shall determine classes is not intuitively natural.' Bernays[65] prefers his distinction between "sets" and "classes" (§ 4.12) to not only the logical grammar of PM, because 'Still the distinction of types here present amounts to a complication which is somewhat cumbersome for the mathematician', but also to Quine's combined stratification requirement and distinction between "elements" and "non-elements", because

'The use of the criterium of stratification has a clearly experimental character' and induces 'some strange features' such as 'the existence of sets or classes having themselves as elements'.

5.1 Rationale of logical grammar

As early as *1903* (§ 492) Russell thought that the principle of logical types 'seems to adhere very closely indeed to common sense'. Five years' further study of paradoxes reinforced this conviction and directed him away from Frege's set-theoretic revision toward 'Mathematical logic as based on the theory of types'. Already in *1910* (p. 37), re-stating his foreword of *1908*, he omitted his earlier qualification that 'this, however, is not a merit upon which much stress should be laid; for common sense is far more fallible than it likes to believe', and stressed that although

the theory of logical types...recommended itself...in the first instance by its ability to solve certain contradictions,....the theory...is not wholly dependent upon this indirect recommendation: it has also a certain consonance with common sense which makes it inherently credible.

And in *1959* (pp. 79–80), in retrospect, Russell wrote that

I settled down to a resolute attempt to find a solution of the paradoxes. I felt this as almost a personal challenge and I would, if necessary, have spent the whole of the rest of my life in an attempt to meet it.... In the end, it became entirely clear to me that some form of the doctrine of types is essential. I lay no stress upon the particular form of that doctrine which is embodied in *Principia Mathematica*, but I remain wholly convinced that without *some* form of the doctrine the paradoxes cannot be resolved... the solution...to be wholly satisfying...should, on reflection, appeal to what may be called 'logical common sense'—i.e....should seem, in the end, just what one ought to have expected all along.... [This] condition is not regarded as essential by those who are content with logical dexterity. Professor Quine, for example, has produced systems which I admire greatly because of their skill, but which I cannot feel to be satisfactory because they seem to be created *ad hoc* and not to be such as even the cleverest logician would have thought of if he had not known of the contradictions.

5.1.1 Systematic analogy and ambiguity. Like Aristotle,[30] Russell[66] concluded that language is pervaded by systematic ambiguities resting on systematic analogies in use between homonyms of different categories or logical types. To ensure consistent determinacy of meaning in an adequate logical reconstruction, it is essential to treat systematically ambiguous logical or mathematical

schemes as representing unbounded hierarchies of different but systematically analogous and true theses ranged in tiers above the basic theses of lowest level. The contextual conventions of PM are designed to maintain valid adjustment of relative types without always requiring explicit indication of absolute types, so that a single formula or deduction may represent valid analogs of higher but parallel levels. Although type restrictions strictly applied would, for example, require parallel arithmetics at successive levels, in practice these stratified but systematically analogous arithmetics are all schematically represented by the basic set of systematically ambiguous formulas. Not even assertions of relative existence or number are falsified by consistently elevating relative types, so long as the number of individuals is treated as an open question.

After studying paradoxes for eleven years, Lesniewski implemented Russell's conclusions by measures designed to attain the same ends without ambiguity. (§ 6.1.8) Neither he nor Russell shared the cost-cutting pragmatism that led Quine[48] experimentally to detach Russell's principle of relative types from its intuitive grammatical foundations for streamlined mechanization in Quine's stratification requirement:

Intuitively all these cleavages and reduplications are of course unwelcome; and technically also, for they call continually for more or less elaborate technical manoeuvres by way of restoring severed connections. (Quine, 1951, § 29)

For, like Aristotle,[30] Russell and Lesniewski saw, not Quine's[48] 'curious reduplication of constants' and 'severed connections' to be restored, but systematic contextual analogy in use between individual constants of the same form but different grammatical category and significance, which homonyms to be univocal must be distinguished.

5.1.2 Prevention of vicious circularity.

Concluding with Poincaré that the paradoxes characteristically "involved vicious circles", in which a generalization about all cases of a certain kind appears to generate a paradoxical case of the same yet not of the same kind, Russell designed his ramified grammar of types to preclude circles of self-reference, in which a proposition refers to itself or a generalization includes itself in its own scope, and "illegitimate totalities containing members involving, presupposing, derived from, or definable only by the totality itself".[66] His order restrictions, in particular, were to preclude "reflexive or impredicative definition[27] of something in terms of an illegitimate totality to which it belongs", by requiring that what is defined always be of higher order than any variable of any generalization in the definiens, and hence not substitutable for any variable of the same order and type. But by proscribing as meaningless unrestricted generalizations "about all propositions (resp. properties, etc.)", which generalizations are themselves not admitted as propositions, these restrictions[31] impeded formulation even of basic logical laws such as that of excluded middle, use of elementary methods such as mathematical induction, and definition (in terms of "class intersection or union") of "what has all or certain specified characteristics". To offset these crippling restrictions and permit deductions he thought indispensable for logical foundation even of arithmetic and analysis, Russell, for lack of a better alternative, felt constrained to overcome his doubts by pragmatic arguments (convenient for justifying dubious assumptions) and to postulate the "axiom of reducibility", a schematic principle authorizing assertion of any number of axioms. By postulating that for any functional "ϕ" there is a coextensive "predicative" equivalent of lowest order compatible with its type, to which it is "reducible" in extensional contexts, Russell virtually nullified order restrictions within classical logic and mathematics, though not in nonextensional contexts of certain extraneous paradoxes. But he himself was the first to suggest that even if the reducibility principle were "pragmatically necessary" for logic, it is not necessarily "logically true", agreeing with critics such as Chwistek,[30] Wittgenstein,[45] and Ramsey (*1925*) that it is not "necessarily even true, but might in fact be false, and even if not false is true by happy chance, not by logical necessity, so that it does not logically prove" its consequences, and ought not to have been postulated at all. As Russell wrote in *1959* (p. 120),

This axiom...seemed necessary if we are, on the one hand, to avoid contradictions and, on the other hand, to preserve all of mathematics that is usually considered indisputable. But it was an objectionable axiom because its truth might be doubted and because (what is more important) its truth, if it is true, seems to be empirical and not logical. Whitehead and I recognized that the axiom was a blot upon our system, but I at least thought of it on the analogy of the axiom of parallels, which had been considered a blot upon Euclid's geometry. I thought that some way of dispensing with the axiom would be found sooner or later, and that meantime it was a good thing to have the difficulties concentrated in one single point.

5.1.3 Formal criteria of meaning. Despite his apologies for the ramifications of his theory, together with the counterbalancing postulate of reducibility, and his indications that he would welcome improvements attaining the same ends by simpler and more intuitive means, Russell[66] never apologized for the underlying grammatical principle of type restrictions. Although never satisfied that his presentation was 'final', in his *1946* reply to his critics (pp. 691–692) he remained 'convinced that some sort of hierarchy is necessary', and hoped for some theory 'simple and adequate, and...satisfactory from the point of view of...logical common sense'. Already in *1919* (p. 135) Russell wrote:

Now the theory of types emphatically does not belong to the finished and certain part of our subject: much of this theory is still inchoate, confused, and obscure. But the need of *some* doctrine of types is less doubtful than the precise form the doctrine should take; and in connection with the axiom of infinity it is particularly easy to see the necessity of some such doctrine. (§ 4.0, § 4.7)

In 1918 (pp. 267–269) Russell had used an Aristotelian[30] illustration of systematic ambiguity to stress that statements about "types" are 'about symbols...never about the things themselves':

The theory of types is really a theory of symbols, not of things. In a proper logical language it would be perfectly obvious. The trouble...arises from our inveterate habit of trying to name what cannot be named. If we had a proper logical language, we should not be tempted to do that. Strictly speaking, only particulars can be named. In that sense in which there are particulars, you cannot say either truly or falsely that there is anything else. The word 'there is' is a word having 'systematic ambiguity', i.e., having a strictly infinite number of different meanings which it is important to distinguish.... This is really important..., that the relation of the symbol to what it means is different in different types.... There is not one single concept of 'meaning'..., so that you can say in a uniform sense 'All symbols have meaning', but there are infinite numbers of different ways of meaning, i.e., different sorts of relation of the symbol to the symbolized, which are absolutely distinct.... You can always only get at the thing you are aiming at by the proper sort of symbol, which approaches it in the appropriate way. That is the real philosophical truth that is at the bottom of all this theory of types.... I think the importance of philosophical grammar is very much greater than it is generally thought to be.

In *1924* (pp. 333–334) Russell emphasized the grammatical rationale of his principles:

Certain contradictions convinced me, after five years devoted mainly to this one question, that no solution is technically possible without the doctrine of types. In its technical form, this doctrine states merely that a word or symbol may form part of a significant proposition, and in this sense have meaning, without being always able to be substituted for another word or symbol in the same or some other proposition without producing nonsense. Stated in this way, the doctrine may seem like a truism. 'Brutus killed Caesar' is significant, but 'Killed killed Caesar' is nonsense, so that we cannot replace 'Brutus' by 'killed', although both words have meaning. This is plain common sense...

Endorsing the distinction between logical and semantic paradoxes, Russell concluded in *1937* (p. xiv) that

This renders possible a great simplification of the theory of types, which, as it emerges from Ramsey's discussion, ceases wholly to appear unplausible or artificial or a mere *ad hoc* hypothesis designed to avoid the contradictions... The technical essence of the theory of types is merely this: Given a propositional function "φx" of which all values are true, there are expressions which it is not legitimate to substitute for "x" in "φx". The theory of types gives rules as to permissible values of "x" in "φx". In the detail there are difficulties and complications, but the general principle is merely a more precise form of one that has always been recognized. In the older conventional logic, it was customary to point out that such a form of words as "virtue is triangular" is neither true nor false, but no attempt was made to arrive at a definite set of rules for deciding whether a given series of words was or was not significant. This the theory of types achieves.

In *1940*, reiterating (p. 26) that "meaning", like "truth" and "falsehood", has 'a hierarchy of meanings, corresponding to the hierarchy of languages', Russell pointed out (pp. 62–63) that 'The conception of a hierarchy of languages is involved in the theory of types, which, in some form, is necessary for the solution of the paradoxes', though his hierarchy (suggested in his 1922 introduction to Wittgenstein's *Tractatus*) differs from Tarski's and Carnap's, and concluded that 'The arguments for the necessity of a hierarchy of languages are overwhelming' (if classical logic is to be maintained). Although he apparently overlooked Tarski's[28] acknowledgment that Lesniewski had first reached this conclusion, even before 1922, later in his *1940 Inquiry* Russell[66] sketched a formal meaning criterion akin in spirit to Lesniewski's grammar of semantic categories: 'No ordinary language contains syntactical rules forbidding the construction of nonsensical sentences' such as 'quadruplicity drinks procrastina-

tion'. Yet 'it must be possible to construct a language' in which
only every sentence constructed according to syntactical rules out
of meaningful words is significant. Even though the concept of
"significance" is not purely syntactical,

it should be possible, in a good language, to give syntactical rules determining whe 叔
a sentence is significant... The rules of syntax in ordinary language are obviously
intended to prevent nonsense, but they fail to achieve their purpose completely...
It must clearly be part of our...problem to construct better rules of syntax, which
shall automatically prevent nonsense.... early...guided by the mere *feeling* as to
what is significant,...we hope in the end to arrive at something better.... It is
customary to say that every *proposition* is true or false, but...nonsensical sentences
are neither. If we are to apply the law of excluded middle..., we must first know
what sentences are significant, since it is only to them that the law can apply...
The distinction between strings of words that signify something and strings of words
that signify nothing is, in many cases, perfectly clear...not always easy, but there
can be no doubt that some forms of words signify something, while others do not,
and that among those that signify something some signify what is true, while others
signify what is false. We must therefore find some way of defining the difference
between strings of words that are nonsense and strings of words that signify something..., to construct rules of syntax which...shall insure that every combination
of words which obeys the rules shall be significant, and every significant combination
of words shall obey the rules. This work has, in fact, been done by the logicians, not
perhaps completely, but with a fair degree of adequacy...guided by feeling, like
the plain man. We cannot rest satisfied with our rules of significance unless we can
see some reason for them...
    We might try to define significance in a more linguistic fashion. We first divide
words into categories, having affinities with the parts of speech. We then say...
any word may be replaced by another word belonging to the same category without
making the sentence lose significance...; but we cannot rest content until we have
found some reason for our linguistic rules.... The syntactical theory of significance—
especially when connected with an artificial logical language—... says "logically
well-behaved people will attach significance to sentences of the following kinds"....
constructing a logical language in which the psychological conditions of significance...are translated into precise syntactical rules.... it is of the essence of the use
of language that we can understand a sentence correctly compounded out of words
that we understand, even if we have never had any experience corresponding to
the sentence as a whole.

Like Russell, Lesniewski[30] made no apology for positive grammatical rules and criteria of meaning, which he considered as natural
and semantically justifiable in formalized as in unformalized languages. He asserted that he would feel compelled to adhere to his
grammar of semantic categories, if he wished to make sense, even
had no "antinomies" ever existed.

But are Lesniewski's categories really semantic or merely syn-

tactic ? This question is prompted by the current distinction between
(1) semantics as the study of symbolic systems in abstraction from
their cultural setting and functions, concerned solely with intralinguistic properties and relations of expressions and their extralinguistic reference, and (2) the intralinguistic, syntactic dimension of
semantics, concerned solely with the formal properties and relations
of expressions in abstraction from their extralinguistic reference.[67]

The question is natural but misleading, for Lesniewski's categories are both: semantic in intention but syntactic in formalization.
Despite Lesniewski's complete formalization of his grammar, it
seems appropriate to follow him in calling his categories semantic,
not merely syntactic, for the following reasons: First, as semantic
pioneer Lesniewski[30] had priority for his usage, having adapted his
terminology from Husserl's '*Bedeutungskategorien*' years before
others differentiated the syntactic subdimension of semantics.
Second, since semantics (in sense one above) includes syntax, even
syntactic categories of an interpreted system or language may be
called semantic as well. Finally, since Lesniewski drew no dichotomy
between formalization and interpretation, but formalized his systems precisely to specify the interpretation he intended, the categories of language L, which include extralogical as well as logical
members, are semantic in the fullest sense. Yet to call them merely
syntactic might further the predominance of just that one-sided
preoccupation with form in abstraction which Lesniewski himself
so vigorously resisted.

Lesniewski was as critical of *pure* formalism as Frege, Husserl,
and Russell; and his logical grammar, though syntactically formalized for rigor and clarity, is as semantic in intuitive foundation
and design as theirs, Aristotle's *Categories*, and grammar of parts of
speech in unformalized languages. Lesniewski[30] called attention to
Husserl's[30] evocation of the idea of a general, purely logical grammar, based on classification of semantic categories, revealing the
import of the grammatical distinction between categorematic and
syncategorematic, "complete" and "incomplete" expressions, and
designed as normative meaning criterion to discriminate sense from
nonsense, rather than logically true from false results, and to prevent
nonsense (*Unsinn*) rather than formal contradiction (*Widersinn*).

Lesniewski implemented this idea by formalizing his intuitive logical grammar of semantic categories for canonic language L, designing it to serve as natural correlate to grammar of parts of speech in unformalized languages.

5.2 Construction of Lesniewski's grammar (§ 7.1)

Recognizing before 1922 the metalinguistic character of the paradoxes against which Russell's order restrictions were directed, Lesniewski concluded that Russell's stratification was not mistaken in principle but simply misplaced.

(Even in his *1940 Inquiry* Russell, in laudable endeavor to do justice not only to logic but to psychology and epistemology, persists in "alternatively defining" key expressions, here logically, there psychologically, and making psychologistic distinctions between expressions of his "object language" and those of higher, "metalinguistic" order.) Suppose simple restrictions of category or type are adequate to preclude logical and mathematical paradoxes, and order restrictions are not essential to preclude extraneous paradoxes in extensional language L. Then order restrictions are dispensable together with their antidote the reducibility postulate. For if the latter is valid, both are logically superfluous, and the original and revised systems of PM alike are replaceable by an extensional system of comparable power, in which every functional "ϕ" of higher order in the ramified system is replaced by the coextensive "predicative" equivalent of the basic order of its type. There is just one, since according to the reducibility principle there is at least one; and at most one, since any two would be coextensive according to the extensionality principle (or even the partial extensionality principle of the revision for functional "ϕ" of the same order, any two being of the same order).[68] So Russell's order restrictions are no more essential in language L than his reducibility postulate itself.

Russell himself recognized in *1910* (pp. 58–59) that his postulate is equivalent to the assumption that "any combination or disjunction of predicates is equivalent to a single predicate". In the spirit of Frege's criticism (in *1884*, § 86) of Cantor for appealing to a mysterious "inner intuition" when he could and should have based his proof on definitions, Russell in *1919* (pp. 71, 73) added that 'The method of "postulating" what we want has many advantages; they are the same as the advantages of theft over honest toil. Let us leave them to others and proceed with our honest toil.... The great advantage of' the method of "construction" or explicit definition over "postulation" is that 'it requires no new assumptions, but enables us to proceed deductively from the original apparatus of logic' without raising new "ontological" questions.

So Lesniewski replaced order restrictions and pseudo-definitions, such as postulates of "reducibility, definability, or class abstraction", (§ 6.1.9) by comprehensive directives of definition, extensionality, etc., embodying a logical grammar of semantic categories simpler than but comparable in scope to Russell's. To guard against vicious circles and semantic paradoxes without barring crucial deductions,[31] Lesniewski as it were transformed, translated into his metalanguage, and retained "metalinguistic ghosts" of Russell's order restrictions, which he replaced by grammatically more intuitive and mathematically less restrictive requirements of hierarchical stratification in construction of language L. Thus Lesniewski's simple but constructively relative grammar of semantic categories has affinities with both simple and ramified grammars of "logical types", yet is not so nearly comparable to either as to a transformation and synthesis of what he considered intuitively and grammatically justifiable in both, combining simple category restrictions in the "object language" with metalinguistic requirements of stratification suggestive of Russell's order restrictions transposed into a more natural key.

What one finds relatively "natural or artificial, intuitive or arbitrary, and clear or unclear" varies according to background, familiarity, and motivation. It is hardly surprising, for example, if grammatical requirements and criteria of meaning seem more reasonable, and set-theoretic restrictions less natural, to someone preoccupied with semantic problems than to others intent on deriving formulas of certain forms within or proving metatheorems about various formal calculi, without considering their interpretation and use outside formalist mathematics, and long accustomed to quote Kronecker and call "integers natural numbers, individuals, entities, objects, or things". So it may be relevant to mention why I decided to study Lesniewski's work at a time when I knew no Polish and little more than his name. Exploring the territory that Frege, Russell, and Whitehead managed in one lifetime to bring under systematic survey in what impressed me as a comprehensive and comprehensible way, I was looking for a system that consolidated, developed, and perfected their pioneer work of deductive unification combined with philosophical clarification. Alternative set-theoretic calculi impressed me, rather, as remarkable ventures in substituting formal ingenuity for semantic analysis and explication. Whereas, looking into Lesniewski's technical key to his unfamiliar systems, I found that, despite its esoteric appearance, I could understand and intuitively justify his requirements to myself on semantic grounds, without having to appeal instead to the apparent provisional success of an internally coherent pragmatic myth.

Lesniewski's grammar, like simple grammars of types, is free from order restrictions; yet is designed to preserve consistent determinacy of meaning in logical reconstruction of foundations of classical mathematics (including Cantor's theories), on the usual hypotheses of infinity and selection or well-ordering. There is just one category of propositions (resp. singulary connectors, binary connectors of propositional arguments,..., nouns, singulary verbs, binary verbs, etc.). So generalizations restricted only by the natural limits of meaning, (§ 6.1.2) whose paraphrases begin 'For every x...' (where 'x's belong to the semantic category indicated by context), (§ 6.1.8) are meaningful propositions in canonic language L. For example, just as the metalinguistic principle of bivalence holds for any proposition, the law of excluded middle holds in Lesniewski's system itself, without restrictions of order: For every p, either p or not p.

Lesniewski's logical grammar, like Russell's,[55] might be described as finite at any stage but constructively unbounded or "potentially infinite". For, although at any stage of construction language L contains expressions of only a finite and countable number of semantic categories, and in practice there is seldom need to go beyond the first few degrees and levels of construction, at any stage language L may be extended and new semantic categories introduced, according to the initial directives, by asserting introductory theses containing expressions of those categories. The unbounded hierarchies of protothetic and ontology begin with (expressions of) the basic semantic categories of non-functorial expressions containing no gaps and taking no arguments but relatively "complete and self-contained": propositions and nouns, respectively; and can be constructively extended, step by step, from expressions of any semantic category already in language L, to functors of yet higher degree or level.

The semantic category of a functor depends on and can be identified by specifying the category of the function together with the number and respective categories of its arguments. So, in the quasi-arithmetical, "fractional" notation devised by Ajdukiewicz in *1935* and developed by Bar-Hillel in *1953*,[30] the semantic category of any expression can be indicated as follows: The two basic, non-functorial categories of propositions (i.e., indicative sentences) and of nouns are indicated by 's' (for 'sentence') and by 'n', respectively. The category of a functor is indicated by a "fraction" whose "numerator" indicates the category of the function as a whole and whose "denominator" is a sequence of one or more indications, in order, of the categories of the respective arguments of the function. For example, the category of binary connectors (i.e., functors, such as 'if and only if', of propositional functions having two propositional arguments) is indicated by 's/ss'; the category of binary verbs (i.e., functors, such as 'is', of propositional functions having two nominal arguments) is indicated by 's/nn'; the category of functors, such as 'non-', of nominal functions having one nominal argument is indicated by 'n/n'; and the category of functors, such as 'precedes with respect to', (§ 1.8) of functions that are binary verbs and that have one binary verb as argument is indicated by

$$' \; \frac{s/nn}{s/nn} \; '.$$

In *1953* Bar-Hillel explains and illustrates how quasi-arithmetical principles and procedures can be based on this notation and mechanically applied in syntactic analysis.

Since the precise details of Lesniewski's grammar are explained in § 7.1 below, I single out here only a few salient principles such as the following: If functions of the same number of arguments belong to the same category, then so do their functors if and only if so do all respectively homologous arguments, occupying the same relative position. No expression belongs to more than one semantic category. Constants C and C' belong to the same category if and only if some and hence every proposition containing C would remain significant, though not necessarily of the *same* significance and truth value, even were C replaced by C'; i.e., if and only if propositions P and P', equiform except that P' contains constants equisignificant to C' at one or more places where P contains constants equisignificant to C, are both significant. (§ 7.1) By this criterion, for example, 'Socrates' belongs to the same category as 'human' and 'non-human', 'is' belongs to the same category as 'equals' and 'is-identical-with', and 'non-' belongs to the same category as 'identical with', in the following propositions, since despite differences in significance and truth value these propositions alike are significant: Socrates is Socrates; Socrates is human; Socrates is non-human; Socrates equals Socrates; Socrates is identical with Socrates. This criterion of semantic category reflects the familiar grammatical principle of "purity of parts of speech", according to which only all expressions belonging to the same "part of speech" are interchangeable without loss of meaning, confusions (such as mistaking other parts of speech for binary or relational verbs) (§ 4.7) yielding not meaningful propositions but only nonsensical mixtures.

Thus Lesniewski's grammar of semantic categories formally resembles simple grammars of "logical types", except for its rigor and generality of formalization and certain other salient characteristics:

(1) *Its exhaustiveness according to its principles of classification:* Providing in advance for introduction of any semantic category of the unbounded hierarchies constructible beginning with expressions belonging to the basic, non-functorial categories of propositions and of nouns, respectively, it is "richer" than non-exhaustive simple type grammars not providing in advance for the "potentially infinite" hierarchies beginning with propositional as well as with nominal expressions. But, as the grammar of extensional language L, whose propositions are all meaningful, true or false *indicative* clauses or sentences, (§ 5.3) it does not provide for interrogative, optative, imperative, or hortative operators, nor for nonextensional modal or attitudinal functors such as 'It is necessary that' or 'So-and-so believes that', nor indeed for nonextensional functors of any kind. (§ 6.1.6) And, since ontology as well as protothetic has just one basic category of non-functorial expressions, Lesniewski's grammar differs in principle also from grammars that classify nouns into different logical types according to referential criteria of existence or number. Since all nominal expressions belong to the one category of nouns, (§ 1.5) regardless how many individual objects they may name, subject and predicate even of singular predication belong to the same semantic category, and existence, inclusion, etc., may grammatically be asserted even of individuals.

(2) *Its "constructively nominalist"* (§ 3.1) *and "contextualist" formalization:* (§ 6.1) Only any individual phrase that is in a proposition but not inside a quantifier, and hence is either a function, generalization, or constant or variable term, belongs to a certain semantic category in language L; expressions or forms of expression in abstraction from propositional context, terms inside quantifiers binding variables, and non-phrases such as punctuators or quanti-

fiers are excluded from category membership. (See T.E. XXXIX' of § 7.1 below) Since no expression belongs to more than one semantic category, only any phrase in a proposition but not inside a quantifier belongs to just one. Since context eliminates indeterminacy of significance, such as ambiguity between homonyms, constants and variables (even of the same category) and expressions of different categories need not be differentiated by using distinctive, predetermined forms of expression. By rigorously applying contextual principles and using brackets of distinctive forms as category indices, instead of subscripts or superscripts on terms, Lesniewski minimized use of category indices, permitted homonymous use of equiform constants to emphasize systematic analogy in use between constants of different category and significance, increased perspicuity and flexibility of expression, and obtained the practical and mnemonic advantages of homonymy or systematic ambiguity without specialized conventions or any actual ambiguity. (§ 6.1.8)

(3) *Its constructive relativity and principle of stratification:* To preserve consistent determinacy of meaning, take the place of order restrictions, and preclude vicious circles generating semantic paradoxes, in metalinguistic descriptions of expressions of the "object language" or stage of language L described, Lesniewski relativized his directives and grammar to stages of construction of canonic language L. More precisely, he formulated his directives, and defined terms used to describe or prescribe rules for expressions of any semantic category, relative to theses representing successive strata or stages of construction of language L. Accordingly, an expression belongs to a certain semantic category and has a certain significance only from a certain stage onward: i.e., relative to a certain thesis and hence to any later thesis of language L. Though I use derelativized metalinguistic expressions such as 'proposition' or 'propositional' freely in uncritical contexts, their implicit relativity needs and can be made explicit, by definitional expansion, in critical or technical contexts. For example, what I loosely call a proposition (resp. propositional) is actually a proposition (resp. is of the semantic category of propositions) relative and only relative to a certain thesis, and hence to any later thesis: i.e., from a certain stage of language L onward.

5.3 Propositions

Lesniewski's directives are designed to assure that any thesis of his system be a proposition, relative to itself and to any later thesis, in the sense of being an individual, (§ 1.3) indicative (declarative) clause or sentence, determinate in meaning and either true or false.

Lesniewski's use of 'proposition' for indicative sentences, after the medieval precedent mentioned by Moody in *1953*, p. 30, should not be confused with other uses: for example, (1) the practice of writers like Russell, who speak of equisignificant indicative sentences as instances or expressions of the same "proposition", treated as an equivalence class (§ 1.8) of indicative sentences with respect to equisignificance; or (2) the familiar manner of speaking of equiform declarations as individual instances of the same "indicative sentence or proposition", treated as an equivalence class of individual declarations with respect to equiformity. (§ 1.3) Following Lesniewski, I define forms, significances, values, etc. as equivalence classes (of individuals) with respect to equiformity, equisignificance, equivalence, etc. and speak of (individual) propositions of the same form, significance, value, etc.

So, just as the law of excluded middle holds in the "object" language or language stage, the principle of bivalence holds in its metalanguage or metalinguistic stage of language L. For in canonic language L, according to Lesniewski's definition, expressions violating his requirements are not propositions at all; so, just as negations of propositions are propositions, "negations" of non-propositions are non-propositions. By refusing the title of proposition to "meaningless, indeterminate, indefinite, or ill-formed" expressions, Lesniewski avoided having either to sacrifice the principle of bivalence or else to call their equally unsuitable "negations" true.[53] His definition is designed to assure that any proposition P be well formed: Any word in P is either a term or punctuator; and any term is either constant, variable, or inside a quantifier serving to bind at least one variable of some ingredient of P. Since any phrase in P but not inside a quantifier belongs to exactly one semantic category, the significance of any constant and the range of substituents (i.e., expressions substitutable) for any variable in P is also unique. Any constant in P is introduced by an axiom or explicit definition that satisfies Lesniewski's requirements for introductory theses, and that uniquely fixes its semantic category and significance, characterizes its use, and, if a definition, also makes it eliminable from any propositional context in favor of constants, already significant in language L, in terms of which it is defined. Having only its assigned significance and delegated capacities, it is used only in the prescribed ways. Punctuators, variables, and terms binding variables are not redundant but also perform their official roles. For example, since brackets in P are properly mated, each pair embracing the one or more arguments of some function, no bracket or function in P is redundant or vacuous. Nor does P contain a vacuous or improper quantifier enclosing no term at all or enclosing a redundant word, such as a punctuator, term binding no variable, or superfluous term uselessly duplicating another term of the same form inside the same quantifier. Any generalization in P belongs to the semantic category of propositions; so does its nucleus, (§ 11) which is either a propositional variable or function, not a generalization or non-propositional expression; and each of its variables is bound by the homomorph inside its quantifier, the terms inside being permutable without altering its significance or truth value.

At any stage one may map maps, describe descriptions, generalize about generalizations. So far as no rule prohibits proceeding indefinitely, there need in theory be no absolutely last stage, finality being unattainable if there is no finality to attain. In the sense that at any stage one may climb a rung higher, the ladder of theory need have no last rung, even if one cannot stand on a rung and at the same time use it as building material for others. But familiar semantic paradoxes suggest vain attempts to catch one's own shadow: to complete the spatiotemporal activity in time, and in such a way, as to make the map of the moment map, the description describe, the generalization generalize about itself truly if and only if falsely. These are not just empty or misleading analogies, since expressions are individual spatiotemporal objects, and no nonentity such as a non-individual expression exists to be named, even by perfectly significant nouns. (§ 1.5) But, to abandon metaphor, suppose for example that E is an expression of a certain semantic category introduced by thesis T of language L. Then any proper name of E is introduced only by some later thesis T', which is not a thesis relative to T. So an expression containing such a name cannot be significant nor belong to a semantic category relative to T; and, although generalization within language L is restricted only by natural limits of meaning, (§ 6 . 1 . 2) a description or generalization containing such a name cannot belong to the semantic category of propositions relative to T, though it can belong to the category of propositions relative to T' or to some yet later thesis.

Semantic paradoxes formulated in terms of proper names of expressions may thus be precluded. But the question arises how to exclude semantic paradoxes relying instead on descriptions of expressions. For example, let language L be developed sufficiently, beyond its basis of protothetic, ontology, and mereology, to admit also (1) Lesniewski's metalinguistic definition of 'proposition relative to', as given in T.E. XXXIX' of § 7.1 below, and (2) introduction of the nouns needed, in addition to the mereological functor 'ingr', (§ 1.7) to compose a faithful translation into language L of the English sentence mentioned below. Let thesis T be the latest thesis introducing such a noun into language L. Now consider the translation that I have just made, in language L and inside a rectangle, of the following sentence in English: The proposition, relative to thesis T, in the rectangle drawn in room 209 in Caldwell Hall in Chapel Hill in North Carolina in 14 September 1960 (E.S.T.), is false. Suppose this translation is in fact the sole proposition, relative to thesis T, in the rectangle drawn in room 209 in Caldwell Hall in Chapel Hill in North Carolina in 14 September 1960 (E.S.T.). Then how can 'false' and 'true' be introduced in such a way as to do their work without entailing, under these circumstances, the paradoxical conclusion that my translation is true if and only if false, and hence is both true and false? (The straightforward way to introduce 'false' into language L would seem to be by a definition to the effect that only any *proposition* (relative to some thesis) that is not true is false, following upon a prior thesis introducing 'true'.)[29] The answer to this question is considerably less clear to me than my answer to the following question. But see Lejewski on the Liar and the concept of truth.

5.4 Do Lesniewski's requirements preclude vicious circles?

Do they not permit "circular, reflexive, or impredicative definitions and illegitimate totalities too large to be consistent"?—Characterizations of such "faults" are too diverse and ambiguous to permit straightforward answer. Even Poincaré[27] and Russell[66] differed in detail despite their vague agreement in principle, and each used the material mode to express equivocal criteria at least verbally different on different occasions. Much of the ensuing discussion assimilates the characteristics of a fogbound cove wherein at certain singular points one falls without warning into vicious circles and, because the exact sources of danger are obscure, trespass must be altogether prohibited.

For example, in classic formulations of criteria, terms such as 'totality', 'collection', 'assemblage', 'class', and 'range' might be taken in either a collective or distributive sense; 'involving', 'presupposing', 'derived from', and 'definable only by' are used interchangeably without being precisely defined;[27] and neither the formal nor the material mode of expression is used strictly enough always to make clear whether "propositions, functions, and classes" are supposed to be linguistic expressions or extralinguistic entities.

Presumably sources of contradiction are "vicious" whether involved in circles or not. But individual definitions can be at most accomplices in suspect systems. So exact location of illicit sources and allocation of collective responsibility for contraband smuggling of illegitimate totalities is not easy to judge. And even the question whether a system is consistent admits no absolute answer, though Lesniewski's system of logic is demonstrably consistent by and relative to classical elementary logic. (§ 6.4)

It is true that Lesniewski's logical grammar permits a defined constant to belong to the same semantic category as variables of generalizations in the definiens; and such a definition or defined constant will loosely be called "formally impredicative" for brevity in the following discussion. But "vicious circularity" cannot fairly be judged by this purely formal criterion alone, which takes no account of the constructive relativity and stratification of canonic language L, nor of Lesniewski's consistent distinction between collective and distributive uses of "class" terminology, "object" and metalanguage, and formal and material mode of expression. In particular, the directives of definition and substitution here in question are formalized and constructively relativized as are his other directives. (§ 7) So the question may best be answered indirectly, by proleptically mentioning certain relevant details of canonic language L. (§ 7)

The "range" of constant terms substitutable for any variable of any thesis is definite and has a finite number of members at any stage, relative to any specified thesis, but may be numerically enlarged in developing the system by introducing new constants of the same category. (In this sense it might loosely and suggestively be called "definite, and at any stage numerically finite, but constructively unbounded, open to admission of new members, and so potentially infinite".) No constant is defined in terms of "itself" (more precisely, in terms of an equisignificant constant, of the same form and category, (§ 1.3) or in terms of another, derivative con-

stant defined in terms of it). Nor does any constant belong to the
category or "range" of a variable, relative to any thesis preceding
its definition; though, if "formally impredicative", it belongs to the
category of a variable of a generalization in the definiens, relative
to its definition and to any later thesis. For, though any constant is
of unique semantic category and significance relative to its introductory thesis and to any later thesis, it is not a significant constant
at all relative to any preceding thesis. And though, like other expressions, it may be substituted for any variable (of the same
category) of any thesis, any resulting substitution instance must
follow its introductory thesis.

To establish a generalization "about members of a class" it is not
always necessary to "comprehend all individual members" and
confirm all substitution instances severally. (If it were, generalizations would always be replaceable by logically equivalent finite
conjunctions or alternations of simple propositions or their negations, and no knowledge would be too general to be expressed by
such "molecular" compounds.) Nor is this even possible when individual members or instances cannot all be enlisted or checked in a
register, as when their number is indefinite or unknown, generalization being useful just when they cannot all be summoned, mustered,
and called to attention for intuitive inspection, so that only inference or conjecture can provide more or less reliable information
about them all, or about arbitrary members not present for roll
call. It is necessary only to establish the generalization itself on
whatever basis is available—individual instances, other generalizations, etc.—, whereupon any substitution instance may logically
follow. For this it is necessary, and may be sufficient, to fix a general
criterion for determining whether or not arbitrary candidates belong
to the class in question and for testing generalizations about whatever satisfies this criterion.

Fortunately, even outside pure logic and mathematics, generalizations can often be established more or less reliably even for classes
whose members cannot be catalogued.

I deliberately use the rather vague terms 'established' and 'knowledge', to cover not
only theses "proved" in logic and mathematics but also extraneous generalizations
which, because meaningful, hitherto unfalsified, and at least partially "confirmed"

or "corroborated" by testing, have so far served as conjectures or hypotheses useful in predicting and explaining individual aspects of reality, and which, so far as is known, may even be true.

For otherwise human knowledge would be incommunicable and non-cumulative, amounting at each moment, for each isolated individual, to little more than the momentary content of his conscious awareness, since even individual knowledge becomes generalized in being communicated.[69] And generalizations may be at least as important as their individual instances. It may for example be as important to know that there is danger (or none) in the field one is about to explore as to know individual names, kinds, numbers, locations, and dispositions of bulls, mines, or what-not. The mere existence of nuclear bombs has proved as disturbing as their unknown total. As Russell wrote in *1940* (pp. 240–241),

If you find a man dead of a bullet wound, you judge that *somebody* shot him, and if you are a good citizen you desire to replace the variable by a constant... But sometimes you are quite content with "there is an x such that fx", and have no wish to replace it by "*fa*". Examining footprints in the jungle, you may say "a tiger has been here"; in this case, unless you are engaged in a tiger hunt, you have no wish to replace the variable by a perceived constant. Or suppose I say "London has 7,000,000 inhabitants", I shall certainly not wish to replace this by "the inhabitants of London are A and B and C and..." to 7,000,000 terms.

Even within the purely logical or mathematical part of a formalized language L it is not always effectively decidable whether or not a proposition is a thesis. It is decidable in protothetic, where the number of "possible values" of any constant is a finite and specifiable power of two (beginning with the two possible values of any propositional constant),[37] but not in ontology, where the number of possible values need not be finite and determinable. But it *is* always effectively decidable whether or not any putative proof, or finite sequence of propositions beginning with the axiom of protothetic, is a proof of its terminal proposition. And criteria of proof need not depend on those of "formal impredicativity". Suppose for example that proposition P contains a "formally impredicative" defined constant. It would indeed be circular if, to establish P, it were necessary to establish a generalization instanced by and not confirmable without first establishing P itself and equisignificant, say, to a generalization in the definiens of the "formally impredicative" definition in question. But it may not be necessary to proceed in this circular way. It is necessary, and may be sufficient, to have a general criterion for determining the truth or falsity of P. And since, in extensional language L, any defined constant is eliminable from any propositional context, whether or not it is "formally impredicative", its definition does provide such a criterion, even for a proposition such as P, which too is definitionally translatable into a logical equivalent not containing the constant in question, or any derivative defined in terms of it.

Consider a metalinguistic example from the grammar of language L, relative to a thesis fixed as parameter: According to Lesniewski's explicit "inductive" definition, with respect to the base relation of belonging *directly* to the same semantic category, only any ancestral descendant (i.e., "inheritor of all hereditary properties") of E belongs to the semantic category of E. Since one such "hereditary property" is membership in the semantic category itself, the question arises whether Lesniewski's definition is viciously circular: whether his criterion of category membership begs the question, by presupposing a catalog of all hereditary properties itself depending on family membership. No. For it follows, as corollary of the definition, that only whatever belongs *directly* to the semantic category of E, or to the category of a fellow member, belongs to the semantic category of E. And whether expressions are linked by the base relation is determinable by inspection. So, by Lesniewski's definition, whether or not expressions are linked by the ancestral relation (i.e., by some finite power of the base relation), and hence belong to the same semantic category, is recursively determinable in a finite number of steps, without circularity; and category membership is always effectively decidable without begging the question, having a catalog of hereditary properties, or even knowing whether such a catalog could ever be completed.

6. LESNIEWSKI'S SYSTEM
OF LOGIC AND FOUNDATIONS OF MATHEMATICS

6.0 Conception of logic

Protothetic, ontology, and mereology together constitute Lesniewski's system of logic and foundations of mathematics, and provide an axiomatic basis for testable description of reality in canonic language L. Protothetic and ontology unite to compose his system of logic, in which as much of classical mathematics can be reconstructed (on similar hypotheses) as in either edition of PM. Their universally valid directives set the pattern for any further theory, such as mereology, in a deductive hierarchy; together with their logically pure axioms, provide a primitive logical basis for deriving further classical laws and rules for deducing propositions; and are designed to establish an exhaustive logical grammar and syntax for language L, assuring that all its propositions be well-formed indicative clauses determinate in meaning and hence either true or false. (§ 5.3)

Since Lesniewski called only any individual, indicative clause in language L a proposition of L, the foregoing generalizations are so worded as to except rules for using nonextensional or non-indicative expressions (modal, moral, legal, attitudinal, imperative, etc.) and also certain rules taken as "valid" in certain calculi supposed to be "indicative and two-valued": for example, rules not valid for all expressions of appropriate category, regardless of questions of extralinguistic reference, existence, or number; rules for manipulating formulas containing expressions redundant, vacuous, meaningless, or indeterminate in meaning according to Lesniewski's criteria; and "convenient fictions or idealizations", such as rules for deducing consequences from "infinitely many expressions, abstract forms of expressions, or potential expressions not actually written down, by infinitely many potential steps not actually carried out". (§ 4.6)

Lesniewski designed the union of protothetic and ontology to embody and define his exact conception of (indicative) logic: Only any axiom or further thesis asserted in protothetic or ontology according to his directives is a thesis, only any constant introduced by such a thesis is a constant, and only any universally valid rule of inference established on this primitive logical basis is a rule of his logic. If he unwittingly failed to provide in advance for any semantic category (of indicative expressions) or universally valid principle not specialized for extralogical constants, then according to his design it too should be appropriated to his logic by consistently strengthening his primitive basis. But, since mereology only enriches language L by new constants and theses, without affecting its basic logic and grammar, Lesniewski called mereology an extralogical theory. And any further specialized theory would also belong to the theoretical superstructure resting on his logical foundations: for example, mathematical theories in which consequents of conditional, purely logical theses were detached and asserted unconditionally on the basis of extralogical postulates of existence, infinity, selection, well-ordering, or the like.

6.1 Formalization

Lesniewski completely formalized protothetic and ontology, prescribing comprehensive directives for their construction at the beginning, instead of scattering ad hoc rules and conventions fragmentarily throughout their development; in particular, he formulated exact rules of definition, in order to leave no gap in formalization through which faulty definitions could admit contradiction. (§ 3.5.1) From the beginning definitions can be asserted as theses, to expand the vocabulary, and proofs can be carried out strictly in symbols, according to directives requiring no later qualification or addition. There is no exception to Lesniewski's rules, no ambiguity or apparent violations of logical laws; nor are auxiliary investigations or conventions required to justify definitions or substitutions and to preclude amphiboly or inconsistency.[26]

For example, no auxiliary conventions of scope and punctuation are needed to preclude amphiboly of compounds, such as 'pretty little girls' camp', and resulting contradictions, such as those Lesniewski proved (§ 3.9) in Von Neumann's systems, (§ 3.10) since univocality of compounds is guaranteed and their resolution into the intended constituents is uniquely determined by the initial directives. The successive arguments of a function need not even be separated by commas to make clear where one argument ends and another begins. Lesniewski carefully formulated general rules for introducing useful compounds of a combinatory character, such as "many-link" (§ 11) and other compound functions. (§ 7.1) But, by requiring that the functor invariably precede all the arguments of a function, he assured univocality without ad hoc punctuation, and uniformity in treatment of functors without "redefinition" (exemplified in *50 and *62 of PM and in D35 of Quine's *Mathematical Logic*). In *1955* (p. 199) the Wundheilers suggest that since such "frontal" language can be translated with the aid of a dictionary alone, thanks to its uniformity in word order, it may be the most suitable for machine translation. Lesniewski's conventions simplify theory so much that, as Quine[70] points out concerning combinatorial use of brackets, to say that

they resolve ambiguities of grouping gives little notion of their far-reaching importance. They enable us to iterate a few self-same constructions as much as we please instead of having continually to vary our idioms in order to keep stock of basic functions, or constructions, and the techniques needed in handling them. They enable us to subject long expressions and short ones to a uniform algorithm, and to argue by substitutions of long expressions for short ones, and vice versa, without readjustments of context. But for...some...convention yielding the foregoing benefits, mathematics would not have come far.... If we were to devise a logic of ordinary language for direct use on sentences as they come, we would have to complicate our rules of inference in sundry unilluminating ways.

* * *

The practice of always placing functors before arguments of functions, suggested by Chwistek in order to spare punctuation, was adopted by most Polish logicians. Indeed Lukasiewicz, whose propositional calculi contain expressions of only a few semantic categories, manages therein without even brackets. Lesniewski, who admits introduction of new semantic categories without finite limit, and relies on brackets of distinctive forms as category indices, cannot afford to be so economical. The term 'functor' for 'function sign' was suggested by Kotarbinski, and was adopted not only by Polish logicians but also by Carnap, who uses it, however, only for "signs of single-valued functions"; that is, for combinators (§ 11) (i.e., functors of functions belonging to the same semantic category as all their arguments, represented by 'x's in the following scheme) which satisfy the uniqueness condition that there be just one $fx_1 \ldots x_n$ for any $x_1, \ldots, x_n$. (See Carnap, *1958*, § 18, § 33.)

6.1.1 Universal validity. Lesniewski did not beg what he considered extralogical questions but designed systems valid for every x ('x' being nominal, resp. of any appropriate semantic category) and, to use the material-mode idiom of validity theory, "valid for every domain, empty or non-empty, finite or infinite, not just for any non-empty or infinite domain". So his systems are logically pure and metaphysically neutral in that they do not *logically* presuppose or imply what is the population of the universe or the denotation of expressions, though they can be used to investigate the consequences of alternative hypotheses, or as logical basis for extralogical postulates that do. For, since no directive is valid only for names, (§ 1.5) and no axiom or thesis immediately asserted according to Lesniewski's directives *logically* implies existence of even one individual (not even an expression, logic text, or the universe itself), neither does any derived rule or theorem. So no principle of Lesniewski's system *logically* depends on existence, number, or kind of individual objects in the universe.

Nor does any further introductory thesis of language L, since any constant is introduced by an axiom or definition without existential import, which uniquely determines its semantic category and significance, characterizes its use, and, together with Lesniewski's logical syntax, helps determine its linguistic properties and relations to other expressions in the system. So, even if not a name, it is univocal in significance, and has whatever further meaning it derives from its intralinguistic relations to names. (§ 1.5) Certain expressions of language L (such as the undefined constant of mereology, and other constants defined in terms of it) must form names of individual objects, or nothing could be described. But which expressions these are is not a question purely of logic and syntax. No more than other questions of interpretation can it be decided by inspecting and noting formal properties and relations of expressions alone, without understanding how the language of which they are part is used to describe individual aspects of reality. (See Hall, *1960*.)

Imagine for sake of illustration that Adam, basing canonic language L on Lesniewski's logical syntax, had already introduced into his aptotic *Ursprache* a primitive nominal vocabulary by theses such as this—For every A, A is equine if and only if A is equine—theses that, being instances of tautology, could not make a valid system inconsistent. (Eve might learn the Adamic language as children learn the language of their parents.) Adam might then resolve to call only any equine with just one straight horn projecting from its mid-forehead a unicorn, and embody his resolution in an introductory thesis. (§ 6.1.9) He would thereby have assigned the noun 'unicorn' a constant significance as definite as that of the constants in terms of which he defined it. But, in thus expanding his vocabulary, he need not presuppose a unicorn waiting for its name to be called. Uncommitted to an ontology of unicorns, he might even use his new constant to deny existence of unicorns in Eden, or even in the universe. Nor need he then conclude that "there exists a class or set of unicorns that does not exist". (See § 4.12 above and § 6.1.3 and § 6.1.9 below.)

So no thesis would be falsified, no inference invalidated, even if no individual were denoted by any expression of language L. Lesniewski's laws being effective and universally valid, all expressions of any category are equal before the law, whose applicability does not depend on uncertain census of the universe or inquiry as to extralinguistic reference of expressions. Expressions which are not names are logically on a par with others of the same category, being subject to the same logical and grammatical rules, raising no peculiar difficulties, and requiring no special restrictions.[26] For example, according to Lesniewski's directives all nominal expressions, whether proper names, nominal functions analogous to Russellian descriptions, or not names at all, may grammatically be used as either subject or predicate of predication, and validly be substituted for any nominal variable of any thesis.

6.1.2 Unrestricted use of variables. In canonic language L, since quantification has no import of extralinguistic existence, variables of any semantic category may be bound without hesitation, and any expression of the same semantic category may be substituted for any variable of any thesis, without even raising the referential and perhaps practically unanswerable question how many individual objects it denotes: none, one, or more.

Naturally the usual precautions are required to prevent illicit capture and binding of variables by internal quantifiers. But these and other syntactical requirements to preclude confusion and amphiboly do not logically depend on questions of extralinguistic reference, existence, or number. So (nouns of language L translated by) 'individual', 'nonindividual', and 'nonentity' would be equally permissible substituents for nominal variables, as would 'mountain', 'Mt. Everest', and 'pure

golden mountain'. (Nouns translated by) 'Loch Ness' and 'Loch Ness monster',
'saucer' and 'flying saucer', 'acorn' and 'unicorn', 'square' and 'round square' could
alike be substituted for nominal variables without first asking for references; and
similarly for expressions of other categories, such as 'even number', 'largest even
number', and 'largest even number equal to no sum of two primes'.

So substitution is free from referential restrictions to "non-empty
expressions or domains"; quantificational inference does not depend
for validity on questions of extralinguistic reference, existence, or
uniqueness;[26] and (bound) variables of any category may be used
rigorously to formulate logical laws and generalizations otherwise
expressible only by use of the material mode, metalinguistic "schemata" or "dummies", (§ 4.12) or other such alternatives. For since
quantification involves no "ontic commitment to extralinguistic
counterparts",[48] there is no need to segregate lower from higher
levels of Lesniewski's system, which has in this respect a uniform
or "monolithic" character. (§ 4.12)

Quantification in language L is an ontologically innocent, strictly
logical device for making generalizations, whose variables stand for
(i.e., in place of) arbitrary substituents, or substitutable expressions
of the same semantic category. Once a semantic category is introduced, by the first axiom or definition containing an expression of
that category, according to Lesniewski's directives variables of that
category may also be used. For generalization in language L does
not logically presuppose or imply "existence of extralinguistic
values of variables named" by their substituents; it merely presupposes availability of expressions of the same category, as substituents for variables, and implies substitution instances of generalizations. Nor is quantification in language L a "mere metalinguistic
or syntactical device for manipulating meaningless counters" in a
'play of insignificant notations'.[48] For, uninhibited by ontological
associations, Lesniewski used variables to make rigorous generalizations within his formalized system itself, instead of using corresponding "schematic dummies" in an unformalized metalanguage.
(§ 4.12) And variables of any proposition are meaningful *as* variables
of a meaningful generalization and of unique semantic category,
standing in general for (i.e., in place of) any substituent, logical or
extralogical, of the same category. (§ 5.4)

Use of (bound) propositional and connector variables in protothetic, for example, no more compels one, willy-nilly, to treat expressions of these categories as names, and to "admit corresponding Facts and Logical Connections to the status of Independent Entities", than use of nominal and verbial variables in ontology commits one to "recognize corresponding Properties, Attributes, and Relations" as individual objects. Generalizations such as those (paraphrased in English) below merely presuppose existence of expressions belonging to the same semantic categories as the propositional variables 'p' and the singulary connector variables 'f', respectively, and imply substitution instances such as those (paraphrased) immediately afterward: For every p, p if and only if p; hence, for every p and f, f(p) if and only if f(p); and so not for every p, p, if and only if not for every p, p; that is to say, loosely, not everything is the case if and only if not everything is the case. Moreover, in language L an assertion (resp. denial) that such-and-such exist(s) is *not* "about statements" at all (unless it is a proposition of semantics, and any such-and-such is a statement), and hence is *not* logically equivalent to the statement that "there exists a (resp. no) true statement into which the term *such-and-such* enters".

Thus substitution in canonic language L is restricted only by the natural limits of meaning. Attempts to restrict substitution by conditions in the generalization itself inevitably break down, since the variables of the resulting conditional generalization themselves escape the intended restriction.[71] So substitution cannot thus be confined to expressions of a certain "range", if meaningful propositions can be derived by substituting other expression too. But natural restriction of substitution to expressions of the same semantic category avoids this difficulty. For, since no meaningful proposition can be derived by other substitutions, the limits of generalization are contextually determined by the natural limits of meaning, which, being implicit in all propositional contexts, unlike narrower restrictions, need not be made explicit by conditions in the generalization itself.

6.1.3 "Unrestricted" as compared with "restricted" quantification. In *1954* Lejewski distinguished between two different interpretations of quantification: the "restricted" and the "unrestricted", as represented by Quine[48] and Lesniewski, respectively; and argued that, under the unrestricted interpretation, what Quine regards as invalid inferences, demonstrating need for restrictions on what Quine calls "universal instantiation" and "existential generalization", are valid without restriction. A few comparisons of similarities and differences pointed out by Lejewski may help to preclude misunderstanding.

Lesniewski's rules of quantificational inference are formally the same as (say) Quine's, in the sense that they may be represented by the same schemes; but in interpretation they reflect that, whereas in most other systems "individual variables" are differentiated from "predicate or class variables", in language L all nominal expressions belong to one and the same category of nouns, however many individuals they name—none, one, or more than one. (§ 1.5, § 5.2) Consequently they may alike be substituted for nominal variables, according to Lesniewski's rule of substitution, which permits unrestricted substitution of nominal expressions for nominal variables; (§ 6.1.2) whereas formally similar rules in other systems are valid only for substitution of unshared *names*. (§ 1.5) As expressed in the material mode, Lesniewski's rules are "universally valid for all domains, empty or non-empty", whereas formally similar rules in other systems, in which the quantifiers are taken to mean "for every (thing which is an individual) object" and "for some (thing which is an individual) object", respectively, are "valid only for all non-empty domains".

Thus for Quine the "individual" variables 'x' in the following examples take names of individuals as substituents—or, as he expresses it, "take individuals as values". Accordingly he regards as logically true the universal generalization '[x] (x exists)' to the effect that "everything (i.e., object) exists"; and argues that universal instantiation must be restricted to names, since otherwise it would permit invalid inference of the false instance that Pegasus exists. But for Lesniewski this is no counterexample, nor to be valid need instantiation be restricted to nouns that are names. For he would regard an inference represented by the same scheme as demonstrating, rather, that a universal generalization of the same form is false—indeed, logically false, since it yields not only the false instance that Pegasus exists but also the contradictory instance that nonentities exist. Similarly, Quine calls the quantifier '[∃x]' and the generalization '[∃x] (x does not exist)' both "existential"; reads the generalization as "there exists something (i.e., object) that does not exist"; and argues that "existential generalization" must likewise be restricted to names, since otherwise it would permit invalid inference of this contradiction from the truth that Pegasus does not exist. But again for Lesniewski this is no counterexample, nor to be valid need (what may noncommittally be called) *particular* generalization be restricted to names. For he would regard an inference represented by the same scheme as demonstrating, rather, that a *particular* generalization of the same form, read noncommittally as 'for some x, it is not the case that an x exists', to the effect (more loosely paraphrased) that "something (for instance, Pegasus) does not exist", is true—indeed, logically true, since it is a particular generalization not only of the particular truth that Pegasus does not exist but also of the thesis that (in particular) it is not the case that a nonentity exists. And Quine himself does not contend that nouns that, like 'Pegasus', name no individual or that, like 'nonentity', are even precluded by definition (§ 1.7) from naming an individual are meaningless or useless. (§ 1.5) Instead he distinguishes between those principles he considers universally valid and those he considers valid only as restricted to names (or, in his words, only "for all non-empty domains"); but is willing to liberalize his notions sufficiently to admit the latter also as logical laws, dismissing the case of an "empty universe" as trivial and easy to check separately; or, by what he calls 'the artificial dodge' of "parsing nouns as predicates" (i.e., replacing nouns by corresponding verbs, or by definite or indefinite descriptions derived from such verbs), seeks to avoid making logical principles depend on factual questions of extralinguistic reference, the answers to which may be and even remain unknown. (Restrictions to be observed in reasoning with nouns definitely known not to be names would, for safety, have to be observed also in reasoning with nominal constants not definitely known to be names, such as 'man alive in 1985'.) But Lesniewski saw no need to resort to such restrictions and concomitant artifices, since for him these difficulties did not arise. Adhering to an older tradition, instead of following Russell in making a distinction of logical type between names of just one individual and other nouns, (§ 5.2) he was able to formulate universally valid principles, independent of factual questions of extralinguistic reference, that are not logical laws by courtesy only, and to parse nouns simply as nouns. (See Lejewski, *1960*.)

Furthermore, whatever is expressible in terms of restricted quantification in other systems is also expressible in terms of unrestricted quantification in language L, though not always by expressions of the same *form*. For example, what is expressed in terms of restricted quantification by any numbered formula at left, below, is expressed by its correspondingly numbered translation in terms of unrestricted quantification at the right of the same line:

1a. $[x]F\{x\}.\equiv.\sim[\exists x]\sim F\{x\}$
    1b. $[x](ob\{x\}\supset F\{x\})\equiv\sim[\exists x](ob\{x\}.\sim F\{x\})$

2a. $[x]ex\{x\}$
    2b. $[x].ob\{x\}\supset ex\{x\}$

3a. $[\exists x]\sim ex\{x\}$
    3b. $[\exists x].ob\{x\}.\sim ex\{x\}$

4a. $[x]\,F\{x\}.\supset F\{y\}$
    4b. $[x].ob\{x\}\supset F\{x\}:\supset F\{y\}$

5a. $F\{y\}\supset[\exists x]F\{x\}$
    5b. $F\{y\}\supset.[\exists x].ob\{x\}.F\{x\}$

6a. $[\exists x].F\{x\}v\sim F\{x\}$
    6b. $[\exists x]:ob\{x\}:F\{x\}v\sim F\{x\}$

7a. $[x]F\{x\}.\supset.[\exists x]F\{x\}$
    7b. $[x].ob\{x\}\supset F\{x\}:\supset:[\exists x].ob\{x\}.F\{x\}$

Wherever in these examples I use defined constant 'ob' of language L (§1.7), Lejewski instead uses 'exists' in Quine's own sense of "exists as an individual object".

Appropriately interpreted, both of the formulas in any one line have the same truth value. What is expressed in terms of restricted quantification by 1a (resp. 2a) and translated in terms of unrestricted quantification by 1b (resp. 2b) is true; whereas what is expressed in terms of restricted quantification by any later example at left, and translated in terms of unrestricted quantification by the corresponding expression at right, is false (unless substitution is restricted to unshared names). Yet all the examples at left except 3a would be accepted by Quine as "logical laws", since even 4a, 5a, 6a, and 7a are "valid for all *non-empty* domains"; and all the examples at left except 2a would *in language L, as interpreted in terms of unrestricted quantification*, be true logical laws, "universally valid for all domains, empty or non-empty alike". Thus apparent conflict concerning truth and validity between restricted and unrestricted quantifiers, due to faulty translation, disappears when homonymy, or differences in interpretation of expressions of the same form, is adequately taken into account.

Indeed, restricted can easily be understood in terms of unrestricted quantification, as but one basic example of the restriction of variables familiar in mathematics and explained by Rosser in his

Logic for Mathematicians. But apparently unrestricted quantification is not so readily intelligible to those habituated to using restricted variables and "existential" quantifiers to the effect that
"there exists an object...". Perhaps their difficulty reflects not only
the habit of years but also a certain asymmetry between the two
interpretations: Although whatever is expressible in terms of
restricted quantification is also expressible in terms of unrestricted
quantification, together with functors of existence, the converse
need not hold. For in terms of unrestricted quantification it is
possible to express or even prove propositions perfectly meaningful
but too weak even to express in terms of restricted quantification,
which Quine has to express in ordinary language in order to reject
as "contradictions in terms". Consider for example *particular*
generalizations of theses, such as "a nonentity does not exist",
containing a "null constant", like the noun 'Λ' or 'nonentity', that
is not a name. (§ 1.5) The *weaker* corollary that "something does not
exist" follows by particular generalization. But the corresponding
existential generalization that "there exists an object that does not
exist" could not logically follow, since unlike the particular generalization it carries existential import and is logically *stronger* not
weaker than the original proposition so much stronger as to be
contradictory.

Thus unrestricted quantification, Lejewski suggests, removes another difficulty from quantification theory. It has been argued that
formulas 6a and 7a above, as interpreted in terms of restricted quantification, are true if and only if at least one individual exists, and
hence, being "valid only for all nonempty domains", should not be
counted as logical laws—the objection that Quine dismisses as relatively pointless, since the case of an "empty universe" is trivial
and easy to check separately. Translations 6b and 7b make clear
that, so interpreted, these two formulas indeed fail for any "empty
universe", when substitution is not restricted to names. But the
same formulas would *in language L, as interpreted in terms of unrestricted quantification,* have no existential import and consequently
no counterexamples, even in an "empty universe", and so would be
universally valid logical laws. Formula 6a would be a *particular*
(not "existential") generalization of an instance '$F\{\Lambda\}v \sim F\{\Lambda\}$',

wherein 'Λ' is an "empty" noun that is not a name, such as 'non-entity'. And the logical truth of 7a, which can be rigorously proved in Lesniewski's ontology, may be made plausible by the following intuitive argument, wherein 'Λ' again is such a noun: If for every x, F{x}, then for instance F{Λ}; and if, in particular, F{Λ} then, for at least one x, F{x}. So the antecedent of 7a logically implies the consequent, even if no noun in language L is a name, whether the universe is "empty" or not.

In conclusion, Lejewski suggests that the unrestricted interpretation is closer to ordinary usage than the restricted interpretation of quantification, since the man on the street, unlike Quine, does *not* affirm that "everything exists", nor see a contradiction in saying that "something does not exist". Without resorting to polls and questionnaires, it can at least be stressed that in canonic language L it is *not* the case, as Quine (in *1951*, § 27) presupposes, that

we presuppose that a noun designates something whenever we deduce a singular statement from a universal quantification by substituting the noun for the variable. The quantification makes an affirmation regarding all entities, and we assume that the substituted noun designates one of those entities. So long as there are primitive expressions whose possession of designata is undecided, the logic of quantification remains indeterminate.

Consequently, in language L, there is no need for what Quine calls the 'artificial dodge of dispensing with primitive names in favor of descriptions or other abstracts' as 'a way of maintaining control over questions of vocabulary independently of questions of fact.' Having analyzed the restricted interpretation of quantification into the unrestricted interpretation compounded with the logic of existence, Lejewski concludes that restricted quantification theory, by merging the two, has misled logicians and philosophers in their endeavors to disentangle the logical problems of existence. (§ 6.1.9)

6.1.4 Universal and particular quantification. Universal quantifiers are introduced into canonic language L by the axiom of protothetic, and are governed by Lesniewski's directives, which like Frege's[34] permit definition only of simple constants. Since particular quantifiers, together with abstraction and description operators, are dispensable and, not being terms, cannot be defined according to Lesniewski's directives, Lesniewski used them only as unofficial abbreviations, according to the classical principle by which 'for some x...' is logically interchangeable with 'not for every x not...'.

Arthur N. Prior has suggested to me that, in any single axiom adequate for a complete system of protothetic but introducing a functor of (exclusive) disjunction (instead of coimplication) as sole undefined constant, particular quantification would have to be primitive, since otherwise no such axiom could be expressed exclusively in primitive notation, solely in terms of this alternative undefined constant and universally quantified variables. (See Prior, *1955*, App. I, §§ 9.3–9.4, pp. 309–310.) In this case, for economy, universal quantifiers might be used only as unofficial abbreviations, according to the appropriate classical principle by which 'for every x...' is logically interchangeable with 'not for even one x not...'.

Why did Lesniewski decide not to introduce particular quantifiers officially?—According to Lejewski, Lesniewski was influenced, not only by their dispensability in favor of universal quantifiers and negation, and by the difficulties of working out exact rules for their official introduction,[87] but also by considerations like the following: There are not just two possible kinds of quantification, to the effect that for every x...or to the effect that for at least one x..., respectively. Restrictions narrower than those of semantic category could also be represented by special quantifiers to the effect that for some x such that..., for every x such that..., or the like. Minimal, maximal, and exact numerical quantifiers could be introduced for any integer n, respectively to the effect that for at least n x..., for at most n x..., and for exactly (i.e., at least and at most) n x...; e.g., for no x..., for exactly one x..., for exactly two x..., etc. Yet other combinations would be possible, to the effect, say, that for at least n x such that..., and so on.[72] But restrictions narrower than those implicitly determined by the natural limits of meaning (§ 6.1.2) can simply and explicitly be expressed by conditions in the generalization itself, as suggested by the schemes 'for every x, if...then' and 'for some x, both...and'. And numerical constants can be defined and used, instead of numerical quantifiers, to express that the number of such-and-such is at least n, at most n, exactly n, or the like. Officially to introduce even a particular quantifier would require additional axioms or directives carefully harmonized with the rest.[87] And there is no compelling reason to stop short at just two kinds of quantifiers and not introduce any number. So, Lesniewski reasoned, why introduce even a particular quantifier to complicate his primitive logical basis? By not doing so he incidentally avoided inviting misinterpretation of his unofficial abbreviation for 'not for every x not' as "existential" in import.

6.1.5 Function of directives. Lesniewski's directives are architect's blueprints, not builder's specifications: they control but do not dictate details of development, relative to (theses representing) stages of construction of his systems. They are general prescriptions, easily adaptable by design to alternative systems, that establish a framework for general theory[33] but do not predetermine the forms of defined constants, definitions, and other theses, nor the order in which theses are subjoined to the axioms. Because of this latitude in development it is advisable in critical contexts to specify *this* as distinguished from *that* alternative system of protothetic, ontology, or mereology. The denotation of the simple names is not univocally determined in advance, since they are not proper but indefinite names shared by all systems satisfying Lesniewski's directives, which control only the general framework of the superstructure erected on the axiomatic foundations. Lesniewski's directives regulate construction in conformity with his architectonic design and over-all scientific, pragmatic, and esthetic standards, so as to preserve truth (and consequently utility too) and to harmonize validity with economy, purity, and elegance.

6.1.6 Extensionality. Accordingly, since we already have unformalized languages as serviceable carry-all vehicles of communication in everyday life, Lesniewski designed his logic as basis for testable scientific description of reality in canonic, extensional language L. Once (a functor of) any semantic category is introduced, his directives permit assertion of a canonic thesis of extensionality which, unlike an axiom or definition, introduces no new constant (§ 6.1.9) but, by guaranteeing extensionality of all expressions of that category, helps make any defined constant of that category eliminable from any propositional context. (§ 7) So it is inappropriate to apply the names he coined for his own systems to others not satisfying his directives of extensionality and other methodological principles.

Lesniewski's directives do not explicitly prohibit introduction of nonextensional functors; but his directives of extensionality, together with the axiom of protothetic and his other directives, assure the extensionality of all expressions of any semantic category in canonic language L. Consequently, for example, even were connectors of the form 'It is necessary that' or 'So-and-so believes that' introduced into language L, they could not play the nonextensional roles of their counterparts in colloquial English, but rather would be logically equivalent to one of the extensional connectors of the same degree, and hence be redundant, in any theory based on protothetic. (§ 7.1)

Frege[73] (who, as Dummett[13] points out, entangled himself in verbal snares by using the material mode) more than once expressed belief that "extensions" need not be "brought into" his foundations of arithmetic, and that objections to writing simply "concept" for "extension of the concept" could be overcome. But, in order to meet the "demand of mathematics and abstract thought to treat the extensions of concepts as objects", he nevertheless postulated a principle of "extensional abstraction", introduced special abstraction operators to form "names of value ranges of functions or extensions of concepts", and exempted these "proper objects representing functions or concepts" from his simple classification of "functions of different types and levels (*Arten* and *Stufen*)". As he remarked in retrospect in *1910*, he had been able in *1879* to develop the fundamentals of logic without even speaking of "classes", so that his rudimentary grammar precluded contradictions like Russell's; and he had hesitated to introduce "classes" even later. But, since he regarded "numbers" as "objects", in order to derive "classes" as "objects" he made the transition from "concepts" to their "extensions"; thereafter made more use of "classes" than was necessary; and thereby fell into error, and into the difficulties connected with use of "classes", in the false confidence due to misplaced trust in the traditional manner of speaking of "extensions of concepts". Even when he learned the price of this exemption of "class symbols" from his grammar of types, he could not bring himself to "regard classes as improper objects, and abstractions as sham proper names".

For he thought it clear that, since only "objects could fall under concepts as arguments, and saturate unsaturated functions, only proper names (*Eigennamen*) of proper objects could fill gaps in names of functions"—though his criteria of whether expressions are *Eigennamen* seem to me essentially syntactical rather than referential. (I usually prefix the otherwise redundant qualification 'extralinguistic' to 'reference', to preclude misinterpretation, just because Frege's term '*Bedeutung*' is often translated by 'reference' rather than by 'extent' or 'value'.) As he expressed himself, "classes do not have the unsaturated, predicative character of functions, concepts, and relations. What we are accustomed to regard as name of a class has, rather, the character of a proper name" which can occur as grammatical subject of a singular proposition. Even logicians like Aristotle, Russell, and Lesniewski recognize the systematic analogies supporting what they interpret as systematic ambiguities. (§ 5.1.1) In Lesniewski's ontology, for example, homonymous constants of the same form, contextually analogous in use but different in semantic category and significance, can be defined and used to say that (where 'x' is an expression of any indicated category) "x is unique". (§ 6.1.8) So, just as *nouns* of form 'V' can be used to say that any numeral is a unique individual object, higher-level functors 'V' can be used to say, in a different but analogous sense, that any integer is a unique cardinal number. (§ 1.5) But Frege was dissuaded by "the unsurveyable diversity of types of objects, and by the difficulty of prescribing just which objects are permissible as arguments of which functions", from carrying through this interpretation. According to his simple syntactical criteria, since one can correctly use the definite article in expressions such as 'the number zero', it seemed that "zero is unique and hence is an object", just as is the following individual object—0—, which I name Sample-Cipher; and that numerals equiform to Sample-Cipher are "names of the number zero", just as expressions of form 'Sample-Cipher' are names of Sample-Cipher. So, presuming it to be an impasse to "conceive classes as improper objects", he concluded that the only way out was to "recognize classes, or extensions of concepts, as objects in the full and proper sense of the word", but to abandon "the traditional interpretation" of the words "extension of a concept", codified in his principle V of extensional abstraction. He would gladly have renounced this postulate had he known any adequate substitute, since he had never concealed from himself (see *1893*, p. vii) that it was not so intuitively evident as his other principles, nor as a logical law ought to be. He replaced it by a set-theoretic modification V', which he apparently found even less intuitive, but which Russell[66] too thought promising in *1903* (§ 496), until deeper study convinced him of the need for a grammar of types, and which Lesniewski later demonstrated to be unsatisfactory.[41] (§ 3.9)

Russell[10] too introduced abstractions or "class symbols" formed by special abstraction operators (by definitions violating Frege's and Lesniewski's principles of simplicity) but classified them into types, like other expressions, and regulated them by grammatical rules axiomatically reducible in extensional contexts to simple type restrictions. But Russell himself recognized that need for special abstractions disappeared when he replaced his principle of reducibility by that of extensionality (of all functional "ϕ" of the same order and extension) and recommended extensional, testable description of reality. In the revision of PM 'there is no longer any reason to distinguish' between "functions and classes". Even if retained, abstractions need not be grammatically distinguished from coextensive expressions, since

there will no longer be any difference between the meanings of the two symbols. Thus classes, as distinct from functions, lose even that shadowy being which they retain in*20. The same, of course, applies to relations in extension. (PM, p. xxxix)

As Russell wrote in *1959* (p. 82, still referring to abstractions, or "class symbols" used distributively, as "classes"), a 'propositional function itself is only an expression', and a "class", equally, 'is only an expression', 'only a convenient way of talking about the values of the variable for which the function is true.' In extensional language L abstractions are notationally redundant; and even in nonextensional systems expressions of a certain form can be regulated more strictly in nonextensional than in extensional contexts,[74] in order to preclude contradiction, without introducing special abstraction operators.

Lesniewski,[74] who from 1922 onward considered the thesis of extensionality as "intuitively" valid as any thesis of the classical logic of propositions, carried Frege's and Russell's extensional tendencies to their logical conclusion. He designed a completely extensional system, regulated by a simple grammar of semantic categories without order restrictions, requiring neither abstraction and description operators nor postulates of "reducibility, definability, class abstraction, or set existence" since, if suitable constants are not already available, new constants can be explicitly defined and used in all the ways in which abstractions and descriptions are used in the revised PM, without ambiguity or specialized conventions and restrictions.[26] And he carried out extensional analyses of practical but relatively vague nonextensional expression in ordinary language, since by design, in canonic language L, only extensional expressions can be used to describe or conjecture what individuals or groups mean, believe, tend to believe, etc., in specified circumstances. (§ 3.4.0)

Although his notes on nonextensional functions were lost during the war, much has already been done by others[74] to develop methods of using extensional propositional functions "about propositions" (§ 5.3) (taking names of propositions as arguments), instead of non-extensional propositional functions having propositional arguments, to express what individuals mean or believe, and to indicate the theoretical status of propositions relative to logical or extralogical grounds of belief. For example, instead of vaguely characterizing a proposition as "necessary", one can describe it as a thesis of a specified theory or language, or as a proposition equisignificant to or logically entailed by others affirmed or believed by specified individuals on specified occasions, and then can discuss the character and rationale of the system or the support of the proposition in question. Coextensiveness (or equivalence) and identity are definable in purely extensional terms, and so are gradations of "synonymy" between these two extremes or limiting relations, stronger than coextensiveness and weaker than identity, such as Olds'[74] extensional isomorphism, or equisignificance as defined in this book. (§ 7.1) In terms of such relations and their respective equivalence classes (§ 1.8) various shades of belief can be described. For even though an individual who believes proposition P may not believe logical equivalents, so that his belief at the time is expressible by P and yet not by an equivalent of P, it is tautologous that he believes any proposition identical with P, and he may tend, under specified circumstances, throughout specified periods, to believe equisignificant or even extensionally isomorphic expressions. Krushchev for example may tend to believe, or at least to affirm on public occasions, from his ascendancy to his decline, extensionally isomorphic Russian translations of the English expression 'Ultimate victory of Communism is inevitable', and never for a moment extensional isomorphs of 'Ultimate victory of Capitalism is inevitable'; yet the two may well have the same truth value, if for the sake of illustration the contrary "antitheses" can be interpreted so as to be meaningful enough to have any truth value.

Many challenging problems remain to be solved, but the direction taken by Russell and Lesniewski should be explored at least by those who take Hume seriously enough to pay his epistemological insights more than informal tribute. Without competing with unformalized languages for the multiple purposes of everyday life, formalized extensional languages may serve purposes to which they are adapted; in particular, they may provide illuminating means or frames of reference for explaining, not what others might have meant by what they are remembered or recorded as saying on various occasions, but what one now means to say oneself, as clearly as circumstances warrant, even if the degree of precision aimed at in theory would be crippling in daily life.[33]

But, since dispositional expressions, such as 'can' or '(-)able', pervade colloquial languages and their technical ramifications, an extensional language without dispositional functors could hardly suffice outside classical logic and mathematics. Even semantics requires dispositional constants to express that names are applicable to whatever they *can* (i.e., do or could) denote. Doubtless different dispositional functors need to be tailored by definition to suit diverse purposes to which members of the family of dispositional expressions are loosely fitted in unformalized languages. In any case, Lesniewski's comprehensive directives for definition provide little temptation to stop short at any arbitrary stage of construction of canonic language L; rather they provide every incentive to investigate and develop the field explored by Reichenbach in his 'Analysis of conversational language' (in *1948*, ch. 7).

One dispositional functor that might, for example, prove useful in extensional language L can be defined by adapting and generalizing the definition of 'soluble' that Storer presented in *1951* and defended in *1954*. (I too oversimplify by not defining relative degrees of solubility in terms of proportion dissolved per temporal unit at specified temperature, as would the chemist in refining a colloquial into a technical term. In the following English paraphrases of expressions and deductions in canonic language L, the expressions of form 'P', 'G', 'x', 'y', 'w', or '*s*' belong to the semantic category of nouns, and the expressions of form 'i' or 'd' belong to the category of binary verbs. Variables of form '*s*' are italicized to distinguish them, in the English paraphrase, from the ending '-s' of English verbs in the third-person singular. 'Every' is used in the technical sense of 'any and at least one'.) (§ 1.7) I say that, by definition, for every w, s, i, and d, w i-*ing can* (i.e., does or could) d s if and only if, for at least one x and y, every w is x, every *s* is y, and every x i-ing some y d-s that y. This definition might be put as follows, loosely and suggestively, in the material mode of expression of informal logic: So-and-so, under appropriate (test) conditions, can (i.e., does or could) act thus-and-so on such-and-such if and only if every so-and-so has a certain property, and every such-and-such has a certain characteristic, such that everything having that property and actually tested under those conditions, in relation to something having that characteristic, acts thus-and-so on what has that characteristic. (§1.8)

Now suppose that individual G is a gallon of hot water, that individual P is a pinch of sugar, and that G incorporates P; and consider the following alternative further suppositions and their consequences: (1) Suppose further that G incorporating can dissolve P. Then by definition, for at least one x and y, every G is x, every P is y, and every x incorporating some y dissolves that y; consequently, since G and P are unique individuals, it follows that (the sole) G is x, (the sole) P is y, and hence that G dissolves P. (2) Suppose alternatively that (any) gallon of hot water incorporating can dissolve (any) pinch of sugar. Then by definition, for at least one x and y, every gallon of hot water is x, every pinch of sugar is y, and every x incorporating some y dissolves that y; consequently, since G is a gallon of hot water and P is a pinch of sugar, it follows as before that (the sole) G is x, (the sole) P is y, and hence that G dissolves P. So by definition in either case (1 or 2) it follows that G, thus put to the test, actually dissolves P. The scheme of the foregoing sample deduction being completely general, it is clear that my definition yields the following general corollary, for every G, P, w, s, i, and d: If (the sole) G is w, (the sole) P is s, G i-s P, and either G i-ing can d P or w i-ing can d s, then G d-s P.

Suppose as before that individual G is a gallon of hot water, and that individual P is a pinch of sugar; and consider the following alternative further suppositions and their consequences: (1) Suppose further that G incorporates and dissolves P. Then, since G and P are unique individuals, every G is G, every P is P, and every G incorporating some P dissolves that P; so by particular generalization, for at least one x and y (namely, G and P, respectively), every G is x, every P is y, and every x incorporating some y dissolves that y; in other words, by definition, G incorporating can dissolve P. (2) Suppose alternatively that (even though G and P may not actually be put to the test) every gallon of hot water actually incorporating some pinch of sugar actually dissolves that pinch. Then, since G and P are unique individuals, every G is a gallon of hot water, and every P is a pinch of sugar; and, by hypothesis, every gallon of hot water incorporating some pinch of sugar dissolves that pinch; so by particular generalization, for at least one x and y (namely, (a) gallon of hot water and (a) pinch of sugar, respectively), every G is x, every P is y, and every x incorporating some y dissolves that y; in other words, by definition, G incorporating can dissolve P. So by definition in either case (1 or 2), whether or not gallon G and pinch P are actually tested, it follows that G incorporating can (i.e., does or could) dissolve P. The scheme of this deduction too being completely general, it is clear that my definition yields also the following general corollary, for every G, P, w, s, i, and d: If (the sole) G is w, (the sole) P is s, and either G both i-s and d-s P or every w i-ing some s d-s that s, then G i-ing can (i.e., does or could) d P.

Suppose instead merely that every gallon of hot water incorporating some pinch of sugar dissolves that pinch. Then, since it is implicit in the wording of the hypothesis that at least one gallon of hot water and one pinch of sugar exist, it follows that every gallon of hot water is a gallon of hot water, every pinch of sugar is a pinch of sugar, and every gallon of hot water incorporating a pinch of sugar dissolves that pinch; so by particular generalization, for at least one x and y (namely, a gallon of hot water and a pinch of sugar, respectively), every gallon of hot water is x, every pinch of sugar is y, and every x incorporating some y dissolves that y; in other words, by definition, every gallon of hot water incorporating can (i.e., does or could) dissolve a pinch of sugar. So, the scheme of this deduction too being completely general, it is clear that my definition yields also the following general corollary, for every w, s, i, and d: If every w i-ing some s d-s that s, then w i ing can (i.e., does or could) d s.

6.1.7 "Constructive nominalism". (§ 3.1) Since language L is completely extensional, and all constants not axiomatically introduced as undefined are explicitly defined, coextensive expressions of any category, being equivalent, are interchangeable in any propositional context, without changing its extension (i.e., truth value); (§ 5.3) and any defined constant is eliminable from any such context, by definitional translation of this context into a logical equivalent that contains no equisignificant constant, nor derivative constant defined in terms of an equisignificant constant, and ultimately into a logical equivalent in primitive notation that contains no defined constant at all. (§ 7) In particular, any proposition of protothetic or ontology is translatable into a logical equivalent that contains no constants except undefined functors of coimplication (i.e., "material equivalence") and of singular predication, the arguments of which functions all belong to the basic, non-functorial semantic categories of propositions and of nouns, respectively. Coimplicators, as connectors of propositional arguments into compound propositional expressions, "biconditional" and "molecular", cannot be used like singular predicators to form simple propositional expressions, unconditional and "atomic", to the effect that So-and-so is such-and-such. (§ 1.7) Consequently, so long as all axiomatically introduced, undefined constants are either nouns or functors (of functions taking singularly nominal arguments) applicable to one or more individual objects in ways that can be taught and learned ostensively, I call canonic language L "constructively nominalist", like its logical basis of protothetic and ontology. For in language L even propositions that others would paraphrase in the material mode of expression, and accordingly interpret as "referring to abstract entities", are translatable into logical equivalents containing no extralogical constants except undefined constants (nouns, verbs, or functors of nominal functions) used to name or describe individual aspects of reality (i.e., one or more individual objects, either singly or in ordered couples, triples,..., or n-tuples, for any n). For example, a proposition to the effect that "hating is (logically) symmetrical", which others, seeing that its "grammatical subject" is a verb 'hate', would interpret as "referring to and being about the relation of hating", is translatable into a logically equivalent proposition to the effect that, of any two individuals (maybe one and the same), the first hates the second if and only if the second hates the first, in which proposition the binary verbs are used as verbial functors (of propositional functions having two nominal arguments) to describe pairs of individuals. (See the end of § 6.1.8 below.)

Lesniewski did not represent his directives schematically but, for exactness, prescribed them verbally, in the formal mode of expression, and strictly in technical terms, precisely defined in preceding terminological explanations. These explanations, too, he expressed formally and combinatorially, on a finite basis; extensionally, without use of subjunctive conditionals; and in terms of individual expressions and their formal properties and relations. So his classical logical syntax too is "constructively nominalist", in the same sense as is his logic itself; and could at a later stage be reformulated, axiomatized, and formalized, for metatheoretic investigations, in the very language L it initially serves to explain, just as a grammar, written in his native tongue, could be translated into the foreign language learned by the translator from that very grammar.

Lesniewski's[3] terminological explanations and directives refer strictly to individual expressions of finite length in spatiotemporal context, not to forms of expression in abstraction from their occurrences, much less to "corresponding extralinguistic entities or to expressions infinite in number or length". He stressed that to overlook that equiform expressions differing in location are different expressions (§ 1.3) might lead to drastic misinterpretation of his system, and asserted that he would not consider a "collection consisting of an infinite number of words" an expression at all. Individual expressions are finite spatiotemporal objects created at certain times and places. Each consists of a finite number of words consisting in turn of a finite number of letters, marks, numerals, or other symbols, and has a certain spatiotemporal "track" and duration. Before its creation it does not exist, and during its lifespan it is subject to the usual hazards of mortal existence. Even Lesniewski's directives, which might figuratively be said to prescribe the "platonic idea" or design of his system, being printed on paper are mortal, and need reincarnation from time to time to preserve the inheritance from one copy to its successors. What Lesniewski calls functions, their functors and arguments, terms, generalizations, or propositions are all concrete individual expressions; and only individual expressions in propositional contexts belong to his semantic categories and have constant significance. So elements of his system and members of his semantic categories can be created, indicated or described, and destroyed at will. Theses are individual expressions actually written down at appropriate times and places, not "potential expressions or forms of expression which, *if* written down, *might* be theses".

Lesniewski conceived his systems not as platonic fossils (§ 4.6) but as flexible growing organisms which, like natural languages, can develop indefinitely and, at any stage of development, are finite but have unbounded potentialities of growth. From their finite primitive basis they grow spatiotemporally, expressively, and deductively, as they are developed and enriched by introducing new forms of expression, their directives like genes controlling without completely determining their growth, so as to preserve the design and maintain proper functioning of the system. Their construction is never "finished": Even protothetic, which in the technical, metatheoretical sense is a "complete" and decidable theory, differs from other systems of propositional logic in that it may be extended "vertically" (to higher levels) as well as "horizontally" (to greater degrees) without finite limit. (§ 7.1)

Each of Lesniewski's systems can be based on a minimal number of universally valid directives and a single axiom satisfying his principles; (§ 3.5) each is constructively unbounded or "potentially infinite" in that it can be indefinitely extended solely by asserting definitions, theses of extensionality, or theorems derived from (one or more) preceding theses, and by introducing new constants and semantic categories of ever higher level and degree, according to initial directives completed once for all as the construction they regulate can never be. At any stage each is avowedly (not just surreptitiously) (§ 4.6) finite and surveyable, consisting of an actual collection of theses: the totality of theses relative to the latest thesis actually written down and incorporated in the system, beginning with the axiom of protothetic, containing any thesis subjoined to the axiom, and ending with the thesis marking its boundary at that stage of development. Since at any stage the number of theses, and of words in any one thesis, is finite and countable, so is the number of phrases in theses, of semantic categories, and of phrases of any one category.[55] (§ 5.2) Since decision procedures terminate recursively in a finite number of steps, questions concerning category membership, variability or constancy, significance, etc., are combinatorially and hence effectively decidable by inspecting (or remembering) the relevant expressions. In practice there is seldom need to go beyond the first few degrees and levels of construction. But whenever need arises the system can be constructively extended according to the initial directives, without adding to the primitive basis, simply by defining homonymous new constants, contextually analogous in use to the old, but of different semantic category and higher degree or level. (§ 7.1) Indeed, thanks to the contextualist character of Lesniewski's formalization, the homonymous new constants may without ambiguity be equiform to the old.

6.1.8 Contextual determinacy. Since in formalizing his directives Lesniewski[3] exploited the dependence of meaning on context, stressed by thinkers such as Aristotle,[30] Hobbes, Frege,[73] Russell, (§ 5.1) Carnap, Wittgenstein, and Quine, the meaning of an expression in canonic language L, as in unformalized languages, depends not on its form alone but also on its use in propositional context. But whereas in unformalized languages context usually *reduces* ambiguity inherent in homonymy, or different but analogous uses of expressions of such forms as 'is', 'exists', 'unique', or 'the', (§ 5.1.1) in canonic language L rigorous general conventions assure that context altogether *eliminate* indeterminacy of significance (as distinguished from referential vagueness, evidenced by borderline cases, which can be minimized but not altogether eliminated in practice). Whether an expression is a proposition, or a sequence of propositions a proof, is always effectively decidable on a finite basis. So is each of the following questions, which depend on but are effectively decidable in propositional contexts: whether an expression belongs to some semantic category; to what category, if any, it belongs; whether a term of any category is variable or constant;

the range of substituents (i.e., expressions substitutable) for any variable; and the significance of any constant. Accordingly, variables and constants even of the same category, and expressions of different categories, may unambiguously be equiform, and need not be formed in ways specified in advance.

By Lesniewski's[3] conventions variability or constancy does not depend on form alone: a term of any category is variable or constant according as it is or is not bound by a homomorph inside a quantifier. So terms of any form may be used either as constants or as variables of any category, even in the same context; and variables need not be selected from a finite alphabet, nor formed in any other way specified in advance. Instead of confining variables to a finite alphabet, and so precluding generalizations containing variables of a greater number of forms, Lesniewski[75] prescribed general conventions according to which new variables can always be formed without adding strokes or other predetermined indices. Since forms of expression, or even individual terms, in abstraction from propositional context are neither variable nor constant, and all the variables of any generalization are bound, variables need not be explicitly described as bound.

Contextual discrimination of variables and constants has further, mnemonic advantages: For example, it permits retention of familiar forms even in generalizing results hitherto established only for special cases, since familiar theorems derivable as corollaries may be suggested, even in the generalization, by using variables equiform to familiar constants. Thus in generalizing (e.g.) recursive characterizations of the succession of integers for progressions, quasi-progressions, or infinite hierarchies,[76] variables of the familiar forms—S, +, 0, 1—may unambiguously be used to suggest substitution instances, or other corollaries, analogous to familiar special cases.

Since constants of the same form are of the same significance if and only if also of the same semantic category, the significance of a constant depends not on its form alone but also on its context, and homonymous constants, contextually analogous in use but different in category and significance, may unambiguously be equiform. So, without ambiguity (or even attaching distinctive category indices to preclude it), equiform constants can be used as homonyms to make systematic analogies prominent and perspicuous; and Frege's and Lesniewski's requirement that a defined constant always be "new" can be satisfied without inventing a baffling multiplicity of new *forms*. Frege[34] pointed out the ambiguous consequences of attempting to eat one's cake and have it, too, by indulging in what he stigmatized as "piecemeal, multiple, or alternative definition". By designing rigorous contextual guarantees of univocality, Lesniewski obtained the tempting mnemonic advantages of "redefinition" without resorting to this careless practice, and those of homonymy or systematic ambiguity without specialized ad hoc conventions (§ 5.1.1) or any actual ambiguity.

For logical laws can be successively extended from one degree or level (§ 7.1) to another, step by step according to his initial directives, simply by first defining homonymous new constants, equiform and similar in use to the old but of different semantic category and significance, and then proving analogous theses as corollaries. The axiom of ontology, for example, can be "elevated" without ambiguity simply by first defining homonymous higher-level epsilons, analogous to the undefined functor epsilon of singular predication (§ 1.7) and also paraphrasable by an 'is', and then deriving corollaries parallel to the axiom. Consequently, homonymous higher-level constants 'V', 'ex', etc., analogous respectively to nouns of form 'V', (§ 1.5) verbs of form 'ex', etc., and also paraphrasable by expressions of form 'unique', 'exists', etc., (§ 1.7) can be defined according to schemes paraphrased as follows in English (the 'x's belonging to the semantic category indicated by context, and the definiendum, as in canonic language L, being to the right): For every x, (the sole) x is x if and only if x *is-unique*; for every x, not-for every y is it not the case that (the sole) y is x (i.e., abbreviated, for at least one y, the sole y is x) if and only if (at least one) x *exists*; etc. Thus Lesniewski provided, without ambiguity, for the systematic analogies between homonyms that rationalize the systematic ambiguities of ordinary language, of mathematics and logic, and of PM, and that motivate abolition of grammatical restrictions in favor of alternative restrictions in set-theoretic calculi. (§ 4.7) For the basic constants, theses, and deductions of his system may suggest and represent unbounded hierarchies of analogs or parallels, of exactly the same form except for use of distinctive forms of brackets as contextual indices of semantic category.

Finally, by consistently using the formal mode to describe individual expressions in context, Lesniewski managed to reconcile dependence of meaning on context with the requirement that constants be univocal in significance, both stressed by Frege, and at the same time to resolve what for Frege[73] was an irreconcilable conflict between the "unsaturated character, or essential incompleteness, of functions and the need to treat concepts or their extensions as objects capable of being arguments". A functor or "function sign" cannot be an argument even in language L. But it may be of the same form, semantic category, and constant significance as an argument of another function whose own functor is of higher level. Yet any such argument is eliminable in favor of equisignificant functors, since any propositional context is translatable into a logical equivalent containing equisignificant constants as functors but not as arguments. (§ 7.1) In the example cited at the end of § 6.1.7 above, for instance, the proposition (in language L) containing the binary verb (corresponding to 'hate') as argument of a function whose functor is the higher-level constant (corresponding to '-ing is logically symmetrical') is translatable into the logical equivalent containing the verb only as functor of a function having two nominal arguments. (See D37 and D34 of T.E. XLIV in § 7.1 below.)

6.1.9 Introductory theses: axioms and definitions. Any constant in canonic language L is introduced at one stroke, in a general propositional context, by a single introductory thesis satisfying Lesniewski's principles. (§ 3.5)

However, in systems of protothetic based on undefined constants other than the coimplicator, or in systems of ontology based on such systems of protothetic, several constants of the same significance (in the usual terminology, several "instances of the same constant") may have to be used to translate into primitive notation a definitional equivalence requiring only one constant of that significance in language L. (See § 1.4 above and Lejewski, *1958*, ID.)

No two nonequisignificant constants are introduced by a single introductory thesis, which, since its nucleus is a coimplication, either is a coimplication defining a propositional constant or is a universal generalization, and which either axiomatically characterizes or explicitly defines a new constant, and in either case fixes its semantic category and significance. (If the constant is a functor, each argument of the function is represented by a variable of the appropriate category, standing in general for any substituent expression of the same category.) Whether axiom or definition, the introductory thesis establishes a logical equivalence without existential import; it does not assume without proof that the new constant is an unshared name or "singular term" (i.e., *Eigenname* in Frege's[73] sense): (§ 6.1.6) For, if one equivalent is of a form presupposing uniqueness, and hence is naturally paraphrasable by use of the definite article, then so too is the other. (§ 3.3.5, § 6.2.3)

Since an explicitly defined constant occurs only at right, in the definiendum, whereas axiomatically introduced constants occur on both sides of the equivalence, it is not at all difficult to distinguish definitions from axioms and other theses in language L, even without aid of the metalinguistic index 'D', 'A', or 'T' respectively prefixed to the number of a thesis. (Similarly, even without aid of such prefixes, theses of extensionality can easily be distinguished from axioms and definitions, since, not being introductory theses, they contain no new constant; and from theorems by their canonic scheme (§ 11) together with absence of any indication, in the right margin, of derivation from one or more preceding theses.) (§ 6.1.6) Furthermore, in ontology definitions containing uniqueness conditions on both sides are explicit definitions in the strict sense that they, too, yield definitional translations which make the constants they define eliminable from all propositional contexts. To preclude other misunderstandings, it may help to make even the obvious point that expressions not satisfying Lesniewski's directives for definition cannot be definitions of his system; and to emphasize that I follow the precedent set in *1903* (esp. § 143) by Frege,[34] who spoke of "creative definitions" only in an ironical sense, rather than the more recent usage[77] of calling "creative" only any definition "fruitful" or theoretically indispensable in the sense that, in the system of which it is part, it makes possible the proof of at least one theorem not provable without its aid but containing neither a constant defined by it nor a derivative constant.

As Frege[34] (in *1884*, §§ 70, 88, 48) distinguished "fruitful" from "unfruitful" definitions, I distinguish theoretically indispensable from theoretically dispensable definitions. More generally, I call *theoretically indispensable* only any thesis T such that, in the system of which T is part, at least one theorem contains no constant introduced either by T or, derivatively, in terms of a constant introduced by T, (§ 11) but yet is provable only with the aid of T. Correspondingly, I call *theoretically dispensable* only any thesis T such that, in the system of which T is part, all theorems containing no constant introduced either by T, or derivatively in terms of a constant introduced by T, (§ 7.1) are provable without aid of T (even if actually proved with its aid). Logically redundant axioms that, being derivable from the other axioms, should be proved as theorems rather than be asserted without proof, for example, may be theoretically dispensable in this sense; so may auxiliary definitions introducing auxiliary constants that are used only as intermediaries in proving theorems, are eliminated in the course of the proof, and neither appear in the result nor are useful elsewhere.

For deductive (as distinguished from expressive) purposes, such auxiliary definitions may be replaced by postulates of the kind sometimes called "axioms of reducibility, definability, class abstraction, or set existence". In set-theoretic systems like Quine's *Mathematical Logic* and Rosser's *Logic for Mathematicians*, for example, particular generalizations are postulated and used as partial substitutes for definitions (just as in many systems recursive characterizations or conditional determinations by cases are not derived as corollaries from explicit definitions but, instead, are asserted without proof in order to introduce new constants, and so are called recursive "definitions" or "definitions" by cases, even when they do not define the new constants completely but, rather, fail to make the "defined" constants eliminable from all propositional contexts).[78] Lesniewski called such postulates *pseudo-definitions*, seeing that, although more questionable in status, they serve as partial substitutes for definitions:

In the first place, they lend themselves to interpretation, not as partial substitutes for definitions without existential import but, instead, as "existential postulates". Thus interpreted, pseudo-definitions take on ontological associations from which definitions are free, and naturally encourage pragmatic experiments in substituting artificial paradox-preventers, devised by trial and error, for criteria of meaning embodied in rules of logical grammar arrived at by semantic analysis. For pseudo-definitions, carelessly treated, generate contradictions as readily as faulty definitions, and engender misconceptions even more easily. Whereas a definition in canonic language L introduces a new constant and establishes an equivalence clearly lacking existential import, a corresponding pseudo-definition asserts without proof that, for some x, only whatever satisfies such-and-such defining conditions is x. So those who read the quantifier as "there exists" accordingly interpret pseudo-definitions as postulating "existence of a class or set" whose members alone satisfy these conditions, and as thereby involving "ontic commitment to abstract entities".

The verbal snares concealed in this "existential" reading and ontological interpretation of pseudo-definitions may be illustrated by the following example: Since any individual is identical with itself, the definition that only any individual not identical with itself is a nonentity, (§ 1.7) far from implying or presupposing existence of one or more nonentities, logically precludes the defined noun 'nonentity' from naming even one individual. However, this definition does entail as a *weaker* corollary, equally clearly lacking existential import, at least as understood in language L, the particular generalization that (1) for some x (namely, a nonentity) only any individual not identical with itself is x. It follows that (2) for some x, no individual is x; i.e., x does not exist (in Lesniewski's sense of being exemplified). (§ 1.7) But it is obvious that, were the noun 'nonentity' useful only as an auxiliary constant in proving this one theorem, its definition could be replaced, for purposes of deduction (as distinguished from expression), by the particular generalization (1), postulated without proof as a pseudo-definition. (See the remark of Russell quoted in § 5.2 above.) Now read the quantifier in the generalization (1) as "there exists"; the pseudo-definition, expressed in the familiar material mode, (§ 1.8) then assumes the appearance of a postulate that "there exists a class (resp. set) having as member only any individual not identical with itself"—a postulate that apparently entails the paradoxical-sounding consequence that "there exists a class (resp. set) that (has no member and in this sense) does not exist". At this point, lost in the jungle of one's own interpretations, instead of retracing one's steps, detecting and resolving the confusion that led to this ambiguous situation, one might persevere in the same direction and try to "interpret" one's way out again, by speaking of "posits" pragmatically justifiable as integral parts of a coherent scheme that appears somehow to be useful on the whole, even if not quite intelligible in detail. Yet one need not find a way out of such a quandary if one does not take the way in, via existential reading of the quantifier, assimilation of categories, and careless use of the material mode. For, as a particular generalization without existential import, (§ 6.1.3) the pseudo-definition is but a *weaker* consequence of the corresponding explicit definition of a noun whose very significance precludes its being a name, (§ 1.5) and in no way implies or presupposes existence of one or more nonentities. In any case, however interpreted or mis-interpreted, pseudo-definitions can no more than recursive or conditional introductory postulates wholly replace definitions, which are required in practice even in systems relying also on such partial substitutes.

For, in the second place, definitions are required at least by human beings, for human comprehension, expression, and communication. Use of defined constants is essential for perspicuity, whose importance for intelligibility is stressed by Wittgenstein in his *Remarks on the Foundations of Mathematics* (esp. pt. II). We need definitions to enable us to survey, recognize, understand, remember, check, form, and transform symbolic patterns, to express and communicate thoughts, that would otherwise be too complex for us to manage and comprehend (as shown by the example cited in § 4.7 above). We could not even conceive, much less carry out, complicated proofs without aid of definitions.

And even if the actual calculations were carried out by machines, still at certain stages problems significant to human beings would have to be predigested or set, machines programmed, and results interpreted and evaluated by human operators, if problems and results were to be intelligible and communicable to other men.

Full automation may one day make machines self-sufficient and human beings practically dispensable, together with their definitions, and retire the survivors to Axel's castle to spend their declining years attending the feelies. But until then— perhaps until 1984 at least—definitions presumably will remain indispensable in practice. Until then, why disdain even in theory, and in vain, to make concessions to the shortness of human life and patience, not to mention human comprehension ? [78]

Moreover, definitions are not dispensable even theoretically, except in favor of such partial substitutes as pseudo-definitions and recursive or conditional introductory postulates. For the latter, unless provably equivalent to corresponding explicit definitions, do not completely define the constants they introduce, but fail to make the new constants eliminable from certain generalized contexts.[78] So they have to be either made equivalent to or replaced by corresponding explicit definitions if the new constants are to be not only introduced and recursively or conditionally characterized but, rather, defined with complete generality. And, just as such postulates (unless provably equivalent to) must be replaced by explicit definitions if the constants introduced are to be eliminable from *all* propositional contexts, so must pseudo-definitions if a new constant is to be introduced for general use at all. Furthermore, pseudo-definitions and recursive or conditional introductory postulates are themselves dispensable, in all "finitely definable" cases, in favor of explicit definitions. (On exceptions such as the hypothesis of selection or "infinite choice", see §§ 4.0, 4.1, 4.7, 4.12, 6.0, 6.1.1, and 6.1.2 above, together with Russell, *1919*, ch. 12.) For certain preconditions must be satisfied if such substitutes are consistently to do their work;[78] indeed, they need to be justified by ad hoc proofs that these conditions hold; yet, if their use is justified, they need not be used at all, since then they can be derived from corresponding explicit definitions. If, on the other hand, such postulates are inconsistent, weaker corollaries can still be derived from explicit definitions, which remain valid even when the preconditions for recursive or conditional introductory postulates fail.

Since Lesniewski too proscribed what Frege[34] stigmatized as "creative, partial, conditional, multiple, alternative, or piecemeal definition", any definition in canonic language L not only is free from existential import but is explicit, unconditional, unique, and complete, being restricted only by natural semantic requirements, prescribed with complete generality for all expressions of appropriate semantic category, so that the restrictions do not break down as would restrictive conditions in the definition itself. (§ 6.1.2) The defined constant is completely and explicitly defined at one stroke in a general propositional context, and is the only new constant in the definiendum, being either a propositional constant, identical with the definiendum itself, or the functor of a function whose arguments are all represented by variables of appropriate category, standing in general for all expressions of that category, any such variables being the only other terms in this function. As Frege[34] required, the defined constant is a simple expression new in significance, (§ 6.1.8) which as a term (no part of which is itself an expression) can have no prior and perhaps conflicting significance as a grammatical compound and which, being introduced for the first and last time, can have no "alternative" and perhaps contradictory definition. Since the defined constant is the only new constant in the definiendum, and all constants in the definiens are already univocally significant, the definitional equivalence, in terms of Frege's[34] algebraic metaphor, has the character of an "equation" explicitly solved for the unknown, whose other side contains nothing unknown. Any definition being explicit and completely general, its consequences have to be investigated and deduced as corollaries, special cases following as theorems, and logical equivalents having to be derived, instead of being asserted without proof as "alternative definitions". No definition is of a specialized form, such as recursive "definition" or "definition" by cases,[78] having logical presuppositions or implications that require ad hoc investigation and justification by proof. (See § 3.3.5 above and T.E. LVI° of § 7.3 below.) "Partial or conditional definitions" that fail to make the "defined" constant eliminable from all propositional contexts, together with pseudo-definitions or definitions "creative" in Frege's[34] ironical sense, are not only ruled out but are made unnecessary by Lesniewski's directives—except, that is, for the purpose of "proving" the infinity of the universe or other hypotheses that Lesniewski did not purpose to prove. (§ 4.0, § 6.1.1) For recursive characterizations and determinations by cases, if they are consistent and their presuppositions are satisfied, can be derived as corollaries of explicit definitions, just as, in all "finitely definable" cases, particular generalizations equisignificant to pseudo-definitions can be deduced as theorems, and therefore need not be postulated as unproved axioms.

In canonic language L, definitions lead no 'double life':[78] They are not treated as metalinguistic conventions of abbreviation or rules of translation; instead, like axioms, they are asserted as introductory theses in the language itself, in order to expand its vocabulary and enrich its expressive and deductive power, by introducing new constants, fixing their semantic category and significance, and characterizing their use. Since Lesniewski dispensed with substitutes in favor of explicit definitions, definitions themselves are not only practically but also theoretically indispensable; they enable us not only to comprehend and express but also to prove what otherwise we could not, without recourse to partial substitutes. Definitions are not rules of abbreviation foreign to Lesniewski's system, nor mere devices for its presentation,[78] but as its means of construction are essential to proof. Without them the primitive notation would remain insufferably cumbrous and forever rudimentary in power of expression and proof. Like axioms, they are introductory theses, but they differ from axioms in two important respects: (1) Being unlimited in number, they are to be asserted according to explicit directives. (2) They make the new constants that they introduce eliminable from all propositional contexts, in favor of constants in terms of which the new constants are defined, and ultimately in favor of undefined constants introduced by the axioms. So any thesis (or other proposition) T containing defined constants is translatable by definition into a logical equivalent T', in primitive notation, containing no defined constant at all. But introduction even of these eliminable constants may increase not only the expressive but also the deductive power of the system, since without aid of definitions T may not be intelligibly expressible nor T' provable.[78] Like a superfluous axiom derivable from the other axioms and therefore provable as a theorem, an individual definition may be theoretically dispensable; but definitions in general, in language L, are no more theoretically dispensable than are axioms.

Definitions and defined constants are as strictly parts of canonic language L as are axioms and axiomatically introduced constants. Lesniewski did not apologize for using definitions, nor ask the reader to pretend that propositions expressed in terms of defined constants are mere abbreviations of primitive notations too long to write out, while conveniently slurring over the distinction in practice.[78] No such theoretical-thinking-of-as-if, or fancy imagining what really isn't so, is required in language L. For propositions containing defined constants are, strictly speaking, propositions, not mere abbreviations of propositions; and remarks ostensibly about them are really about them, not about definitional expansions actually in the system but not literally in the text. (§ 4.7) What is properly meant by calling propositions theorems is that they are theorems, just as they stand.[78]

Since introductory theses are propositions in language L itself, not rules in its metalanguage, definitions are meaningful and true in precisely the same sense as axioms.[47] No more than axioms are they mere theoretically superfluous expressions of volition, concerned wholly with symbols, that need not be treated with care.[78] To assert a definition, axiom, extensionality thesis, or theorem is indeed an act of will. But the act, though voluntary, is not arbitrary, if the results are to be consistent, true, and hence useful too. Definitions and axioms alike, though as introductory theses they embody resolutions and prescriptions, are not themselves resolutions or prescriptions, but like other theses are propositions (i.e., indicative sentences) and in this respect differ from theorems and theses of extensionality only as follows: Being immediately asserted in order to introduce and explain (i.e., characterize or define) new constants, they are not meaningful propositions relative to any preceding thesis. But, once asserted, they are meaningful propositions henceforth,[34] relative to themselves and to all later theses. (§ 5.2) The sign of assertion as an axiom or definition indicates the tacit imperative: The new constant introduced by the following proposition is to be of the semantic category and significance thus determined, and is to be used as thus characterized or defined, according to the directives of the system. The law must be fulfilled and all propositions be good and faithful servants, since by prescription in canonic language L other expressions are not recognized as propositions at all. (§ 5.3) So definitions asserted as introductory theses are usually no more "about symbols" than are axioms: They do not as a rule "mention" (i.e., contain names of) expressions at all; and even semantical theses introducing names of expressions cannot safely mention their own constituents, if vicious circularity and reflexive paradoxes are to be avoided, and so do not mention expressions of the same semantic category and significance, *relative to themselves*, as these names. (§ 5.3) Like metalinguistic rules of abbreviation, introductory theses do explain the meaning of new expressions; but, unlike such rules, they do so not by explicitly mentioning them but, rather, by actually exemplifying their proper use and fixing their significance in canonic language L. Whereas metalinguistic rules are prescriptions for acting, introductory theses are the stage setting in and by which the new actors are introduced to begin playing their constant roles. The novices, cast bodily into the medium, have to perform the first time, and take on significance in the act. Once on stage, whether introduced by axiom or definition, they are official and significant parts of the system, subject to the same rules as senior members of the cast.

6.2 Lesniewski's system of logic

Axioms and directives (i.e., "primitive", underived propositions and rules) are complementary: The weaker the one, the stronger the other must be, to compensate and thereby to maintain the deductive power of the system whose primitive basis they together establish. Where one system relies on an axiom in the system itself, another may rely instead on a corresponding directive. Axioms proper, finite in number, may trivially altogether be replaced by directives for asserting corresponding theses, on the basis of suppositional deductions or of nothing at all, as so-called "theorems" or "logical consequences of the null class" or of an arbitrary proposition. And theses unlimited in number, such as definitions, theorems, or theses of extensionality (assertible for functors of each semantic category), can be rigorously asserted only according to special directives. So directives, though perhaps reducible in number, cannot even trivially be altogether eliminated; and can hardly be

formulated so rigorously as axioms in the formalized system itself—
especially without asserting at least one axiom, as propositional
basis for explaining terms used to prescribe the directives themselves. Therefore Lesniewski considered it less trivial to discover
that a directive, being derivable from the one or more axioms and
remaining directives, could be eliminated from the primitive basis;
and sought what he considered not the one-sided technical or even
trivial primitive economy of directives alone but, rather, the ideally
balanced logistic economy of a primitive basis consisting of a minimal number of directives, together with a single axiom satisfying
his principles of formalization. (§ 3.5.3)

6.2.1 Primitive logical basis. Lesniewski's primitive logical
basis consists of the logically pure axioms (§ 4.0) of prototethic and
ontology together with his universally valid (§ 6.1.1) directives for
definition, distribution, detachment, substitution, and extensionality. His individual directives may be comparatively weak, since
stronger rules can be derived and so need not be taken as primitive.
His directives for definition permit definition only of constant terms
(i.e., simple constants, not compound expressions such as quantifiers or abstraction and description operators). His directive for
distribution permits derivation only of the result of distributing
universal (not particular) quantifiers through coimplication (not
implication). His directive for detachment permits detachment
only of the consequent of a coimplication (not an implication, nor a
generalization whose nucleus (§ 11) is a coimplication) with the aid
of a thesis, equiform to the antecedent, that is a closed and independent proposition (not an open propositional expression). His
directive for substitution permits only "simple" substitution of
expressions of the same semantic category for variables of independent (§ 1.4) generalizations (not substitution of expressions of
another or of no determinate semantic category, nor "formula"
substitution for compound expressions of the same category, even
when the result would be a meaningful and well-formed proposition).
His directives for substitution and for distribution do, however,
permit and incorporate the usual rules for "reiteration" (or
deriving homomorphs of theses), for "alphabetic variation" (i.e.,

revision by inessential "rewriting" or "relettering" of variables of independent generalizations), and for "permutation" of terms inside universal quantifiers. And, although weaker in isolation, his directive for substitution, together with the rest of his primitive basis, particularly the directive of extensionality, makes it possible to eliminate defined constants from consequences derived by "simple" substitution, and thereby to derive the results and rules of "formula" substitution. Finally, for economy, Lesniewski's directives of extensionality provide extensionality theses only for (expressions, once introduced, of) any semantic category except the category of propositions, since a thesis of extensionality for propositional expressions is independently derivable. Yet this primitive logical basis is adequate to establish all other classical rules for deducing consequences of propositions. (§ 6.0) So, for example, by deriving the classical introduction and elimination rules of "natural" deduction, (§ 3.7) such as the "deduction theorem" and rule of detachment for implication, the facility of the suppositional method can be combined with the rigor and economy of Lesniewski's primitive logical basis.

For his implicational calculus containing expressions of only a few semantic categories Lukasiewicz (*1951*, § 2, § 3) devised a method of definition he considered more direct than Lesniewski's. But whether, or in what sense, it is more direct is open to question. For the two methods yield corresponding results in reverse order, equivalences corresponding to Lesniewski's definitions being derivable from Lukasiewicz's definitions, and counterparts of Lukasiewicz's being derivable from Lesniewski's according to laws of extensionality. And, whereas definitional equivalences established by asserting theses according to Lesniewski's rigorous and comprehensive directives can be used to expand the vocabulary from the start, without presupposing new constants and semantic categories, definitions according to Lukasiewicz's partial and informal suggestions contain "delta" variables of higher level than the constant defined, which as hangers-on (so to speak) gate-crash into the system without proper, official introduction, thus violating Frege's and Lesniewski's principles. Similar remarks seem applicable to Lukasiewicz's claims for his loose adaptation, to his propositional calculus, of the familiar procedure of substituting compound functors, formed by quasi-abstraction operators (commas of ellipsis indicating gaps to be filled), since the same results and rules are derivable according to Lesniewski's more rigorous directives. The need for precautions, embodied in carefully formulated procedural rules, is demonstrated by the contradiction derived by Prior in *1956*, p. 209.

Though Lesniewski's two logical systems may be distinguished and described separately, ontology theoretically incorporates the "proto-theses (*Ursätze*)" of protothetic to constitute his unified system of logic. (§ 7.0) Protothetic is his "logic of propositions", and ontology his "logic of nouns", in that the basic, non-functorial category of the system in question is that of propositions and that of nouns, respectively. But protothetic as well as ontology is extensible both "horizontally and vertically" to admit functions or terms, constant or variable, of any greater degree or level (§ 11) in the unbounded hierarchies beginning with (expressions of) the basic categories. Thus the logic, not only of propositional and nominal expressions, but also of functors of functions having any number of exclusively propositional or nominal arguments, and of higher-level functor-forming functors of any semantic category, can be developed within his system, which might therefore be characterized as a classical, universally valid propositional, nominal, and functional or functorial logic, "constructively nominalist (§ 3.1) but unbounded, and so of potentially infinite degree and level". Introduction of the undefined functors of coimplication and singular predication by the axioms of protothetic and ontology, respectively, makes it possible immediately to expand the vocabulary by subjoining explicit definitions, according to directives that make pseudo-definitions, conventions of systematic ambiguity, and abstraction and description operators unnecessary.

6.2.2 Protothetic. Protothetic is Lesniewski's indefinitely extensible logic of propositions, connectors, connector-forming functors, higher-level functor-forming functors—indeed of constants and variables of any semantic category in the unbounded hierarchies constructible on the basis of propositional expressions in language L. The shortest known adequate single axiom for protothetic as based on coimplication, worked out by Sobocinski in 1945, takes the following forms in Lesniewski's and in more familiar notation, respectively:

AP.

$$\llcorner pq \lrcorner \ulcorner \phi \Big(\phi \, (pq) \llcorner f \lrcorner \ulcorner \phi \Big(f \big(pf(p \llcorner u \lrcorner \ulcorner u \urcorner) \big) \llcorner r \lrcorner \ulcorner \phi \big(f(qr) \, \phi \, (qp) \big) \urcorner \Big) \urcorner \Big) \urcorner$$

$$[pq] :: p \equiv q . \equiv \therefore [f] \therefore f\big(p, f(p, [u].u)\big) . \equiv :[r]: f(q,r) . \equiv . q \equiv p$$

Axiom of protothetic AP consists of fifty-four words, and is an organic thesis of protothetic, (§ 1.4) not a mere translation, into terms of coimplication, of the conjoined axioms of some set such as A1, A2, and A3. (§ 3.6) By introducing the coimplicator as sole undefined constant, AP makes it possible from the beginning to assert definitions rigorously as theses, in order to expand the vocabulary, without introducing another, special sign of definitional equivalence. In *1960* Sobocinski shows how to derive from AP (1) a classical logic of negation, implication, conjunction, alternation, tautology, and contradiction, having the structure of an elementary but indefinitely extensible Boolean algebra;[79] in fact (2) a complete classical logic of propositions or "theory of deduction", together with further generalizations expressible (as generalizations) (§ 6.4) only by using functorial variables; and, in particular, (3) Lesniewski's effective method for deciding whether any *proposition* (§ 5.3) purely (i.e., containing constants only) of protothetic is tautologous (resp. contradictory) and for proving it (resp. its negation), if it is a generalization, by proving a finite number of instances[37]—a method suggested by the familiar decision procedure of "truth-value analysis and evaluation", in the special case of propositional expressions, but rigorously generalized for expressions of any semantic category in protothetic. (§ 3.6) The fundamental principles of bivalence and extensionality for propositional expressions can be derived from AP without even using the directive of extensionality. Also derivable are the classical rules of natural deduction by the suppositional method, together with all other universally valid classical principles (i.e., theses or corresponding rules) of quantification for variables of any semantic category (once introduced) in canonic language L. (§ 6.0) Ample illustrative theses and proofs in or relevant to protothetic are to be found in Lesniewski, NS, *1929*, and *1938;* Slupecki, *1955;* Sobocinski, *1960;* and Tarski, *1923*.

6.2.3 Ontology. Ontology is Lesniewski's indefinitely extensible logic of nouns, verbs, functors of nominal or of verbial functions—indeed of constants and variables of any semantic category in the unbounded hierarchies constructible on the basis of nominal expressions in language L. The shortest known adequate single axiom for ontology as based on singular predication, developed by Lesniewski in 1929, is to the effect that, for every A and b, (the sole) A is b if and only if, for at least one C, (the sole) A is C and (the sole) C is b. It is an organic thesis of ontology written as follows in Lesniewski's and in more familiar notation, respectively:

AO. $_{\llcorner}Ab_{\lrcorner}\ ^{\ulcorner}\phi\Big(\varepsilon\{Ab\} \vdash \big(_{\llcorner}C_{\lrcorner}\ ^{\ulcorner}\vdash \big(\phi(\varepsilon\{AC\}\ \varepsilon\{Cb\}))^{\urcorner}\big)\Big)^{\urcorner}$

  $[Ab] : \varepsilon\{Ab\}.\equiv.\sim[C]\sim(\varepsilon\{AC\}.\ \varepsilon\{Cb\})$

By introducing the singular predicator epsilon as the undefined constant, axiom of ontology AO makes it possible immediately to subjoin, as theses of language L, definitions equating in value singular propositional expressions to the effect that (the sole) A is thus-and-so, according to the scheme that, for every A, (the sole) A is such-and-such if and only if (the sole) A is so-and-so. From AO can be derived a classical law of "substitutivity of identity" (as distinguished from equality) (§ 1.7) to the effect that, for every A, B, and f, if A is an individual identical with B, then A f-s if and only if B f-s. This special case, being derivable, is not provided by Lesniewski's directive for asserting theses of extensionality. Also derivable is a theorem equisignificant to his original axiom of 1920, to the effect that, for every A and b, (the sole) A is b if and only if there is at least one A, there is at most one A, and any A is b. This thesis, reminiscent of Russell's treatment of descriptions, makes it possible to translate the subject of any singular predication into the predicate position (say) for purpose of definitional elimination, and is expressed primitively as follows in familiar notation:

  $[A\ b] \therefore \varepsilon\{Ab\}.\equiv:\sim[C]\sim(\varepsilon\{CA\}):[C\ D]:$
  $\varepsilon\{CA\}.\ \varepsilon\{DA\}.\supset.\ \varepsilon\{CD\}:[C]:\varepsilon\{CA\}.\supset.\ \varepsilon\{Cb\}$

This axiomatic characterization of singular predication represents Lesniewski's analysis of use of the copula in singular propositions "about individuals", both in traditional logic and in Indo-European languages—particularly languages like Greek, Latin, and Slavonic languages such as Polish and Russian (and to a lesser extent German and Romance languages—see Quine, *1960*, p. 118) that are relatively free from idiomatic complications involving use of definite or indefinite articles—for example those illustrated by paraphrasing an instance of a thesis of ontology first into Latin and then into English: *Si Socrates est coniunx Xantippae, et coniunx Xantippae est homo, Socrates est homo et coniunx Xantippae est Socrates*; i.e., if Socrates is (a or the sole) husband of Xanthippe, and (the sole) husband of Xanthippe is human (resp. a or the sole human being), then Socrates is human (resp. a or the sole human being) and (the sole) husband of Xanthippe is (a certain or the one and only) Socrates. This instance suggests several respects in which Lesniewski's logic of predication approximates more closely to traditional and colloquial usage than do Russellian and set-theoretic treatments. Lesniewski's epsilon of singular predication, like copulas such as 'est', 'jest', 'ist', and 'is', as distinguished from most epsilons of "membership or elementhood", may grammatically be used with a predicate naming just one individual object. Moreover, subject and predicate both being nominal, no matter how many individuals they denote, existence and inclusion are meaningfully assertible even of individuals, and "being" (§ 1.7, § 1.8) is logically transitive: i.e., it is a thesis that, for every A, B, and c, if (the sole) A is B, and (the sole) B is c, then (the sole) A is c. Re-examining the Russellian theory of descriptions in *1960*, Lejewski explores the differences in detail between Russell's and Lesniewski's treatment of predication and description, and explains the import of these differences.

It should be remarked that Lesniewski followed the older precedent according to which the predicates in the foregoing Latin example are the expressions '*coniunx Xantippae*', '*homo*', and '*Socrates*', respectively, rather than a more recent usage according to which both copula and predicate (in this sense) are swallowed by the so-called "predicates" '*est coniunx Xantippae*', '*est homo*', and '*est Socrates*'. Verbs (or "predicates" in this latter-day sense) are *not* nominal expressions, since the functor is always of higher level than any argument of a function, according to Lesniewski's as well as Russell's or Frege's logical grammar.[30] Russell's epsilons of "class membership" approximate more nearly to Lesniewski's bracket notations for "functional application" than to Lesniewski's epsilon of singular predication, which corresponds more closely to the epsilon of Quine's *Mathematical Logic*, as used to say that an individual is "member of a class of one or more individuals". But this partial analogy holds only where the subject in Quine's formula is singular; and, even apart from divergence elsewhere, it is difficult significantly to compare formulas in virtually grammarless set-theoretical calculi like Quine's with propositions meaningful according to the criteria of Lesniewski's grammar of semantic categories or Russell's grammar of logical types. (See §§ 3.3, 4.0–4.4, 4.7, 4.8, 5.0–5.3, 6.1.0, and 6.1.6 above.)

Ontology embodies Lesniewski's universally valid (§ 6.1.1) synthesis of principles derived from complementary logical traditions but freed from what he considered their logical defects. In particular, his logic of verbs (including predicative logical verbs) (§ 1.7) is comparable to a transformation, reconciliation, and union of Aristotelian[9] and logistic treatments of predication, as powerful as Russell's[10] logic of abstraction and description combined with a quasi-Aristotelian syllogistic but without the specialized restrictions[26] of either. (§ 6.1.3) In consequence, it provokes no temptation to dispense with useful expressions such as conventional proper names, or to transmogrify nouns into verbs by "parsing them as predicates" (§ 6.1.3) in Quine's sense; and needs no abstraction and description operators, (§ 6.1.6) attended by ad hoc conventions,[26] in order to make clear distinctions between predications or negations respectively with or without import of existence or uniqueness: (§ 1.7) for example, between affirmation that the sole man alive in 1985 is non-radioactive and denial that the sole man alive in 1985 is radioactive, which are equivalent if and only if there is exactly one man alive in 1985. Within ontology can be developed not only a classical algebra of logic, extended by Lesniewski's logic of singular predication and rules of definition, and having the structure of an indefinitely extensible and complete atomic Boolean algebra,[79] ontological individuals corresponding to Boolean "atoms", but also all theses of the universally valid syllogistic extended to nominal negation and conjunction and called $S'(n-k)$ by E. J. Lemmon in *1958* (pt. 1, §§ 1–8).

Consequently ontology also provides all theses of the systems (due to Slupecki, Bochenski, and Shepherdson) cited and extended by Lemmon. Comparing systems in *1955* (p. 38), Slupecki overlooks the fact that all theses of his own syllogistic are provable in Lesniewski's ontology if, instead of the definition *D 3.2* (p. 33) of the functor paraphrasable by 'at least one so-and-so is (individual but) not', thesis *b'* (p. 38) is taken as definition of the Aristotelian "O" constant paraphrasable by 'not every (§ 1.7) so-and-so is', in accordance with medieval practice as explained by Moody.[9] Two pages earlier Slupecki proves (as *Theorem I*) that, although Lukasiewicz's formalization of *Aristotle's Syllogistic* is not valid for nouns other than names, (§ 1.5) consequents corresponding to all theses of Lukasiewicz's syllogistic are implied in Lesniewski's ontology by antecedents expressing Lukasiewicz's existential presuppositions for all nominal expressions involved.

For all constants of these systems are definable in terms of the undefined constant, and all theses are derivable from the axiom, of Lesniewski's ontology. Also derivable are all classical principles (i.e., theses or corresponding rules) of natural deduction peculiar to ontology; in particular, those of universal and particular generalization, and other principles of quantificational inference or "quantification theory", as specialized for nominal expressions and expressions of any other category in ontology. Within ontology can also be reconstructed as much of arithmetic or number theory, analysis, abstract algebra, and other theories of classical mathematics, including Cantor's, as is meaningfully expressible according to Lesniewski's logical grammar, (§ 5) is universally valid (§ 6.1.1) as required by Russell and Lesniewski, (§ 4.0) and is derivable in either edition of *Principia Mathematica*[81] on hypotheses (logically equivalent to those) of infinity and selection. (§ 4.0) Ample illustrative theses and proofs in ontology are to be found in Kotarbinski, *1929*; Lejewski, *1954, 1958* (LO), *1960* (BA), *1962* (Syllogistic); Slupecki, *1955*; and Sobocinski, *1934, 1949–50*.

Theses provable in ontology include the Cantorian theorem that (as expressed in the distributive idiom of the material mode) "a class is never equinumerous to the class of all its subclasses, but has a greater number of members, 2^n as contrasted with n". (§ 4.10) Although it is a thesis of ontology that, for every b, any b is individual, it is for instance demonstrably false that (the sole) nonentity is individual (since, for every c, if the number of c is greater or less than one, it is false that c is individual), and hence demonstrably false that, for every b, (the sole) b is individual. That is to say, loosely and distributively, although it is a thesis that "all classes are included in the universal class", it is demonstrably false that "the null class is a member of the universal class" (since "no class having more or fewer members than one is a member of the universal class"), and hence demonstrably false that "all classes are members of the universal class". Consequently it is not a thesis that "the universal class is equal and hence equinumerous to the class of all its subclassess". So ("the universal class of") individuals is not an "over-sized" exception to Cantor's law, as in certain set-theoretic systems are "non-elements, classes too large to be represented by sets, or non-Cantorian classes". (See § 3.3.2 above; and, in contrast to PM, vol. 2, **116.72, 117.66, and 117.661, see the writings of Quine, Bernays-Fraenkel, and Rosser cited in § 4.10 above, esp. n. 56.)

Lesniewski[22] himself characterized ontology as a modernized traditional logic, closely related to Schröder's "theory of (distrib-

utive) classes and of individuals" (citing Schröder, *1891*). Kotarbinski[22] describes it as an extension and improvement of traditional
Aristotelian formal logic and, at the same time, a perfected logistic
of nouns, of all systems known to him the most mature, natural,
and practical in its applications. In the material mode of expression (§ 1.8) it might be called a universally valid (§ 6.1.1) "theory
of individuals, (distributive) classes (§ 4.10) or properties, (§ 3.3)
relations, functions, equivalence classes or properties, (§ 1.8) structures, numbers, groups, lattices, etc.", and in this sense, according
to Kotarbinski, a truly ontological "theory of what there is, or
general principles of being". (§ 3.2)

6.3 Mereology

Mereology might be called an axiomatic extralogical theory of
"parts or wholes, as pieces or aggregates, and their most general
relations". For mereological collections (or "collective sets") and
totalities (or "collective classes") are individuals literally consisting
of their constituent elements (§ 3.3) or (§ 1.7) ingredients, (§ 4.10)
as social sets or classes consist of persons, planetary systems of
planets, armies of subgroups of one or more men, oceans of water,
rain of raindrops, papers of paper, expressions of words, Morse
signals of dits or dahs (resp. dots or dashes), multiple images of
component images, and headaches of assorted aches or pains. As
Frege pointed out in his *1895* critique of Schröder, (§ 4.10) no more
than woods without trees can collections or totalities of (individuals
that are) b exist without (being composed of one or more individual) b–s. (§ 4.9) If and only if at least one individual b exists,
so does at least one collection (resp. the totality) of b; otherwise
it is simply false (but meaningful to say) that it exists. Since any
collection of collections of b is itself a collection of b, and either
any ingredient of an ingredient or any collection of ingredients of
A is itself an ingredient of individual A, collections of (individuals
that are) b are diversely analyzable into, and hence have no unique
number of ingredients, if they have more than one, though any
individual is identical with the collection (resp. totality) of itself.
Since any individual is the (same individual as the) totality of itself,

and is in itself, no individual is a totality (of individuals) that is not in itself, nor *a fortiori* a totality of such totalities. So it is simply false (but meaningful to say) that the "Russellian" totality of such totalities is anything at all, even itself, or in itself. (§ 4.9) Since any (§ 1.7) sole ingredient of any individual is the totality of ingredients of that individual, and any totality of ingredients of any individual is the same individual, it follows that any sole ingredient of any individual is the same individual; i.e., any (§ 1.7) individual ("collective singular class") having just one ingredient is identical with that sole ingredient. And, for every B, only whatever is identical with B is the totality of individuals identical with B. (§ 4.10)

Mereology resembles but antedates and differs significantly from Whitehead's informal "theory of events", (§ 3.9) and Leonard and Goodman's reformulation of Lesniewski's axiomatization of *1921* (§ 6.5) as the "calculus of individuals". (§ 3.3.3) In Sobocinski's opinion it has a certain affinity with scholastic ontology, though, like Lesniewski's other systems, it is universally valid and metaphysically neutral in the sense that it does not prejudge the number or kind of individuals populating the universe, nor even logically imply that either an individual or (equivalently) the universe exists. For it is not even a thesis that the universe exists, though it is a thesis that, if and only if at least one individual exists, then so does the totality of individuals. Within mereology can be developed a "theory of ingredience" having the structure of an indefinitely extensible "Boolean algebra of individuals", consisting of theses "about individuals" analogous to just those Boolean formulas that would be true if Boolean inclusion were interpreted as mereological ingredience: (§ 4.10) i.e., just those Boolean formulas "valid for all existent (non-null) Boolean elements".[79] Mereology is too general to be counted a geometrical theory but (if mereological ingredience is interpreted spatiotemporally) may be taken, together with the underlying logic and grammar of protothetic and ontology, as basis for systems of geometry proper (§ 3.2) such as those constructed by Lesniewski and Tarski.[23] It might also be used like Whitehead's later and less rigorous (§ 3.9) "theory of events" (§ 3.3.3) to analyze and construct concepts and theories of (1) spatiotemporal topology and relativity theory, (2) phenomenal and physical reality, (3) things, hierarchies, cells, and organisms,[76] and (4) "constructively nominalist" (§ 3.1) syntax and semantics.[80]

Alternative relatively short single axioms for mereology, each introducing a single basic form of undefined constant, have been worked out in recent years by Lejewski and Sobocinski, who is preparing a monograph on mereology.[86] To illustrate the meaning and use of a few mereological constants without exceeding the scope of this book, I loosely paraphrase into English certain characteristic theses selected from the hundreds due to Lesniewski and his associates, without indicating their status as axioms, definitions, or theorems. As the first thesis indicates, a single mereological constant can take the place of three Polish expressions—*ingredjens, element, podzbior*—originally introduced by different theses but later proved coextensive.

Only any individual (literally) in A is a constituent element (resp. "collective individual subset") of A. Any individual is in itself, and any ingredient of an ingredient of A is also in A. If A is in B, then B (as well as A) is an individual, and if in A is the same individual as A. Only whatever is either A or part of A is in A. Any part of part of A is also part of A. But, since only any ingredient of A not identical with A is part of A, no individual is part of itself; and if A is part of B then B is an individual not part of A. A overlaps (resp. is an overlapper of) B if and only if at least one ingredient of individual A is in B; i.e., A and B have at least one common ingredient. So A overlaps B if and only if B overlaps A. Since any individual is in itself, any individual A or any ingredient of A overlaps A, and hence overlaps at least one ingredient of A. If every part of A overlaps B then every ingredient of A also overlaps B. A is in B if and only if every ingredient of A is in B, this being the case if either every part of A is part of (resp. in) B, A is an individual all ingredients of which overlap B, or every ingredient (resp. overlapper) of A overlaps B. Since only all mutually ingredient individuals are identical, any one of the following five conditions is necessary and sufficient for A and B to be the same individual: (1) only every ingredient of A is in B; (2) every part of A is in B, and every part of B is in A; (3) A is an individual all ingredients of which overlap B, and which is overlapped by all ingredients of B; (4) every ingredient of A overlaps B, and every ingredient of B overlaps A; or (5) only every overlapper of A overlaps B. Being in, being part of, and overlapping are all relations holding only between individuals. Being in and being part of are transitive relations; but being in is antisymmetrical and reflexive; whereas being part of is asymmetrical and irreflexive; and overlapping is symmetrical and reflexive.

A is (a or the sole) collection of b if and only if at least one ingredient of every ingredient of A is in at least one b in A. That is, only any individual all ingredients of which overlap at least one b in itself is (a or the sole) collection of b. Since there is at most one collection of b if and only if there is at most one b, and at least one collection of b if and only if there is at least one b, there is exactly one collection of b if and only if there is exactly one b. So only any individual is the (same individual as the) collection of itself, and hence is the (same individual as the) collection of the collection of itself, etc. At least one b is in any collection of b, and any b is in any collection of b if there is at most one b. Only any collection of b is a collection of collections of b. Since any b or collection of collections of b is itself a collection of b, any ingredient of any collection of collections of b overlaps at least one b in that collection.

A is (a and hence the sole) totality of b if and only if (1) every b is in A and (2) some ingredient of any (and hence every) ingredient of A is in at least one b. So any ingredient or overlapper of any totality of b overlaps at least one b. The interdefinability of various constants is further illustrated by the following corollaries: Only any individual in which all b are ingredient and all ingredients of which overlap at least one b (i.e., only any individual containing all b and only overlappers of at least one b), only any individual overlapping (resp. overlapped by) only all overlappers of at least one b, or only any collection of b in which all b are ingredient (i.e., only any collection of b containing all b; in short "collection of all b") is totality of b. Since A is (a or the sole) collection of b if and only if, for at least one c, A is totality of c and all c are b, it follows that only any individual totality of b which are in that individual is a collection of b. A is in B if and only if, for at least one c, B is totality of c, and A is c; that is to say, loosely, only any individual that is "something" of which B is totality is in B. Since there is at most one totality of b, any totality of b is the (same individual as the) totality of b. Any totality of b contains every b, since it contains all b, and exists only if at least one b exists. For instance, if at least one individual exists, so does the totality of individuals (i.e., the universe), which then contains every individual. For only any individual containing all individuals (i.e., only any individual which, for every B, is not part of B) is the totality of individuals. If some b is the totality of individuals, then the (resp. any) totality of b is the totality of individuals, since if any totality of b is also totality of c then the totality of b is (the same individual as) the totality of c. Any b, collection of b, collection of collections of b, etc., is (the same individual as) the totality of b which are in itself, and is in the totality of b; and if all b are c then (1) it is also a collection of c and (2) any totality of b is a collection of c in any totality of c. Since any totality of b is a collection of b, and any individual is identical with the collection of itself, and hence with the collection of the collection of itself, etc., it follows that any individual is also identical with the totality of itself, with the totality of the totality (resp. collection) of itself, etc., and also with the totality of its own ingredients. And, since any totality or collection of b is individual, only any totality of b is the totality of the totality of b, the totality of collections of b, the collection of the totality of b, etc., these being the same individual provided at least one b exists.

A is outside B if and only if (1) A is individual and (2) every ingredient of B is an individual not in A. So only all nonoverlapping individuals are outside each other, and being outside is a symmetrical and irreflexive relation holding only between individuals. Only any totality of individuals which are in B but outside A, A itself being in B, is (a and hence the collective) complement of A with respect to B; i.e., (collective difference) B minus A. Only any totality of (individuals which are either) A or B, A being outside B, is (a and hence the collective) sum of A or B (resp. A plus B). If and only if nonidentical c are always outside each other, then c are-discrete; and only any individuals A and B such that individuals being A-or-B are-discrete are outside each other. Only any totality of c, c being discrete, is (a and hence the collective) union (resp. sum total) of c. So only any collective union of (i.e., sum total of individuals which are either) A or B is the collective sum of A plus B. If all b are c, and c are-discrete, so are b. Any collection of c being discrete if and only if there is at most one c, the collection of B is-discrete if and only if B is individual. If b are-discrete and c are-discrete, and only any collection of b is a collection of c, then only any b is c; i.e., b as well as c being discrete, collections of b equal collections of c only if b equal c. A Cantorian theorem is provable in mereology too: If there are at least two different b, and b are-discrete, then there are fewer b than collections of b. Moreover, if b are-discrete, c are-discrete, and b and c are equinumerous, then collections of b and collections of c are also equinumerous.

6.4 Demonstrable relative consistency

Each of Lesniewski's systems is demonstrably consistent relative to classical elementary logic; i.e., relative to the classical logic of propositions, together with classical principles of definition, extensionality, and quantificational inference for nominal expressions as well as for expressions of propositional logic. Moreover, their consistency does not logically depend on what is the population of the universe.[81] By means of elementary logic, Lesniewski himself proved that his other systems of protothetic are inferentially equivalent, and hence consistent relative to his axiomatization of case-analysis as a method of evaluation and proof in his "computative systems". For protothetic, though richer and accordingly more concise in means of expression than systems not permitting use of (bound) variables of all protothetical categories, (§ 4.12) is inferentially equivalent to the complete classical logic of propositions: Protothetical generalizations containing functorial variables can be translated into logical equivalents containing variables of just the basic category of propositions; and even propositional variables can be eliminated, by using the principle of bivalence to translate any generalization into a logically equivalent conjunction of a finite number of instances or "possible cases", derived by substituting standard tautologies (§ 11) or contradictions (§ 7.1) for its propositional variables. For example, axiom of protothetic AP (§ 6.2.2) can thus be translated into a conjunction of 128 classical tautologies.

This conjunction can quickly be reduced by familiar classical laws to a conjunction of only thirty-two different instances: Consider the four main groups of conjuncts, corresponding to the four possible combinations of truth values for the variables 'p' and 'q'. Those representing the mixed cases for opposite truth values are logically equivalent to alternations (corresponding to particular generalizations) easily validated by the tautologous connector of propositional arguments (resp. by the functor of either implication or coimplication). (§ 7.1) So only the two groups representing the cases for the same truth values remain to be validated, each of which has sixteen instances.

Since Lesniewski's directives are universally valid, (§ 6.1.1) any thesis of protothetic is thus translatable into a classical tautology, and a contradiction is not provable in protothetic unless a corresponding contradiction is provable in classical propositional and hence in classical elementary logic, by which all these conclusions follow. Consequently, if classical elementary logic is consistent, so is protothetic. And, if protothetic is consistent, so are ontology and mereology. For, if the epsilon functor of singular predication introduced by the axiom of ontology were the protothetical functor of conjunction of propositional arguments, then the axiom of ontology would be a thesis of protothetic, and the only two directives of ontology not holding as primitive directives of protothetic would nevertheless be derivable as valid rules of inference. So a contradiction is not provable in ontology unless a corresponding contradiction is provable in protothetic. Finally, mereology can be proved consistent relative to an interpretation in ontology.[81]

Naturally, consistency proofs are not absolute, but are relative to the consistency of the system taken as model and to the validity of the logic used in the proof; and hence carry conviction only to the extent of one's confidence in their presuppositions. Anyone having more confidence in Lesniewski's system than in informal logic, or in other formalized systems, would tend to use his system, instead, as touchstone for these. There is no absolute guarantee or substitute for one's intuitive judgment of systems not known to be inconsistent, since, unlike contradiction, consistency cannot without circularity be demonstrated within the system itself.

6.5 Grzegorczyk on Lesniewski (§ 3.10)

In *1955* Grzegorczyk discusses the question how Lesniewski's investigations are related 'to the whole trend of logical research in the first half of the twentieth century'. Although he does 'not feel competent to give a proper historical account of Lesniewski's role in the development of logic', Grzegorczyk introduces 'a formal logical discussion' of Lesniewski's systems by describing logistic and set-theoretic attempts in the early 1920s to save logic and the foundations of mathematics from contradiction, adding that 'this period was marked by an interest in the possibility of a consistent formalization'. Whitehead and Russell's logistic synthesis was 'fundamental for its day', and for more than a decade after its publication 'it was thought indispensable for research workers to have at least a superficial knowledge' of *Principia Mathematica*. Grzegorczyk does not suggest that, in many philosophically significant as distinguished from purely formal respects, PM has not yet been superseded, and is still fundamental today.

So too Rosser, in his *1953* preface, mentions that he has 'omitted a few topics which seem to be little used nowadays', and has 'improved on the symbolic machinery' of PM, 'which is out of date and extremely unwieldy. By using techniques invented since its writing, we have succeeded in condensing most' of PM 'into the present text'. If every later alteration, truncation, mutilation, or innovation is an emendation, then Rosser has "improved" PM, by abolishing Russell's logical grammar in favor of Quine's invention of stratification, (§ 4.7, § 5.1) and by omitting more than a few topics not in the focus of current mathematical as distinguished from philosophical interest. (§ 4) One of the techniques Rosser uses, to condense three volumes into one, consists in drastically abbreviating or altogether omitting proofs, as often as not, and stating theorems as exercises to be proved by the reader. Doubtless the 'symbolic machinery' of the English language too could be "simplified" by abolishing its grammar of parts of speech; and the 'three large volumes' of PM itself could have been condensed by Russell and Whitehead into one by the convenient technique of cutting out proofs.

'In that atmosphere', especially in Poland, consistent logical reconstruction and rigorous formalization of foundations of mathematics 'seemed particularly fascinating':

Logicians felt the need of thinking out that problem for themselves. Lesniewski took an interest in it and solved it with great precision... Lesniewski's treatment of logic was in his times the most exact; it was simpler than the *Principia* and had it been published simultaneously with the second edition of the *Principia*, it would have played a considerable part in the development of logic.

Grzegorczyk neither suggests that Lesniewski's treatment of logic is still the most exact nor mentions any other equally exact. Nor does he distinguish between difficulty and unfamiliarity, in referring to Lesniewski's notation without mentioning its schematic simplicity, (§ 3.8) uniformity, (§ 6.1) and ideographic design. (§ 8)

The system of the *Principia*, in the second edition, still contained numerous in-accuracies and drawbacks from which Lesniewski's systems were entirely free. Un-fortunately Lesniewski published very little, he introduced a new terminology, used a difficult symbolism and delayed publication of his works. That is why his direct influence outside Poland was insignificant.... The two works of Lesniewski which might have made his systems...known outside Poland...were written in such a difficult manner that only his close collaborators made use of them. Towards the end of the interwar period, when a systematic publication of Lesniewski's works in the new periodical

Collectanea (Grzegorczyk says *Studia*) *Logica* was contemplated (§ 2.3) 'the works in question had to a large extent become obsolete', according to Grzegorczyk, who does not mention in what respects they have since been surpassed, nor for whom he speaks (other than himself) in generalizations like the following:

About the year 1930 the interest in constructing formal systems had decreased considerably. Between 1925 and 1930 the conviction became firmly established that

it is 'easy' to reconstruct PM exactly according to a simple grammar of types. Grzegorczyk gives no grounds for firmly established con-victions about the ease of consistently reconstructing this 'huge work' of synthesis, so as 'to formalize all known intuitive mathe-matical proofs'.

Before the appearance of Gödel's work on undecidability it could have been supposed that there exists a possibility of constructing a system of logic whose consistency can be proved. Therefore a continued search for new formalizations of logic seemed to be appropriate.

Grzegorczyk gives no sound reasons why anyone should ever have supposed that any system could be proved consistent without pre-supposing and using some system of logic in the "proof", (§ 6.4) nor why search for new formalizations should cease to be appro-priate as soon as it was made unmistakably clear that consistency proofs are relative, not absolute. He does not suggest that one might want a system which one could interpret as logical basis for meaning-ful description, not just as a formal calculus with certain conven-tional rules, (§ 4) and in whose consistency one had sufficient in-tuitive confidence to use it as a touchstone for investigating, perhaps among other things, the relative consistency of systems inspiring less confidence. (§ 6.4) He only asserts that

The works of Gödel put an end to such hopes. Other comparative metalogical observations led to the easy conclusion that all systems of the simple theory of types are, in a way, formally equivalent.

Grzegorczyk does not specify in *what* way, attempt to justify this 'easy conclusion', nor even indicate the diversity of "the" various simple theories of types. (§ 5.2) Again he speaks in general terms, as if fortunate unanimity enabled him to speak for everyone:

Investigations concerning the possibility of a consistent formalization of logic were recognized as being completed: the interest in the construction of new systems of logic faded away. Gödel's studies directed the attention of scholars towards metalogical research; Lesniewski, however, was then engaged in perfecting various details of his theories. He shortened the axioms, deduced scrupulously theorems whose deducibility from axioms was at the time regarded as obvious and hence of no interest. He was gradually completing the programme...of constructing a formally perfect logical system of the foundations of mathematics—thus remaining outside the main trend of logical investigations in the fourth decade of this century.

Grzegorczyk mentions neither that Lesniewski proved many results that were far from obvious (such as his extremely general metatheorem about the logic of equivalence, (§ 3.9) and various theses not even expressible as generalizations within other systems) (§ 6.1.2, § 6.2.2) nor that Leibniz, Frege, Peirce, Cantor, Whitehead, and Russell remained outside the main trend of investigations in their decades too.

To sum up, Lesniewski's investigations in the years 1917–1921 dealt with problems that interested all logicians; they were of the nature of discoveries and they were not published. In later years they gradually lost their actuality.

Grzegorczyk does not explain in what sense they no longer have 'actuality' except as follows:

Lesniewski's main conceptions, as to which his priority is unquestionable, date back to the first period. These are: the construction of a system of the simple theory of types (called by Lesniewski the system of semantic categories) simultaneously with Chwistek, and a philosophical explanation of that system on the basis of an analogy with everyday language; the establishing of...ontology...on the basis of a semantic analysis of the word "is"...; the construction of...mereology...; the development of numerous syntactical concepts and the construction of many rules of inference which have henceforth become a part of the logical achievements of the 20-th century, above all the formulation of a rule of definition, the only one that was sufficiently exact; a contribution to the elucidation of several problems which were obscure at the time, such as the differentiation between language and metalanguage, with Lesniewski's own solutions of all known logical antinomies; and finally numerous critical remarks with regard to contemporary systems of logic.

Just as he neglects the distinction between Lesniewski's grammar of semantic categories and his original "simple generalized theory of types", (§ 3.4.1) Grzegorczyk neglects other semantically important distinctions and contributions, in his concentration on purely formal comparisons. What Lesniewski considered fundamental,

the philosophical foundations of his systems and their philosophical interpretations seem particularly interesting. We shall not deal here with this aspect of his work and we shall concentrate on comparing Lesniewski's systems with other known systems... from a purely formal point of view, without analyzing the interpretations which Lesniewski attached to them.

Remarking that Lesniewski's systems 'greatly resemble other systems created independently about the same time or somewhat later', Grzegorczyk does not add that, from a purely formal point of view, all classical systems greatly resemble one another; otherwise they would not be classical systems. From this point of view the 'greater generality' of protothetic,

as compared with ordinary propositional calculi, is of little practical importance. In ordinary deduction...there is no need to use other functors than the functors of negation, conjunction, implication, alternative and equivalence. This generality has a certain purely theoretical value. It makes possible the formulation within the system itself of many theorems which, with a different treatment..., belong to the metasystem.

Grzegorczyk loosely but formally characterizes Lesniewski's three systems as Boolean algebras,[79] without bothering to contrast the meaningful propositions of interpreted language L with the uninterpreted, grammatically indeterminate, schematic formulas of an abstract Boolean algebra, or even to stress the formally significant point that classic characterizations of Boolean algebras mention nothing like Lesniewski's comprehensive directives of definition and extensionality, nor his rules for using quantifiers (internal as well as external) and variables of any semantic category. Since protothetic has a 'very poor and well known' Boolean model,

deduction of theorems in protothetics is not interesting for the mathematician. We know beforehand what these theorems may tell us. It is worth while to know that protothetics exists, but in practical deductions we can make use of less elaborate systems.

True, just as we could restrict ourselves to using Basic English, we could forego using non-propositional variables and write the fifty-four word axiom of protothetic AP as a conjunction of one hundred and twenty-eight tautologies. (§ 6.4) But Grzegorczyk does not explain why, if we know so much beforehand,

we do not know whether the following law of generalization:

$$(f)\Big(f\big(f((s)s)\big) \equiv (q)f(q)\Big)$$

together with the theory of equivalence may constitute a system of axioms of protothetics. It is true that on the basis of that law we can easily obtain the whole theory of deduction and the rules of quantifiers, but we have failed so far to obtain on this basis the ordinary law of generalization or the ordinary law of extensionality for propositions.

Again using the singular, Grzegorczyk assimilates Lesniewski's grammar of semantic categories, despite its distinctive characteristics, (§ 5.2) to "the" simple theory of types:

The theory of semantic categories is more often called today simple theory of types. Lesniewski constructed the theory of types all by himself when studying the semantic categories of expressions of everyday speech. He believed that theory to have a linguistic justification, quite independently of the fact that with its aid various antinomies of typeless logic are avoided. Moreover, ontology contains the greatest wealth of types ever conceived in the simple theory of types.

If Lesniewski's grammar of semantic categories *is* "wealthier in types" than, say, Carnap's simple theory of types (as expounded in *1937* and *1958*), this "greater wealth" itself would seem to be an important distinction. Referring to Tarski's "general theory of classes" as 'the simplest system of the simple theory of types', Grzegorczyk overlooks the fact that the "definitions" by which Tarski "reduces relations to classes" actually violate the rules of Lesniewski's grammar of semantic categories and of various simple theories of types. (§ 4.7)

Even if the "language" of this "simpler theory" does not make sense outside the realm of pure formalism, still

For the formalization of mathematical proofs the language of the general theory of classes is entirely sufficient. The variety of types of ontology is more suitable for practical deduction than simpler theories. When speaking of a certain relation we regard it as a relation between the individuals in question and not as a class of classes of a certain type. However, for metalogical investigations made hitherto the system of the general theory of classes has been much more convenient.

But in following passages Grzegorczyk omits this crucial qualification 'made hitherto'.

The language of ontology seems most appropriate when we yield to what seems a natural tendency to use always the lowest possible types. In the language of Tarski a great number of variables of very high types are usually needed for the proof of properties of elements of a certain type. On the other hand when using Lesniewski's semantic categories the same process of reasoning requires a relatively small number of minimally higher types. The problem of conducting proofs with the use of minimally higher types is interesting from the constructivist point of view. It is connected with the tendencies inherent in the so called ramified theory of types and with mathematical practice in which we do not raise types needlessly. Indispensable for such investigations is just that kind of language in which variables of arbitrary type appear. However, not many investigations have been made in this field and but few interesting results were obtained.

Grzegorczyk does not suggest that this is an excellent reason why such investigations should be made by the only persons likely to do so: namely, those with "constructively nominalist" (§ 3.1) sympathies who, like Lesniewski himself, dislike appealing to "useful fictions" or "idealizations", and are willing to let others investigate the formal consequences of postulates that seem to be more "convenient" for autistic oversimplification than true. (§ 4)

In metalogical research, systems with different kinds of variables for different types are much more convenient. However, Lesniewski's systems are almost entirely unsuitable for metalogical investigations owing to the fact that they are presented not as completed systems but as systems developing in the course of time....being continually enriched by...definitions.

Grzegorczyk does not stress that this is just how systems or languages actually manifest themselves in reality, even when accompanied by a conventional request to imagine or pretend otherwise.

This property of Lesniewski's systems is suitable for deductive practice. When defining a new concept in mathematics we add the symbol...to the constant symbols of the system. As we know, however, the systems of the simple theory of types containing definitions are equivalent to the systems not containing definitions but containing the so-called axiom of definability or of subsets. Both can equally well serve for mathematical proofs.

Grzegorczyk does not inquire whether they can equally well serve outside the syntactical realm of formal calculation, (§ 4.7) nor whether even mathematics itself can dispense with definitions in practice; (§ 6.1.9) neither does he suggest that Lesniewski relied on definitions to the exclusion of pseudo-definitions for sound reasons, since they are more economical, being indispensable in practice even in systems using pseudo-definitions as partial substitutes, and being too clear in status to be interpreted as "postulating extralinguistic entities". (§ 6.1.9) Again Grzegorczyk neglects to restrict his generalizations to metalogical investigations made hitherto of whatever abstract forms (if any) satisfy presuppositions not entertained by Lesniewski: (§ 4.6)

Systems without definitions are, however, much easier to describe and hence they are much more convenient for strictly metalogical investigations. Therefore, although the exact...rule of definition given by Lesniewski was at the time a great theoretical success, his systems are most inconvenient for metalogical research.

Grzegorczyk does not specify how, since that time, Lesniewski's directives for definition have been improved on. Neither does he cite any sources or grounds for the following opinion:

On account of the above peculiarities of the language of Lesniewski's systems, such an obvious theorem of the completeness of prototheties is very difficult to prove precisely and, according to some logicians, it is even impossible to prove.

Grzegorczyk does not even mention that two years earlier, in *1953*, and in the very journal in which his own article appears, Slupecki[37] had presented what at least purports to be a proof that protothetic is deductively complete.

Grzegorczyk mentions no exceptions to the following generalizations, though Lesniewski at least was evidently an exception:

This inconvenience of Lesniewski's systems is explained by the fact that between the years 1925 and 1935 the attitude of scientists investigating the foundations of mathematics towards formal logical systems changed considerably. Formerly systems were constructed in the belief that the creative and intensive work of logicians would consist in the systematic deduction of more and more new theorems within systems previously established once and for all. For that kind of work Lesniewski's system was very well adapted: it was perhaps the best possible. But the development of logical research went in another direction.

Grzegorczyk does not predict for how long, and perhaps he is wise, fashion being a fickle and whimsical mistress, like the more modish and voguish of its creations and creatures. He does not suggest that there are questions enough for everyone; nor that Lesniewski's systems are still very well adapted to Lesniewski's kind of work, and may yet contribute to construction and analysis, in the swings of the dialectical pendulum, as the world turns in the spiral way of successive approximation to (or retrogression from) clarity. Rather Grzegorczyk speaks in the past tense, as if logic would nevermore be used except metatheoretically to investigate formal relations of formulas in "comparative logic", in the effort to classify and subclassify the varieties of formal calculi proliferating like mushrooms in the cloudy atmosphere of our day, and as if the judgment of the centuries would surely coincide with that of the uncertain decades.

Logicians soon realized which kinds of intuitive reasoning could be formalized in the simple theory of types and they returned to those reasonings being in general convinced that "somehow or other everything is always formalizable". Such an attitude was of course more economical. Investigations within the system itself gave way to the investigation of deductive systems; for such investigations the systems of Lesniewski were not suited. Lesniewski himself, whose interests were logico-philosophical rather than logico-mathematical, did perhaps not notice that change early enough.

Again no qualification indicates that the course of history ever deviates from an ideal line of progress; nor that Lesniewski was not given to being "in general convinced", and never sought to "formalize everything somehow or other", no matter how. Grzegorczyk does not even suggest the possibility that Lesniewski, in the decade preceding his death, did perhaps notice the change of fashion following Gödel and Tarski, yet nevertheless carried on the work of Aristotle, Leibniz, Frege, Peirce, Whitehead, and Russell, in the unshaken conviction that it too was important, and that not everyone need drop prior pursuits to follow the trend and jump into the metalogico-metamathematical, ultra-high-frequency wave band. Nor does Grzegorczyk suggest this reason why Lesniewski was not shocked by Gödel into abandoning his life work: Lesniewski saw no need for agonizing reappraisal, since long before 1930 he had relativized his directives (§ 3.4) according to principles of constructive stratification, (§ 5.2) and did not imagine his systems were disembodied forms in abstraction from context somewhere platonic not in space and time. (§§ 3.4.2, 4.6, 6.1.7)

Pointing out that Lesniewski based his grammar on semantic analysis of linguistic structure, Grzegorczyk continues to miscall this grammar "the" simple theory of types:

Even for formulas of fairly high logical types it is easy to find equivalent expressions of everyday language. Logical types resemble to a certain extent grammatical parts of speech. In a sentence of everyday speech a verb can only be replaced by another verb, a noun—by another noun, other substitutions lead to meaningless expressions. The principle of purity of types is a transfer of this restriction to the field of logic. Thus interpreted it seems quite a natural requirement. Lesniewski believed that irrespective of the problem of antinomies the simple theory of types would have anyhow arisen as a natural treatment of logic.... probably many of those who favour it do not realize that Lesniewski was the first to carry it out in a consistent manner, and that it was in fact this interpretation upon which he constructed the theory of types.... However at present we do not wish to enlarge upon the subject.

Grzegorczyk describes ontology as

a system which formally proved to be identical with the theory of atomic and complete Boolean algebras with constants and functions of arbitrarily high type. From a formal point of view Lesniewski's result can be reduced to the observation that the relation ε defined above may act as primitive relation of the atomic and complete Boolean algebra and that

certain axioms form 'a sufficient basis of this algebra'—provided, of course, that the algebra be enriched by the grammatical and logical rules distinguishing ontology from classic Boolean algebras, as it was by Tarski[79] after Lesniewski's formulation of these rules; in particular, by the rule of definition, which

ensures the possibility of defining arbitrary functions of Boolean algebra. It was Lesniewski who gave the first exact...rules and this was an achievement of historical value.

Again Grzegorczyk uses the past tense, without indicating why Lesniewski's achievement is not still of more than historical value, or how it has been surpassed and made obsolete in the three decades since. Here too

history brought Lesniewski a certain disappointment. Instead of deducing theorems from Boolean algebra considered as a theory, logicians became more interested in various so-called Boolean algebras considering them as models of that theory as well as of weaker theories, and they discussed these models in an intuitive manner not strictly connected with any system.

Grzegorczyk does not recommend historicist interpretation also of the disappointments history has repeatedly brought to Poland. Neither does he provide a statistical basis for his generalization about logicians (other than Lesniewski), nor distinguish intuitive from loose and unconnected manners of discussion.

Grzegorczyk repeats after Chwistek (§ 3.10) that 'Lesniewski opposed the concept of empty class'; and compounds this misleading interpretation (§ 3.3, § 4.10) by adding that because of 'absence of the zero element' mereological theses cannot be written without using quantifiers, and 'for this reason the... axioms of mereology cannot be written out in the form of equalities alone', like formulas of Boolean algebra. It *is* true that according to Lesniewski's principles, as explained by Sobocinski in *1955–56*, axioms *should not* be written in the form of equations if (and for the reason that) "defined" constants are thereby introduced, proleptically, into the axioms themselves; rather, axioms should be written in primitive notation, and only later translated into logically equivalent corollaries containing defined constants. But Grzegorczyk does not mention that Lesniewski defined and used nouns such as 'Λ', which is not a name: Among other things he used this "zero element" or "null concept" to prove it false that either ("the empty distributive class" of) nonentities (§ 3.3, § 4.9, § 4.10) or the ("empty collective class" or) totality of nonentities exists. And this "null constant" can perfectly well be used to write in the form of equations mereological theses which can also be expressed without using internal quantifiers in several other ways.

Grzegorczyk's example ("the disjunctness of two elements A and B") can thus be expressed in many logically equivalent ways such as the following: common ingredients of A and of B equal nonentities; it is not true that A and B overlap; A and B, if individuals, are outside each other.

Grzegorczyk, however, does not recognize that the following evaluations and comparisons rest on false foundations.

The zero element is of course not the most interesting element of algebra. Hence every more interesting theorem of Boolean algebra can be expressed as a mereological proposition.

This is an understatement (unless by "proposition" Grzegorczyk means thesis—i.e., *provable* proposition): for *all* Boolean theorems can be so *expressed*, though the "less interesting" ones would be false. But Grzegorczyk here seems no more to distinguish between expression and proof than, in the quotation below, he distinguishes between simplicity and mere familiarity. Having just pointed out Boolean theorems whose analogs in mereology are not true, or are demonstrably false, he continues:

There is no essential difference between mereological investigations and investigations in Boolean algebra. It is therefore worth while to consider the advantages of using either of the two theories.

He does not specify for what purpose: formal calculation, mathematical recreation, or true description of reality.

The absence of the zero element which is "philosophically doubtful" and uninteresting in itself, speaks in favour of mereology. Mathematicians, however, prefer Boolean algebra on account of the simplicity of its formulas. Using the zero element it is possible to express certain relations in a much simpler way. E.g. the disjunctness of two elements A and B can be expressed in Boolean algebra in the form of the equality

$$A \cdot B = 0,$$

while in mereology the same relation must be presented in the form of a proposition containing quantifier:

$$\sim (\exists C) \, (C \; ingr \; A \cdot C \; ingr \; B)$$

Presumably the 'A' and 'B' in the equation, if not constant, are to be interpreted as variables implicitly bound by a tacitly prefixed quantifier. But, even if by 'quantifier' he means *internal* quantifier, still his assertion is simply mistaken. The use of "equalities", which he misunderstands to be impossible in mereology,

facilitates greatly both the investigation of Boolean algebras and their application to other theories, e.g. to topology. Here again we encounter a similar phenomenon... Boolean algebra proves to be a more convenient instrument for mathematicians than the equivalent and competitive theory of Lesniewski, though the latter has certain philosophical advantages.

Lesniewski believed it to have the advantage of being true. But no more than he specifies for what ends Boolean algebra is more convenient does Grzegorczyk explain just how an uninterpreted algebra can compete with, and at the same time be equivalent to, an interpreted theory whose theses are supposed to be true. Perhaps he means, rightly, that Boolean algebra, interpreted in the *same* way, would be false if mereology is true—a novel kind of equivalence. For he does not point out any individual example of a totality of nonentities; i.e., a "collective class consisting of nothing at all". Whatever he means, he continues:

Mathematicians do not avoid "philosophically doubtful" elements, they often introduce them in order to obtain simpler formulas, as for instance the "points in infinity" in geometry.

Preoccupied with pure form, he does not remark that mereology, if true, could be formally "simplified" into a system having the structure of an orthodox Boolean algebra[79] in two alternative ways: either (1) by falsifying refractory theses, or (2) by divesting them of meaning and letting them regress into naked forms. He does add that

> Mereology may be applied to those theories in which it is important that all elements should have physical equivalents in reality, thus for instance, to the geometry of events or to the geometry of time-space solids. In such theories the zero element would have no physical interpretation. It even seems that such was Lesniewski's intention in developing mereology when he said that "a part" means as much as "a piece" and "a class of A's" as much as "a heap of A's". Such was also the intention of H. S. Leonard and N. Goodman when, about fifteen years after Lesniewski and independently of him, they formulated a theory, exactly like mereology, which they called the calculus of individuals. J. H. Woodger uses mereology in formalizing biology. In formalizing various empirical sciences mereology may still render valuable service.

According to Grzegorczyk, Leonard and Goodman 'mention the fact that they obtained their theory about the year 1930 independently of Lesniewski'. But, in the article he cites, Leonard and Goodman[82] themselves mention the fact that

> The calculus of individuals...is formally indistinguishable from the general theory... developed by Lesniewski.... Inasmuch as his system is rather inaccessible, lacks many useful definitions, and is set forth in the language of an unfamiliar logical doctrine and in words rather than symbols,

they attempt to 'restate the calculus' in what they consider a 'more usable form' and 'transparent English terminology'—though, in trying to *substitute* their reformulation of Lesniewski's theory of totalities or "collective classes" for a "theory of distributive classes or properties", they find it difficult, for example, to express that there are more b than c, twice as many, etc., to make numerical comparisons, and to define adequate substitutes for the ancestral functors (§ 1.8) of Frege and Russell.

7. TERMINOLOGICAL EXPLANATIONS AND DIRECTIVES

7.0 Preliminary explanations

To formalize a deductive system is to stipulate exact and comprehensive directives for its construction in purely syntactical terms, referring solely to forms and formal relations of expressions. Formalization therefore presupposes precise explanation or definition of metalinguistic terms used to describe and prescribe rules regulating expressions of the system. Such terminological explanations, being prescriptive for technical usage rather than representative lexical explanations of colloquial usage, are sometimes classed as rules together with the directives, but called "syntactical rules of formation" for classifying expressions, as distinguished from "logical rules of transformation or inference" governing deductive relations between expressions.

This dichotomy, though familiar and suggestive, is arbitrary and relative to peculiarities of individual systems—a point illustrated by borderline cases such as theses (i.e., axioms, definitions, extensionality theses, or theorems derived from one or more preceding theses) in language L, and by the reliance of one system on a rule of inference or abbreviation where another relies instead on an axiom or definition within the system itself. (§ 6.2.1)

For rigor, Lesniewski carefully prescribed comprehensive directives for his systems once for all at the beginning, and in extensional technical terms precisely defined in preceding terminological explanations. For distinctness, he separated those several conjuncts of the definiens that, for economy, he had so worded as to be logically independent. He welcomed refinements, and several of his terminological explanations are the result of successive logical simplifications of his original formulations. Certain complications that might appear needless are in fact designed to secure mutual independence and maximum economy without use of subjunctive conditionals, and must therefore be accounted to logical elegance at the expense of ready intelligibility. My own supplementary exposition and commentary is intended to counterbalance debits and credits in the opposite direction.

Certain variables for example appear only to "disappear" later. Yet these variables, which may appear superfluous, might be foregone, or eliminated immediately, only by letting variables in otherwise mutually independent conditions fall within the scope of a single quantifier. And certain "improprieties" mentioned earlier, in discussing propositions, (§ 5.3) are permitted in isolated quantifiers, functions, generalizations, or the like, but are excluded from *propositions* in canonic language L by definition XXXIX' below, and from theses by directives assuring that all theses be propositions.

It is possible, and was Lesniewski's practice (exemplified in his *1931* article on definitions), to illustrate every terminological explanation by examples violating each of his separate requirements in turn while satisfying all the others, thus demonstrating their mutual independence.

Since his terminological explanations and directives belong to the working metalanguage used to formalize and discuss his system, and common to author and reader, Lesniewski customarily expressed them in ordinary language and illustrated them by such examples. But in publishing blueprints for the foundations of protothetic and ontology, in *1929* and *1930* respectively, to save space he deviated from his usual practice by omitting examples, and by condensing into twenty-four pages of Latin abbreviations and logical symbols his complete terminological explanations and directives—to the exposition of which, according to Lejewski, he usually devoted more than two semesters in advanced courses. Not knowing that these condensations were to be the only accounts published in his lifetime, he thus obtained a degree of conciseness and precision that would facilitate later axiomatization and formalization of his logical syntax in canonic language L itself, but at the expense of the reader, and at the price of discouraging potential readers, thereby paying for logical gains by intelligible losses.

Lesniewski's blueprints for protothetic and ontology were published in different journals in different years; were based on his 1922 axioms of protothetic A1, A2, and A3, (§ 3.6) and 1920 axiom of ontology; (§ 6.2.3) and, as indicated by the distinctive suffixes 'p' and 'o' of his Latin abbreviations, were relativized to theses of protothetic (thp) and theses of ontology (tho) respectively. But most of his terminological explanations for ontology differ from the corresponding numbers for protothetic only in these suffixes and in the distinctive superscripts '°' added to their Roman numerals. Lesniewski provided for definitions and extensionality theses of two kinds in ontology (as contrasted with only one in protothetic), which he differentiated by prefixing distinctive '1's and '2's to 'defo' and 'extnsnlo' in his Latin abbreviations, and which, since they are analogously related to propositional and to nominal expressions, I call *propositive* and *nominative* (§ 1.5) respectively, as suggested by the distinctive prefixes 'prop' and 'nom' of Lesniewski's Latin abbreviations in explanations XLI°–XLIII° of § 7.3 below.

These two kinds are sometimes distinguished as "propositional" and "nominal", or "protothetical" and "ontological", respectively. But I avoid this usage in order to preclude confusion. For, since all theses in language L belong to the semantic category of propositions, not of nouns, definitions of either kind alike are propositional, not nominal; yet alike might be called "nominal", as contrasted with "real" or "ontological" definitions, in terms of the traditional dichotomy; and alike may be ontological in the quite different sense of being theses of Lesniewski's ontology.

The technical terms defined by terminological explanations L°–LVII° in § 7.3 below are used to formulate the only two directives for ontology that differ significantly from their counterparts for protothetic: namely, the directives for nominative (as distinguished from propositive) definition and theses of extensionality. Terminological explanation XXXII° in § 7.3 below, used to prescribe and explain the theoretical priority of protothetic to ontology, establishes a certain difference in theoretical import between subsequent explanations and directives and their protothetical prototypes. But, excepting these eight explanations, two related directives, and other indicated peculiarities, terminological explanations XXXIII°–IL° for ontology follow XXXIII–IL for protothetic word for word, just as the first five directives for ontology (§ 7.4) duplicate the complete directives for protothetic. (§ 7.2)

So, to save space and repetition, I here delete the distinctive

references to protothetic and ontology where these alone differentiate the *1929* prototype from its *1930* counterpart for ontology,
and thereby condense and combine Lesniewski's separate directives
into a single set for his unified system of logic, (§ 7.4) consisting of
ontology based on and incorporating protothetic. (§ 6.1, § 6.2.1)

Since in any deductive development ontology presupposes an effective proto,
thetical basis, I take my license to do so from Lesniewski's remark in *1930* (GO
pp. 128–129) that the directives for ontology could be reformulated so as to depend
on the general relation of precedence between any two theories in canonic language
L, rather than on the particular priority of protothetic to ontology. Although
ontology, developed according to his *1930* directives, theoretically "incorporates"
protothetic in the sense that homomorphs of all theses obtainable in protothetic can
be obtained as theses of ontology, he adds that his directives could easily be re-
worded so as to preclude this derivation and keep protothetic and ontology "outside" each other, though a thesis of ontology might then have to be doubly relativized, both to a thesis of protothetic and to a thesis of ontology. In language L
only any thesis of protothetic actually preceding the axiom of ontology belongs
effectively to protothetic, just as only any thesis of ontology actually preceding the
first extralogical axiom—say, the axiom of mereology—belongs effectively to ontology. But theses of Lesniewski's unified system of logic might be sorted out into
those proper to protothetic and to ontology, respectively—perhaps as follows:
Only any axiom of ontology, subsequent thesis not obtainable without use of a
directive or axiom proper to ontology, or logical thesis not legitimate as definition
or thesis of extensionality until immediately after some such thesis, is proper to
ontology; and only any other logical thesis (including any thesis effectively belonging to protothetic) is proper to protothetic.

But, although I have thus generalized Lesniewski's explanations
and directives to avoid reiteration, their original forms can be
restored simply by duplicating the *relativized* explanations, and
reattaching the deleted qualifications 'of protothetic' and 'of ontology' to phrases like 'relative to thesis B of this system', as indicated
by the respective suffixes of his *two* Latin abbreviations, which I
have left intact, following the Roman numeral of the explanation.
Otherwise I have modified his original explanations only to the
extent of referring, for examples, to the relatively short single
axiom of protothetic AP (§ 6.2.2) and axiom of ontology AO,
(§ 6.2.3) which I have substituted for the older, longer axioms used
as "primitive propositions" of protothetic and of ontology by him
in *1929* and *1930*, respectively.

Since he explicitly stated that his symbolic formulations were only
abbreviations of what, granted adequate space, he would express

in ordinary language, I translate his terminological explanations and directives into English. Wherever possible I paraphrase his Latin abbreviations by whatever familiar terms seem appropriate, rather than coin unfamiliar metaphrases. But such terms as, for example, 'word', 'bracket', or 'nucleus' apply to expressions of canonic language L strictly in the technical sense prescribed by his explanations. (§ 1.4)

I translate his abbreviation 'prnt' by 'bracket', not only because 'bracket' is relatively short, but also in order to leave open the possibility of using the familiar term 'parenthesis' as an alternative to the unfamiliar technical term 'parentheme', to signify "parenthetical expression inclusive of the outermost brackets", as explained in XVI of § 7.1 below. The sense of 'cnf' seems better conveyed by the translation 'equiform' than by the cognate 'conformable' or 'conformal'.

I try to combine logical rigor and economy with intuitive clarity by first translating each of Lesniewski's terminological explanations literally, but then sometimes adding auxiliary explanations of my own, without attempting to preserve mutual independence of separate requirements in this supplementary exposition. My commentaries are intended, not to suggest omissions in, much less to replace, but rather to supplement his exact definitions, which are distinguished from mine by his prefixed Roman numerals and Latin abbreviations, and by absence of any indication like 'I say' or 'I call'. (§ 1.4)

The *Polish* terminological explanations coded into the symbolic abbreviations of *1929* and *1930* were customarily worded by Lesniewski according to the following scheme: I (Lesniewski) say of (any) individual A that it is such-and-such if and only if it is so-and-so...; as for example in T.E. V below: I say of (any) individual A that it is a term if and only if (1) A is a word, (2) A is (individual but) not a bracket, etc.

For accuracy in explaining technical terms, and to reconcile precision with clarity, I add the following conventions to those of § 1 above: Stylistic variants corresponding to the same Latin abbreviation are used only for greater flexibility and idiomatic convenience of expression in context, and are to be logically interchangeable. To prevent cumbersome English phrases such as 'relative to thesis B of this system' from becoming too obtrusive, I indicate relativization (indicated in Lesniewski's Latin abbreviations by suffixes too short to be troublesome) wherever idiomatically convenient in context. In my supplementary remarks, though not in the preceding literal translations, the relativization may be indicated once for all at the beginning and left tacit throughout the rest of a passage or, where implicit in context, even be omitted altogether, in comments of a loose and general nature. When no dangerous ambiguity results, I use the Roman numeral of a terminological explanation as name of that explanation, either alone or together with the accompanying commentary; and use the Roman numeral followed by a dot and Arabic numeral as name either (1) of the correspondingly numbered separate conjunct of its definiens or (2) of a conditional generalization, derivable from that explanation, whose consequent is equiform to that conjunct and whose antecedent is equiform to the definiendum.

For example, it should be clear in context whether 'V.1' denotes conjunct number one of the definiens of T.E. V—namely, 'A is a word'—or the derivable generalization that, for every A, if A is a term then A is a word. Outside the immediate context of T.E. V, 'V.1' would usually indicate the generalization that any term is a word.

Lesniewski's terminological explanations are such that the following generalizations hold: Any capitalized variable in an explanation may be qualified, in case of doubt, by some appropriate indication of uniqueness of expression, as in (e.g.) 'the sole expression A' or 'individual expression A', without changing the logical force of the explanation or of any of its propositional parts. For, to use the material mode of expression, (§ 1.8) any member of a class, or of the field of a relation, is an individual expression (§ 1.3) if represented by a capitalized variable in his explanation. Similarly, a definite article may be used in the English paraphrase of any constant which is defined by a terminological explanation and the Latin abbreviation of which begins with a capital letter, corresponding to my parenthetical use of '(the)' or '(a and hence the)' and indicating uniqueness, according to the scheme of the following example from T.E. VIII and XI of § 7.1 below: Whereas (a) quantifier (qntf) *in* a generalization may be only one of several, (a and hence the) quantifier (Qntf) *of* a generalization B is unique: there being at most one, any quantifier of B is the sole quantifier of B. But confusion may be avoided by re-emphasizing that, since in canonic language L all nouns belong to one and the same semantic category, such contextual indications of uniqueness indicate no corresponding distinction of semantic category (§ 1.7) between nouns naming just one individual and nouns naming fewer or more than one. (§ 1.5) Parenthetical definite or indefinite articles may be inserted where required by English idiom but be omitted elsewhere; (§ 1.7) and parenthetical qualifications, such as '(of this system)', or '(universal)' in T.E. VIII of § 7.1 below, may likewise be omitted as superfluous when not needed to prevent ambiguity.

For example, 'A ε Cmpl(b)' of T.E. VII in § 7.1 below may be paraphrased by 'A is the complex of expressions that are b' instead of by 'individual A is (a or the sole) complex of expressions that are b'. For capitalization indicates uniqueness; and capitalization of the Latin abbreviation in particular indicates that it follows, as a consequence of Lesniewski's definition, that, there being at most one, any complex of expressions (that are) b is the sole complex of expressions b. Incidentally, were Lesniewski's symbolic formulations to be reformulated at a later stage in canonic language L itself, this abbreviation would take the form 'ε {A Cmpl(b)}'; and more complicated examples, such as 'A ε var (B, C)' and 'A ε prntm(B, c)' in XIV and XVII of § 7.1 below, would take the forms 'ε {A var(BC)}' and 'ε {A prntm(Bc)}', respectively. For Lesniewski used braces or "curly" (resp. angled) brackets to embrace exclusively nominal arguments of propositional (resp. nominal) functions; (§ 1.7) and in language L functors invariably precede arguments of functions, whose arguments need not be separated by commas. (§ 6.1.0)

Lesniewski defined his other metalinguistic constants in terms of logical constants and the mereological constant 'ingr' already explained, (§ 1.7, § 6.3) together with the primitive metalinguistic vocabulary abbreviated and explained as follows. In axiomatization at a later stage within canonic language L itself this vocabulary could, as parenthetically indicated, be reduced to the following undefined metalinguistic constants, in terms of which all the rest are definable: cnf, prntl, prntsym, thp, prcd.

Constant	Corresponding English paraphrases used in this translation
cnf(A)	(individual) expression equiform (§ 7.0) to (individual) A; *homomorph of* A
expr	(individual) *expression* (§ 1.3) (i.e., expression equiform to itself)
vrb	(individual) *word* (i.e., simple (§ 1.4) expression)
prntl	(individual) left bracket (§ 7.0)
prntsym(A)	(individual) bracket symmetrical to (individual bracket) A
prnt	(individual) *bracket* (i.e., expression equiform to or bracket symmetrical to a left bracket)

thp   (individual) thesis of (this (§ 6.1.5) system of) protothetic
prcd(A)   (individual) preceding (individual) A; individual that precedes (in-
                 dividual) A; (individual) predecessor of (individual) A
AP (§ 7.0)   (the) *Axiom AP of this* (§ 6.1.5) *system of protothetic*, printed and
                 named in § 6.2.2 above (i.e., first thp: thp preceded by no thp)
scd(A)   (individual) *following* (i.e., preceded by individual) A; individual that
                 follows (individual) A; (individual) *successor of* (individual) A
Uprcd(A)   (the) *last word preceding* (individual) A (i.e., word immediately (§ 1.4)
                 preceding individual A)
Uingr(A)   (the) *last word in* (resp. *of* individual expression) A (i.e., word in ex-
                 pression A followed by no word in A)
$_1$ingr(A)   (the) *first word in* (resp. *of* individual expression) A (i.e., word in ex-
                 pression A preceded by no word in A)
$_2$ingr(A)   (the) *second word in* (resp. *of* individual expression) A (i.e., word in
                 expression A preceded by exactly one word in A)
etc.

Lesniewski's supplementary comments and examples are designed
to preclude misinterpretation, illustrate the intended use of certain
expressions, and refine them into precise metalinguistic technical
terms applicable strictly to expressions in canonic language L:
(§ 1.4)

The following eight expressions are examples of *words*: man,
word, p, ◊ , ∟, ⌐, (, }. The following three expressions are examples of
collections of words but are not themselves words: the man, (p),
f∟) word. The expression 'the man' consists of two words, the expression '(p)' of three words, and the expression 'f∟) word' of four
words. Axiom AP (§ 6.2.2) consists of fifty-four words. Individual
letters merely part of words consisting of at least two different
letters are not words; nor, I add, are numerals, numerical or other
indices, or further signs if merely part of such words. Compound
expressions, consisting of at least two words, are not words.

I find it useful to have a broader description for quasi-expressions
that may or may not be expressions. So I characterize as *string* only
any individual sign or letter of some alphabet, punctuation mark,
index, technical symbol of logic, mathematics, or other discipline,
or collection consisting of any finite number of *consecutive* signs,
letters, marks, indices, or symbols, whether or not the collection
is an expression. In a quite general sense, I call *sign* (resp. *letter,
mark, index, symbol*—whichever seems most appropriate to the
case in question) only any simple string, from which compound

strings are formed. So only any string containing no string as part
is a sign. But any sign is a string, and any concatenation of a finite
number of strings is a string. Any string consists of a finite number
of *consecutive* signs. Any expression is a string; but a string need not
be an expression, since it may for example be merely part of a word
and hence contain no expression.

Clearly only any simple expression is a *word*, which is an expression no part of which is grammatically itself a word, and is a string
consisting of one or more consecutive signs. Partition of a compound expression into its constituent words is usually indicated by
spacing those words noticeably farther apart than any two consecutive signs merely part of the same word. A string that might
otherwise appear to be a compound expression may be treated as a
single word by juxtaposing or hyphenating parts to preclude their
being taken for separate words, as in the following six examples
of words: ⋄ ⋄, converse-13, cnv-21, cnv-23, cnv-31, cnv-32. So
expressions such as the following five indexed examples are likewise
to be treated as single words:

$$(, (, (, \diamond, \diamond.$$

Any word is an *expression*. Any collection of any finite number of
consecutive words of any expression is itself an expression. But the
collection of the first, third, and fourth words in an expression is not
an expression. Every expression consists of one or more consecutive
words. But, according to Lesniewski, no "collection consisting of an
infinite number of words" would be what he would call an expression.
So any expression consists of a finite number of consecutive words,
and hence is a string of finite length. Any compound expression
is a string consisting of words (i.e., simple expressions), and any string
consisting of words or other expressions is itself an expression.

The following six words are examples of *brackets*:

$$(, (, (, [, \{,).$$

So, I add, in order to assure an inexhaustible supply of analogous
but not equiform brackets, are words equiform to brackets already
used except for having distinctive indices such as numerals, dots,

slashes, bars, or other curlicues, as in the following four examples
of brackets:

$$(, \{, \underset{2}{(}).$$

All but the last bracket in each of these two sets of brackets are
left brackets. The following two words are not brackets: ⌐ ⌐.

Each of the three brackets—

$$(, (, \Big($$

—is a *bracket symmetrical* to each of the following three brackets—

$$),), \Big)$$

—and conversely. Each of the two brackets—}, }—is a bracket
symmetrical to each of the following two brackets—{, {—and conversely. None of the four brackets—(,],), }— is a bracket symmetrical to the following bracket: (. I add that the two brackets in each of
the following pairs of brackets are symmetrical to each other, but
that no bracket in any one pair is symmetrical to a bracket in any
other pair:

$$(\underset{2}{)}, (\underset{3}{)}, (\!(\,)\!), (\underset{2}{)}, \langle \rangle, \langle \overset{2}{)} \rangle.$$

Symmetry of brackets is clearly a symmetrical and irreflexive relation. Brackets respectively symmetrical to homomorphs are themselves homomorphs.

Any expression is an *expression equiform* (i.e., individual *homomorphic*) *to* itself, or in other words a *homomorph of* itself. (§ 1.3)
The sixth word in Axiom AP (§ 6.2.2) is an expression equiform to
the eighth word in AP. The collection of (individuals being either)
the second or third word of AP is an expression equiform to the
collection of (individuals being either) the tenth or eleventh word
of AP. The following two brackets are equiform expressions: (, (;
so are the following two words: ⌐, ⌐. The following two brackets
are not equiform expressions: (, [; nor, I add, are any of the following
three brackets:

$$(, (, \underset{2}{(}.$$

Clearly any expression equiform to a word is itself a word, and expressions respectively equiform to symmetrical brackets are themselves symmetrical brackets. For sake of perspicuity Lesniewski lets equiform brackets, or pairs of corners '⌐' and '¬', vary arbitrarily in height within the same propositional context without affecting its sense. But equiform expressions differing in location are *different* expressions. (§ 1.3)

Any individual (resp. expression) is ingredient in but not merely part of itself. For example, each of the fifty-four words part of AP, any other expression part of AP, and even AP itself is in AP; but AP is not part of itself.

I add that the *precedence* relation between expressions in canonic language L is the same as in Western Indo-European languages, the order of precedence being from left to right in the line, from top to bottom in the page, and from front to back as between pages of the same script. This relation, like its converse, is transitive, asymmetrical, and irreflexive; and, with its field restricted to discrete expressions in one context, is also connected and so serial. I use stylistic variants such as 'foregoing', 'before', 'earlier', and 'above' interchangeably with 'preceding'; and 'succeeding', 'after', 'later', and 'below' interchangeably with 'following', for the converse relation, where no dangerous ambiguity results.

7.1 Terminological explanations (§ 1, § 7.0)

Terminological Explanation I. A ε vrb$_1$ For every A: A is (a) *left lower corner* if and only if A is an expression equiform to the first word in Axiom AP; i.e., is of form '∟'.

Term. Expl. II. A ε vrb$_2$ For every A: A is (a) *right lower corner* if and only if A is an expression equiform to the fourth word in Axiom AP; i.e., is of form '⌐'.

T.E. III. A ε vrb$_3$ For every A: A is (a) *left upper corner* if and only if A is an expression equiform to the fifth word in Axiom AP; i.e., is of form '⌐'.

T.E. IV. A ε vrb$_4$ For every A:

A is (a) *right upper corner* if and only if A is an expression equiform to the last word in Axiom AP; i.e., is of form '⌐'.

I call *lower corner* only any left lower corner or right lower corner; *upper corner* only any left upper corner or right upper corner; *corner* only any lower corner or upper corner; and *punctuator* (in canonic language L) only any bracket or corner.

T.E. V. A ε trm   For every A:

A is (a) *term* if and only if (1) A is a word, (2) A is (individual but) not a bracket, (3) A is (individual but) not a left lower corner, (4) A is (individual but) not a right lower corner, (5) A is (individual but) not a left upper corner, and (6) A is (individual but) not a right upper corner.

Since only any word not a punctuator is a term, any word is either a term or punctuator but not both. Even truisms like these may shed light in obscure places in my commentaries: Any homomorph of a word (resp. term, corner, bracket, punctuator) is itself a word (resp. term, corner, bracket, punctuator) of the same form; and any word A is the same individual as the sole expression in A, the sole word in A, the first word in A, the last word in A, and indeed each word in A.

T.E. VI. A ε int(B)   For every A and B:

A is (a) *word inside (expression)* B if and only if (1) B is an expression, (2) A is a word, (3) A is in B, (4) A is (individual but) not the first word in B, and (5) A is (individual but) not the last word in B.

So only any word in expression B except (and hence between) the first and the last is a word inside B. I call (*expression*) *inside* (*expression*) B only any expression every word in which is inside expression B; and, conversely, call (*expression*) *enclosing* A only any expression inside which A is an expression. Clearly any word inside B is an expression inside B; any expression inside B is merely part of B; and any expression enclosing an expression contains at least three words.

I call only any e which is a union (§ 6.3) of b, in which every simple e is in exactly one b, and all b are e, (a and hence the) *complex of* (the one or more) e *(that are)* b. As suggested, any complex of e that are b is the sole complex of e that are b, and is an e consisting of (the one or more) e that are b: discrete ingredients that together compose it. Figure A here, for instance, is the complex of quadrilaterals that are squares in A, but is neither a complex of quadrilaterals that are rectangles in A, of squares that are in A, nor of squares that are rectangles in A.

(A)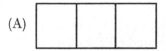

I call only any complex of the one or more expressions that are words and are inside expression B (a and hence the) *interior of (expression)* B, which is itself an expression inside and hence part of B. Only any expression inside B is an expression in the interior of B.

Schematically, I call only any complex of strings that are one of the individuals $B_1, \ldots, B_n$, wherein (for every i) B_i contains the last simple string (i.e., sign) preceding B_{i+1} and so itself immediately precedes B_{i+1}, (a and hence the) *concatenation of* $B_1, \ldots, B_n$. So only any complex of strings that are either B or C, wherein B contains the last sign preceding C and so itself immediately precedes C, is the concatenation of B and (resp. with) C; only any concatenation of B with the concatenation of C and D is the concatenation of B, C, and D; and so on, recursively. Only any string that is the collective sum (§ 6.3) of string B plus an immediately following string C is the concatenation of B and C. The order in which the specified constituents are mentioned is clearly essential in describing a string as a concatenation, but not in describing it as a complex, order of mention then being permutable at will. The complex of strings that are either C or D equals the complex of strings that are either D or C; and, if C precedes D, also equals the concatenation of C and D, but not the concatenation of D and C, which then is nonexistent. For every individual is what it is and not otherwise; and, the relation of precedence being asymmetrical, any predecessor of D is an individual not preceded by D. So some individual is the concatenation of C and D only if none is the concatenation of D and C. The only words of which SSP in VII below is the concatenation are its first, second, and third words in that order, whereas SSP is the complex of expressions that are one of these three words mentioned in any order whatever.

T.E. VII. A ε Cmpl(b)   For every A and b:

A is (the) *complex of* (the one or more) *expressions* (*that are*) b if and only if (1) A is an expression; (2) for every C, if C is a word in A then, for at least one D, C is in D, and D is b; (3) for every C, D, and E, if C is b, D is b, and E is a word in C and in D, then C is the same individual as D; and (4) for every C, if C is b than C is an expression in A.

—I.e., A is an expression, any word in A is in at least one b, no two b contain a word in common, and all b are expressions in A. So every word in expression A is in exactly one b, and every b is an expression in A. Since words equal simple expressions, any such A is simply the complex of the one or more expressions that are b, according to my generalized definition above.

Although the resolution of any complex of (e.g.) expressions that are b into its one or more constituent b is uniquely determined, its resolution into other components need not be so, as suggested by Figure A above. For instance (as Von Neumann recognized in hindsight) (§ 3.10) any compound expression can be analyzed in more than one way. Consider for example the following compound of three words—   (p)   —, which I name Sample-Simple-Parentheme and nickname SSP for short. (Ensuing comparisons may further clarify similarities and differences between complexes and other collections of expressions.) Since any individual A that is e is an individual identical with the complex (resp. collection, totality) of e that are A, SSP is an individual identical with the complex (resp. collection, totality) of expressions that are SSP. But SSP is also the complex (resp. totality) of expressions that are words and are in SSP, and is describable as a complex in many other ways. For example, it is also the complex of expressions that satisfy any of the following six alternative descriptions: (1) that are either the first, second, or

third word of SSP; (2) that either are the first word of SSP or are
the concatenation of the second and third words of SSP; (3) that
either are the third word of SSP or are the concatenation of the
first and second words of SSP; (4) that are ingredients of SSP
equiform to SSP; (5) that either are brackets in SSP or are expressions of form 'p' in SSP; (6) that are either SSP or SSP or nonentities (such as expressions of infinite length. Such reiterations or redundancies would not falsify a true description but would merely be
pointless.) Furthermore, whereas any expression is an individual
identical with the totality of its ingredients (resp. parts), and so
with the totality of expressions that are in (resp. are part of) itself,
any compound (e.g.) expression is an individual not identical with
the complex of expressions that are expressions in itself. For example, in violation of requirement VII.3, every word in SSP is in more
than one expression in SSP: namely, itself, SSP, and each concatenation of two words of which it is one. There is no complex of
expressions that are of infinite length, since no expression is of
infinite length; and no word is a complex of expressions that are
merely part of itself, since no simple expression contains an expression as part.

T.E. VIII. A ε qntf   For every A:

A is (a *universal*) *quantifier* if and only if (1) the first word in A is a
left lower corner; (2) the last word in A is a right lower corner;
(3) for at least one B, B is a word inside expression A; (4) for every
B, if B is a word inside A then B is a term; and (5) for every B and
C, if B and C are equiform words inside A, then B and C are the
same individual.

So only any expression in which the first and last words are
respectively left and right lower corners, every word inside being
a term, no two such being equiform, is a (universal) quantifier.

Here and elsewhere parenthetical qualifications, such as 'universal' above, may be
omitted as superfluous when not needed for clarity—in this case because all quantifiers officially in canonic language L are universal, particular quantifiers being
used only as informal abbreviations. (§ 6.1.4)

It follows that no individual is a word inside two different quantifiers. The reasons for Lesniewski's requirements are clear: A quan-

tifier enclosing no term to bind variables would be useless; punctuators inside quantifiers, instead of playing their proper roles, would only confound rules of punctuation and substitution; and, since one term inside a quantifier suffices to bind all equiform variables of the generalization, homomorphs inside the same quantifier would be superfluous duplicates.

    T.E. IX. A ε sbqntf   For every A:

A is (a) *subquantifier* if and only if (1) for at least one B, B is a word inside A; (2) for every B, if B is the first word in A or is a word inside A, then there are fewer left upper corners in A that follow B than right upper corners in A that follow B; and (3) for every B, if B is a word inside A or is the last word in A, then there are fewer right upper corners in A that precede B than left upper corners in A that precede B.

So only any expression which encloses at least one word, and in which every word but the last (a right upper corner) is followed by fewer left than right upper corners, and every word but the first (a left upper corner) is preceded by fewer right than left upper corners, is a subquantifier. It follows (by an inductive argument of the kind outlined by Kleene in *1952*, pp. 23–24, 73–74) that any left and right upper corners inside any subquantifier are also equinumerous and properly matched and mated in uniquely determined pairs. I call *quantificate* only any (and hence the) interior of a subquantifier.

The definiens of IX is the result of a twofold deductive simplification, by Lindenbaum and Lesniewski, of a conjunction originally of five factors. The expression that Lesniewski abbreviated by 'sbqntf' lacks connotations of agency or activity: A subquantifier is not "what subquantifies" but rather, as the name also suggests, is what in a generalization follows and falls "under" its quantifier, as its "corpus" or "body", minus its quantifier; and consists of its quantificate, the quantified expression, together with the outermost upper corners, the punctuators that enclose this nucleus and mark its scope. To avoid the inept connotations of the English cognate 'subquantifier', 'sbqntf' might perhaps be translated instead by 'corpus', 'subquantification', or 'quantificatum'; but not by 'subquantificate', which would hardly suggest the body of a generalization, incorporating its quantificate as part.

T.E. X . A ε gnrl   For every A:

A is (a *universal*) *generalization* if and only if (1) for at least one B, the first word in A is in B, and B is a universal quantifier in A; (2) for at least one C, the last word in A is in C, and C is a subquantifier in A; and (3) for every B and C, if the first word in A is in B, B is a universal quantifier in A, the last word in A is in C, and C is a subquantifier in A, then A is the complex of expressions that are either B or C.

—I.e., A is the complex of expressions that either are a universal quantifier in A that contains the first word in A or are a subquantifier in A that contains the last word in A; in other words, is the concatenation of the universal quantifier and subquantifier of A. As illustrated by the following freakish examples, a universal generalization according to definition X need not be significant, as are all *propositional* (§ 5.3) generalizations, such as theses or other propositions beginning with quantifiers: (§ 7.0)

$$\llcorner p \lrcorner \ulcorner \llcorner \urcorner \urcorner, \quad \llcorner p \lrcorner \ulcorner q \urcorner, \quad \llcorner p \lrcorner \ulcorner \llcorner q \lrcorner \ulcorner r \urcorner \urcorner, \quad \llcorner p \lrcorner \ulcorner q \llcorner r \lrcorner \ulcorner s \urcorner s \urcorner.$$

Although by 'quantifier' or 'generalization', used without qualification, I always mean a quantifier or generalization that, being universal, may officially be part of canonic language L, (§ 6.1.4) I sometimes use the terminology of particular quantification analogously and loosely as suggested by the following proleptic remarks: I call *unabbreviated particular generalization* only any negation whose negate is a universal generalization, as represented by the following scheme:

$$\vdash \left(\llcorner \ldots \lrcorner \ulcorner \vdash (\ldots \ldots) \urcorner \right);$$

call *particular generalization* only any informal abbreviation of such a negation, as represented, say, by the following analogous scheme:

$$\bot \ldots \bot \ulcorner (\ldots \ldots) \urcorner;$$

and call *particular quantifier* only any part of such an abbreviation corresponding to the universal quantifier of a universal generalization, as represented by the abbreviation '⊥ ... ⊥' in the second scheme above.

T.E. XI. A ε Qntf(B)   For every A and B:

A is (the *universal*) *quantifier of* (generalization) B if and only if (1) B is a universal generalization, (2) A is a universal quantifier in B, and (3) the first word in B is in A.

So only any universal quantifier (part of B and) containing the first word in universal generalization B is (a and hence the) universal quantifier of B. This initial quantifier, as my use of the definite article indicates, is unique, though there may be other, *internal* quantifiers inside the quantificate of a generalization. So *having* must be distinguished from the weaker relation of merely *containing* a quantifier: For, whereas any (and hence the) quantifier of B is in B, a quantifier *in* B need not be the quantifier *of* B. For instance, no quantifier of part of B is the quantifier of B.

Lesniewski adds in a footnote that, since, on the basis of preceding explanations, together with his tacit presuppositions about expressions, it could be demonstrated that any quantifier containing the first word in a generalization is itself in that generalization, the requirement that A be in B is implicit in the remainder of the definiens and so might be omitted from XI.2 above; but that he retains this requirement, despite its redundancy, in order to establish, independently of his own presuppositions, that any generalization contains its quantifier.

T.E. XII. A ε Sbqntf(B)   For every A and B:

A is (the) *subquantifier of* (generalization) B if and only if (1) B is a universal generalization, (2) A is a subquantifier, (3) A is in B, and (4) the last word in B is in A.

So only any subquantifier that is part of B and contains the last word in generalization B is (a and hence the) subquantifier of B. This terminal subquantifier is unique, though there may be other subquantifiers *inside* the subquantifier of B. So *having* must be distinguished from merely *containing* a subquantifier: For, whereas any (and hence the) subquantifier of B is in B, a subquantifier *in* B need not be the subquantifier *of* B. For instance, no subquantifier of part of B is the subquantifier of B.

I call only any interior of the subquantifier of B (a and hence the) *quantificate of* (generalization) B. This is also unique, being the subquantifier of B minus the two outermost upper corners, which

serve only as punctuators, marking the scope of the quantifier by
enclosing what is quantified. So any generalization is the complex
of the expressions that are either its quantifier or its subquantifier; in other words, is the concatenation of its quantifier and its
subquantifier. As illustrated by the third independent example in
X above and represented by the following scheme—

$$\llcorner ab\ldots\lrcorner \ \ulcorner\llcorner kl\ldots\lrcorner \ \ulcorner f(ab\ldots kl\ldots)\urcorner\urcorner$$

—, the quantificate of a universal generalization may itself be a
universal generalization, unlike that of a *propositional* (§ 5.3)
generalization, (§ 7.0) which is always represented instead by the
following scheme:

$$\llcorner ab\ldots kl\ldots\lrcorner \ \ulcorner f(ab\ldots kl\ldots)\urcorner.$$

T.E. XIII. A ε Essnt(B)   For every A and B:

A is (the) *nucleus of* (expression) B if and only if either A is the complex of expressions that are words and are inside the subquantifier
of B or, alternatively, A is the same individual expression as B
but is not a universal generalization.

Since only any quantificate of generalization B or any non-
generalization identical with expression B is (a and hence the)
nucleus of B, this too is unique: if B is a generalization, it is the
same individual as the quantificate of B; if not, it is the same
individual as expression B itself, just as "the nucleus of an atom
without planetary electrons is the atom itself". Conversely, I call
only any individual (expression) of which A is nucleus (a and hence
the) *nucleate of* (expression) A.

The sense of 'Essnt' seems better conveyed by the translation 'nucleus' than by the
natural cognate 'essence', which has inappropriate connotations in English.

T.E. XIV. A ε var(B, C)   For every A, B, and C:

A is (a) *variable of* (generalization) C *bound by* (the equiform term)
B (inside the quantifier of C) if and only if (1) B is a word inside the
quantifier of C; (2) A is an expression equiform to B; (3) A is in the
nucleus of C; and (4) for every D and E, if D is in C, E is a word

inside the quantifier of D, and A is in D and is an expression equi-form to E, then D is the same individual as C.[83]

Since the nucleus of any generalization is identical with its quantificate, and any word inside a quantifier is a term, only any term which is in the quantificate of generalization C, is equiform to term B inside the quantifier of C, and is not in any *part* of C whose quantifier encloses a term of the same form[83] is a variable of C bound by B. I call *variable of* (§ 3.5.2, § 6.1.8) (generalization) B only any variable of generalization B bound by some individual; i.e., any term in the scope of, and bound by the equiform term inside, the quantifier of B (hence not both in the scope of, and bound by a term of the same form inside, the quantifier of some part of B).[83] I call *variable* (§ 6.1.8) only any variable of some individual (generalization); i.e., of the generalization whose quanti-fier encloses the binder of that variable. So *having* must be distin-guished from merely *containing* a variable: For, whereas any variable of B is a variable in B, a variable *in* B need not be a variable *of* B. For instance, no variable of part of B is a variable of B. Nor is a word inside a quantifier a variable, according to this definition, in contrast to the usage of others who call such binders "variables bound by or to themselves". For instance, all terms in the quantificate of each of the first two of the following four inde-pendent generalizations (including the ' ϕ 's) (§ 6.1.8) are variables of that generalization:

$$\llcorner \phi \lrcorner \ulcorner \phi \, (\mathrm{pp}) \urcorner, \quad \llcorner \phi \mathrm{pq} \lrcorner \ulcorner \phi \, (\phi \, (\mathrm{pq}) \, \phi \, (\mathrm{pq})) \urcorner, \quad \llcorner \mathrm{p} \lrcorner \ulcorner \phi \, (\mathrm{pp}) \urcorner,$$

$$\llcorner \mathrm{p} \lrcorner \ulcorner \phi \, (\llcorner \mathrm{q} \lrcorner \ulcorner \phi \, (\mathrm{pq}) \urcorner \llcorner \mathrm{q} \lrcorner \ulcorner \phi \, (\mathrm{pq}) \urcorner) \urcorner.$$

But only the 'p's in the quantificate of each of the last two of these four independent generalizations are variables of that generaliza-tion, in which the ' ϕ 's are not variable at all, the 'q' in the quan-tificate of each generalization that is merely part of the fourth being a variable of that part.

T.E. XV. A ε cnvar(B, C) For every A, B, and C:

A is *convariable with* (variable) B *of* (generalization) C if and only if

(1) for at least one D, A is a variable of C bound by D; (2) for at least one D, B is a variable of C bound by D; and (3) A is an expression equiform to B.

For greater flexibility and idiomatic convenience, I call only all pairs of individuals one of which is convariable with the other variable of generalization B *convariables* (resp. *related variables*) *of* (generalization) B; and call only all convariables of some individual (generalization) *convariable* (resp. *related*).[83] Since equiformity is an equivalence relation, and no quantifier encloses two equiform terms, only all equiform variables *of* a generalization, bound by the term of the same form inside its quantifier, are convariables (of that generalization). But equiform variables *in* a generalization need not be convariables (*of* that generalization), since they may be variables of different ingredients of that generalization, bound by terms of the same form but inside different quantifiers. For instance, all the equiform variables in each of the first two of the four independent generalizations given as examples in XIV above are related, but only the variables 'p' in each of the last two are related (variables of that generalization), though the variables 'q' in each generalization that is merely part of the fourth are related (variables of that part). Since convariability is an equivalence relation, the order in which convariables are mentioned is inessential, and only any variable (of some generalization) related to itself is a variable (of that generalization).

T.E. XVI. A ε prntm   For every A:

A is (a) *parentheme* if and only if (1) for at least one B, B is a word inside expression A; (2) for every B, if B is the first word in A or is a word inside A, then there are fewer ingredients of A that both follow B and are expressions equiform to the first word in A than ingredients of A that both follow B and are brackets symmetrical to the first word in A; and (3) for every B, if B is a word inside A or is the last word in A, then there are fewer ingredients of A that both precede B and are brackets symmetrical to the first word in A than ingredients of A that both precede B and are left brackets (and expressions) equiform to the first word in A.

So only any expression which encloses one or more words, and in which every word but the first (a left bracket) is preceded by fewer brackets symmetrical to than by left brackets equiform to its first word, and every word but the last (a right bracket) is followed by fewer expressions equiform to than by brackets symmetrical to its first word, is a parentheme. Since XVI was simplified in the same way as IX above, it follows by the same argument that brackets of these respective forms inside any parentheme are also properly matched and mated in uniquely determined pairs. Parenthemes are "parentheses" understood as parenthetical, bracketed expressions together with the outermost brackets, (§ 7.0) the punctuators that embrace them and mark their scope; and are analogous to quotations understood as quoted expressions together with the outermost quotes. The following are three independent examples of parenthemes:

$$(V), \quad (\llcorner r \lrcorner \ulcorner r \urcorner), \quad (\cap (PQ)) .$$

Though no concatenation of parenthemes, such as '⟦p⟧(q)', is a parentheme, parenthemes may enclose other parenthemes, as in the third independent example above; indeed, the possibility of such nesting without limit, in compound functions, gives mathematical logic much of its combinatorial power. (§ 6.1.0) For the reason explained in XXI below, parenthemes that enclose no phrase, like these three independent examples— (⌣), (()), (⌐(⌣)⌐⌐)—, are useless, and therefore are excluded from propositions. (§ 5.3, § 7.0)

T.E. XVII. A ε prntm(B, c)   For every A, B, and c:
parentheme A *of* B is c if and only if (1) A is c; (2) for every D, if D is c then D is a parentheme; (3) B is the complex of expressions that are either c or the first word of B; and (4) the first word of B is a term.
—I.e., A is one of the one or more c, which are all parenthemes (in B), and B is the complex of expressions that are either c or the first word of B, which word is a term. So the parentheme of each of the first three of the four independent examples in XIX below is the complex of expressions that are words which in that example follow its initial term.

T.E. XVIII. A ε prntm(B)   For every A and B:
A is (a) *parentheme of* (function) B if and only if, for at least one c,
parentheme A of B is c.

T.E. XIX. A ε fnct   For every A:
A is (a) *function* if and only if, for at least one B, B is a parentheme
of A.

So only any compound expression having (not just containing)
at least one parentheme is a function, and contains every function
of which each of its one or more parenthemes is parentheme. A
function is the concatenation of its own first word, which word is a
term, and its one or more parenthemes, which, being discrete and
non-overlapping, fit together with one another and with its initial
term to compose it. I call *many-link function* only any function
having (not just containing) more than one parentheme, such as the
following sample many-link function—

$$\text{Cnv} \left(\cap_2 \underset{2}{(PQ)} \right) \{xy\}$$

—, which I nickname SMF for short. SMF is the counterpart of
'x{Cnv'(P∩Q)}y' in PM, (§ 1.0) p. 239, since in canonic language L
every parentheme of any function F follows the initial term of F,
(§ 6.1.0) as indicated by loosely representative schemes such as the
following:

f(ab...), f[kl...](ab...), f⟨xy...⟩[kl...](ab...), etc.

Since no two parenthemes of any function B contain a word in
common, any term in B except the first is inside just one parentheme
of B. But *having* must be distinguished from merely *containing* one
or more parenthemes, and many-link functions distinguished from
merely compound functions: For, whereas any parentheme of B is
in B, a parentheme *in* B need not be a parentheme *of* B. For instance, no parentheme inside a parentheme of B is a parentheme
of B. The parentheme (e.g.) of the function

$$'\cap_2 \underset{2}{(PQ)}'$$

inside the first parentheme of SMF above is a parentheme in but not of SMF. Similarly, though any many-link function contains more than one function, and hence is a compound function, not all compound functions are many-link functions, as illustrated by the third of the following four independent examples:

$$\vdash (V), \quad \vdash (\llcorner r \lrcorner \ulcorner r \urcorner), \quad \mathrm{Cnv} \left(\cap (PQ) \right), \quad \phi (\!(p)\!)(q).$$

The first two are both simple functions; the last two are both compound functions; but only the fourth is, like SMF, a many-link function. The only parentheme of the first is the contained expression of form '(V)'; that of the second is the contained '($\llcorner r \lrcorner \ulcorner r \urcorner$)'; that of the third is the contained

$$'\left(\cap (PQ) \right)',$$

that of the enclosed function being the nested

$$'(PQ)';$$

and the only two parenthemes of the fourth are the contained '$(\!(p)\!)$' and '(q)'.

For the reason explained in XXI below, functions such as the following three independent examples— $-(\llcorner)$, $\phi (())$, $f(\llcorner (\ulcorner (\llcorner)\lrcorner) \urcorner)$—are as useless as their parenthemes, which enclose no phrase, (§ 1.4) and therefore are likewise excluded from propositions. (§ 5.3, § 7.0)

T.E. XX. A ε arg(B, c)   For every A, B, and c:
argument A *of* (parentheme) B is c if and only if (1) B is a parentheme; (2) the complex of the one or more expressions that are words and are inside B is the complex of the one or more expressions that are c; (3) for every D, if D is c then D is either a term, universal generalization, or function; and (4) A is c.

—I.e., the interior of parentheme B is the complex of the one or more expressions that are c, which are all phrases (§ 1.4) (inside B), and of which A is one. Consider the first three independent examples of parenthemes in XVI above: The only argument of the first is the enclosed term 'V'; the only argument of the second is the enclosed generalization '⌊r⌋ ⌈r⌉'; and the only argument of the third is the enclosed function

$$\text{'}\cap (PQ)\text{'},$$

the only two arguments of whose own parentheme are the enclosed terms 'P' and 'Q'.

T.E. XXI. A ε arg(B)   For every A and B:
A is (an) *argument of* (parentheme) B if and only if, for at least one c, argument A of parentheme B is c.

So only any parentheme whose interior is the complex of one or more expressions that are phrases, (§ 1.4) of which A is one, is (a and hence the) parentheme of which A is argument. The interior of any parentheme in a proposition (§ 5.3, § 7.0) is the complex of the one or more expressions that are its arguments, which need not be separated by commas, since it is always clear where one ends and another begins, without ad hoc conventions of scope and punctuation. (§ 6.1.0) I call *argument* only any argument of some individual (parentheme). Since any argument is a phrase, containing at least one term, no non-phrase can be an argument. For this reason, parenthemes enclosing no phrase (as at the end of XVI and XIX above) have no argument; therefore, like functions having such a parentheme without an argument, they are useless, and consequently are excluded from propositions. (§ 5.3, § 7.0)

Having must be distinguished from merely *enclosing* one or more arguments: For, whereas any argument of B is a phrase that is an argument inside B, not even a phrase that is an argument *inside* B need be an argument *of* B. For instance, no argument of a parentheme inside B is an argument of B. The terms 'P' and 'Q' in the examples in XVI or XIX above (e.g.) are arguments, not of the enclosing parentheme

$$\text{'}\big(\cap (PQ)\big)\text{'},$$

but instead of its own argument the enclosed function

$$\text{'}\cap (PQ)\text{'}.$$

I call simply *argument of function* B only any argument of the last parentheme of function B, as distinguished both from an argument merely of a parentheme, and from what I call (a) *parameter of* (many-link function) C: namely, only any argument of some parentheme of C other than the last. No ambiguity attends this usage, since no function is a parentheme. Since any parentheme in a *proposition* (§ 5.3) has at least one argument, so does any function in a proposition. (§ 7.0) I call only any function having exactly n arguments (a) *function of* (resp. *with*, *having*) n *arguments;* resp. n-*place*, or n-*adic*: one-place or monadic, two-place or dyadic, three-place or triadic, etc. Consider for example the various functions in SMF in XIX above: The terms 'x' and 'y' are the two arguments of dyadic function SMF, a compound and many-link function whose only parameter is the function

$$\text{`}\cap \underset{2}{(}PQ\underset{2}{)}\text{'},$$

itself a simple function of the two arguments 'P' and 'Q' that has no parameter, and that is in turn the one argument of the monadic function

$$\text{`}Cnv \underset{2}{(}\cap \underset{2}{(}PQ\underset{2}{)}\underset{2}{)}\text{'},$$

a compound but not many-link function that, like a simple function, has no parameter.

T.E. XXII. A ε Sgnfnct(B)　　　　　　For every A and B: A is (the) *functor of* (§ 6.1.0) (function) B if and only if (1) A is an expression, (2) A is in B, and (3) the complex of expressions that are words and are in B but are not in A is a parentheme of B.

So only any complex of the one or more expressions that either are the first word in B or, alternatively, both are parenthemes of B and precede the last parentheme of B is (a and hence the) functor of B, which in other words is function B minus the last parentheme of B; and only any function is the concatenation of its functor with its last parentheme, which alone of its one or more parenthemes is not in its functor, and which encloses all its arguments, as distinguished from its parameters, if it has any. Only any many-link function has one or more parameters, each of which is inside some parentheme of the functor. The first word in any function is the same individual as the first word in its functor, and is a term; the remainder of the function is the complex of the one or more expressions that are its parenthemes. Any individual is functor of at most one function. Since any simple function has just one parentheme, its functor is the same individual as its initial term; whereas the functor of any many-link function is itself a function, identical with the concatenation of its initial term and each of its parenthemes but the last. XIX above provides examples illustrating both the foregoing and the following remarks. The functor of the sample many-link function SMF, for instance, is itself the compound function

$$\text{'Cnv}\left(\underset{2}{\cap}\left(\underset{2}{PQ}\right)\right)\text{',}$$

whose own functor is in turn the term 'Cnv', and the functor of whose argument is the term '$\cap$'.

Since no parentheme is a function, arguments of the last parentheme of a function may safely be called simply arguments of that function. But such arguments cannot, without ambiguity, in all cases be called "arguments of its functor", since the functor of any many-link function is itself a function. Such ambiguous usage would not make clear, for instance, whether the description "argument of the functor of SMF" in XIX referred to the parameter

$$\text{'}\underset{2}{\cap}\left(\underset{2}{PQ}\right)\text{'}$$

of SMF, as argument of the compound function

$$\text{'Cnv}\left(\underset{2}{\cap}\left(\underset{22}{PQ}\right)\right)\text{'}$$

that happens to be the functor of SMF, or to the terms 'x' and 'y', as arguments of SMF and hence of its functor.

I call simply *functor* only any functor of some individual (function). Any functor is either a term or function but not both, and therefore is a phrase but not a generalization. No argument is a functor; though arguments and functors alike may be functions, as mentioned above, and an argument may belong to the same semantic category and be of the same form as a functor. (§ 6.1.8) So *having* must be distinguished from merely *containing* a functor:

For, whereas any functor of B is a functor in B, a functor *in* B
need not be the functor *of* B. For instance, no functor of part of B
is the functor of B. Neither the functor '∩' of the parameter, nor
the functor 'Cnv' of the functor, of (e.g.) SMF is the functor of
SMF itself.

T.E. XXIII. A ε simprntm(B)   For every A and B:
A is (a parentheme) *similar to* (parentheme) B if and only if (1) A
is a parentheme, (2) B is a parentheme, (3) the first word in A is an
expression equiform to the first word in B, and (4) arguments of
A and arguments of B are equinumerous.

For greater flexibility and idiomatic convenience, I call only all
pairs of similar parenthemes *homotypes*; and call *types* only all
"equivalence classes" (§ 1.8) with respect to the equivalence relation of being similar parenthemes (resp. homotypes). So only all
parenthemes having the same number of arguments, and having
initial (and hence terminal) brackets of the same form, are similar
parenthemes (resp. homotypes, of the same type); and the type of
a parentheme can be represented by schemes such as '(– –)', indicating the forms of its outermost brackets and the number of its
arguments, which are represented by dashes. Relative "argument
positions" or "places" can be defined as equivalence properties
(§ 1.8) with respect to the relation of being homologous arguments
of certain individuals. (§ 1.4)

T.E. XXIV. A ε genfnct(B)   For every A and B:
A is (a) *generating function with respect to* (function) B if and only if
(1) A is a function; (2) parenthemes of A are equinumerous to or less
numerous than parenthemes of B; and (3) for every C and D, if
C is a parentheme of A, D is a parentheme of B, and parenthemes of
A that follow C are equinumerous to parenthemes of B that follow
D, then C is a parentheme similar to D.

—I.e., function A has at most the same number of parenthemes as
B, which therefore must also have at least one parentheme and so be a
function, and all terminally homologous parenthemes of A and of B
are similar. Then and only then, for brevity, I call A *generant of* B
and, conversely, call B *generate of* A. Since a generant may have fewer

parenthemes than one of its generates, generation is not an equivalence relation, as is the symmetrical relation of homogeneity
defined as follows: I call *homogenes* (resp. *homogeneous*) only all
pairs of functions whose terminally homologous parenthemes are
all similar; i.e., functions of which at least one is a generant of the
other; and call *genus* only any "equivalence class" with repect to
homogeneity. (§ 1.8) So if A is a generant of B, then B is of the
same genus as A even if not a generant of A.

T.E. XXV. A ε Anarg(B, C, D)   For every A, B, C, and D:
argument A *of* (parentheme) C is *analogous to* (argument) B *in* (resp.
of parentheme) D if and only if (1) C is a parentheme similar to
parentheme D, (2) A is an argument of C, (3) B is an argument of
D, and (4) arguments of C that precede A are equinumerous to
arguments of D that precede B.

—I.e., individuals A and B are (initially) homologous arguments
of similar parenthemes C and D respectively; in other words, occupy
the same relative argument position in parenthemes C and D of the
same type; when and only when, for greater flexibility and idiomatic convenience, I use obvious stylistic variants such as these:
I say that A is *analogous, as argument of* (parentheme) C, to (argument) B *in* (resp. *of* parentheme) C; call (*argument*) A *of* (parentheme)
C *analogous to* (resp. the *analog to* or *of*, the argument *having* as
analog) B *in* (resp. argument B *of* parentheme) D; call (*arguments*)
A and B *analogs in* (resp. *analogous arguments of* parenthemes) C
and D, respectively; etc. I call only all analogous arguments of
respective individuals (i.e., parenthemes) simply *analogous arguments*. So only all homologous arguments of homotypes are thus
analogous, and only any argument of B is the argument of B analogous to itself in B. For XXV might loosely be said to define an
"equivalence relation between pairs of individuals", in this sense:
Suppose argument A of B is analogous to C in D. Then argument
A of B is analogous to A in B and argument C of D is analogous to
C in D ("reflexivity"); argument C of D is analogous to A in B
("symmetry"); and if argument C of D is analogous to E in F, then
argument A of B is analogous to E in F ("transitivity").

T.E. XXVI. A ε Ansgnfnct(B, C, D)   For every A, B, C, and D: (the) *functor* A *of* (function) C is *analogous to* (the functor) B *in* (resp. *of* function) D if and only if (1) A is the functor of function C; (2) B is the functor of function D; and (3) for certain E and F, E is a parentheme of C that follows A and is similar to F, and F is a parentheme of D that follows B.

—I.e., individuals A and B are respectively the functors of functions C and D, the last parenthemes of which functions are similar (so that analogous functors A and B immediately precede parenthemes of the same type). Then and only then I use obvious stylistic variants patterned on those mentioned in XXV above, 'argument' being replaced by 'functor' and 'parentheme' by 'function'. I call only all analogous functors of respective individuals (i.e., functions) simply *analogous functors*. So only all (and hence the) functors of homogeneous functions are thus analogous, and only any (and hence the) functor of B is the functor of B analogous to itself in B. For XXVI too might be said to define an "equivalence relation between pairs of individuals": Suppose functor A of B is analogous to C in D. Then functor A of B is analogous to A in B, and functor C of D is analogous to C in D; functor C of D is analogous to A in B; and if functor C of D is analogous to E in F, then functor A of B is analogous to E in F.

T.E. XXVII. A ε An(B, C, D)   For every A, B, C, and D: *argument or functor* A *of* C is *analogous to* (argument or functor) B *in* (resp. *of*) D if and only if either argument A of parentheme C is analogous to argument B of parentheme D or, alternatively, the functor A of function C is analogous to the functor B of function D.

Then and only then, for greater flexibility and idiomatic convenience, I say that A is *analogous, as argument or functor of* C, *to* (argument or functor) B *in* (resp. *of*) D; call (*argument or functor*) A *of* C *analogous to* (resp. the *analog to* or *of*, the argument or functor *having* as *analog* argument or functor) B *in* D; and call A and B *analogs* (resp. *analogous, analogous arguments or functors*) *in* (resp. *of*) C *and* D, respectively. I call only all analogous arguments or functors of respective individuals simply *analogous* (*arguments or functors*). So only all pairs of individuals that either are homologous arguments of parenthemes of the same type or, alternatively, are the functors of functions of the same genus are analogous arguments or functors, and only any argument or functor of B is the argument or functor analogous to itself in B, the alternatives being mutually exclusive. For XXVII too defines what, like its two mutually exclusive subrelations, might be called an "equivalence relation between pairs of individuals": Suppose argument or functor A of B is analogous to C in D. Then argument or functor A of B is analogous to A in B, and argument or functor C of D is analogous to C in D; argument or functor C of D is analogous to A in B; and if argument or functor C of D is analogous to E in F, then argument or functor A of B is analogous to E in F; moreover, if argument C of parentheme D is analogous to E in F, then argument A of parentheme B is analogous to argument E of parentheme F; whereas, if functor C of function D is analogous to E in F, then functor A of function B is analogous to functor E of function F.

T.E. XXVIII. A ε Arg$_1$(B)   For every A and B:
A is (the) *antecedent of* (*parentheme*) B if and only if, for at least one C, C is in Axiom AP, and argument A of parentheme B is analogous to the tenth word of AP, in C; i.e., to the first argument of parentheme C, C being of form '(pq)'.

Lesniewski considered the requirement that C be in Axiom AP implicit in the remainder of the definiens of XXVIII (resp. XXIX below) but, as in XI above, retained this redundant requirement in order to establish the ingredience of C in AP independently of his own tacit presuppositions.

T.E. XXIX. A ε Arg$_2$(B)   For every A and B:
A is (the) *consequent of* (*parentheme*) B if and only if, for at least one C, C is in Axiom AP, and argument A of parentheme B is analogous to the eleventh word of AP, in C; i.e., to the second argument of parentheme C, C being of form '(pq)'.

So only any first (resp. second) argument of parentheme B, a parentheme of type '(– –)', is (a and hence the) antecedent (resp. consequent) of parentheme B. I call *antecedent* (resp. *consequent*) only any antecedent (resp. consequent) of some individual (parentheme); and call only any antecedent (resp. consequent) of the last parentheme of function B (a and hence the) *antecedent* (resp. *consequent*) *of* (function) B.

T.E. XXX. A ε Eqvl₁(B)   For every A and B:
A is (the) *provisory coimplicans of* (dyadic function) B if and only
if (1) the functor of function B is an expression equiform to the
sixth word in Axiom AP and (2) for at least one C, C is parentheme
of B, and A is the antecedent of parentheme C.

T.E. XXXI. A ε Eqvl₂(B)   For every A and B:
A is (the) *provisory coimplicate of* (dyadic function) B if and only
if (1) the functor of function B is an expression equiform to the
sixth word in Axiom AP and (2) for at least one C, C is parentheme of B, and A is the consequent of parentheme C.

So only any antecedent (resp. consequent) of function B, whose
functor is a term of form ' φ ', is (a and hence the) provisory
coimplicans (resp. coimplicate) of dyadic function B; and is the
same individual as the coimplicans (resp. coimplicate) of coimplication B, *provided* that B is propositional and its functor is not
variable. The qualification 'provisory' is accounted for by this
proviso, (§ 7.0) which will be clarified by later explanations, especially XLIV below, and which is violated by the first two examples
of form ' φ (pp)' and ' φ (pq)' in XIV above.

I translate the Latin abbreviations of XXX and XXXI in terms of "coimplication"
in order to facilitate formation of derivatives, such as 'coimplicator', 'coimplicant',
'coimplicans', and 'coimplicate', analogous to counterparts for "implication"; and
to reserve the terminology of "equivalence" for metalinguistic relations between
expressions such as the arguments of true coimplications. (See § 2.0 above, together
with XLIV in § 7.1 and n. 17 in § 9 below.)

T.E. XXXII. A ε thp(B) (§ 7.0)   For every A and B:
A is (a) *thesis relative to* (*thesis*) B (§ 5.2) (*of this* (§ 6.1.5) *system*) if
and only if (1) A is a thesis of this system, (2) B is a thesis of this
system, and (3) A is an individual either preceding or identical with B.

So only any thesis of this system either preceding or identical
with thesis B of this system is a thesis relative to B; and only any
thesis is a thesis relative to itself or, equivalently, belongs to the
field of being a thesis relative to an individual (thesis), which is a
simple-order relation, reflexive, transitive, antisymmetrical, and
connected: Suppose A is a thesis relative to B. Then A is a thesis
relative to A, and B is a thesis relative to B; if B is a thesis relative

to C, then A is a thesis relative to C; and if B is also a thesis relative to A, then B is the same individual as A. So of any two theses of this system (i.e., members of the field) at least one is a thesis relative to the other.

Lesniewski's and my own (auxiliary) definitions are such that, the relation being transitive, any meaningful generalization holds that is obtainable by replacing 'so-and-so', in the following represent- ative scheme, by any nominal expression defined relative to any thesis taken as parameter:

Relativity Scheme RS of XXXII:

> If A is a thesis relative to B, then
> any so-and-so relative to A is
> a so-and-so relative to B also.

One instance expresses the transitivity of the relation itself: If A is a thesis relative to B, then any thesis relative to A is a thesis relative to B also. Since Axiom AP is a thesis relative to any thesis whatever, it follows that any so-and-so (e.g., thesis) relative to AP is a so-and-so (e.g., thesis) relative to any later thesis as well. Instances of the relativity scheme RS above may henceforth be taken for granted and not explicitly stated.

T.E. XXXIII. A ε frp(B), A ε fro(B) (§ 7.0) For every A and B: A is (a) *basic propositional phrase relative to* (*thesis*) B (*of this system*) if and only if either (i) A is a thesis relative to thesis B of this system; (ii) for certain C and D, A is the antecedent of parentheme C, C is in D, and D is a thesis relative to thesis B of this system; (iii) for certain C and D, A is the consequent of parentheme C, C is in D, and D is a thesis relative to thesis B of this system; or (iv) for certain C and D, A is the complex of expressions that are words and are inside C, C is a subquantifier in D, and D is a thesis relative to thesis B of this system.

So, relative to any one thesis specified as parameter, only any thesis, antecedent or consequent of some ingredient of a thesis, or quantificate in a thesis is a basic propositional phrase, these four alternatives being mutually exclusive. Hence the relation of being a basic propositional phrase relative to an individual (thesis) is antisymmetrical and transitive. For all individuals that are basic propositional phrases relative to each other are necessarily theses relative to each other, and hence are the same individual. And if A is a basic propositional phrase relative to B, and B is a basic propositional phrase relative to C, then, since B is necessarily a thesis relative to C, it follows (according to relativity scheme RS of XXXII above) that A, being a basic propositional phrase relative to B, is a basic propositional phrase relative to C also. No basic propositional phrase is a functor.

The translation of 'frp' and 'fro' that I adopt corresponds more closely in meaning to Lesniewski's original *'frasa'* than would the shorter alternative 'frame', and likewise is rationalized by the following considerations: Any basic propositional phrase is a phrase in a thesis but not inside a quantifier, belongs to the basic semantic category of propositions, and hence is a propositional phrase, "basic" too in this further sense: Any new constant or founding member of a new semantic category is introduced into canonic language L, and so to speak "framed" in a general propositional context, by a thesis that, like the definiendum of any definition, is a basic propositional phrase.

I call *thetic (relative to thesis* B) only any phrase that is in some thesis, relative to an individual thesis B of this system, but is not inside a quantifier. So the following generalizations hold relative to any one thesis specified as parameter: Any basic propositional phrase is thetic; and Lesniewski's requirements for theses are such that any thetic is either (1) a thesis, (2) a quantificate in a thesis, (3) a variable of some ingredient of a thesis, (4) an argument of some ingredient of a thesis, or (5) the functor of some ingredient of a thesis. To anticipate, only any thetic is a categoric ingredient of some thesis; i.e., an ingredient belonging to some (one) semantic category. Of the subcases enumerated above, only all those indicated as follows are mutually exclusive: Case 1 is incompatible with 2, 3, 4, or 5; 2 with 4 or 5; and 4 with 5.

T.E. XXXIV. A ε $_1$homosemp(B, C), A ε $_1$homosemo(B, C) (§ 7.0) For every A, B, and C: A is (a) *thetic direct homoseme of* (thetic) B *relative to* (*thesis*) C (*of this system*) if and only if either (i) A and B are

both basic propositional phrases relative to thesis C of this system;
(ii) for certain D and E, A is convariable with variable B of generalization D, D is in E, and E is a thesis relative to thesis C of this
system; or (iii) for certain D, E, F, and G, D is in E, F is in G, E
and G are both theses relative to thesis C of this system, and
argument or functor A of D is analogous to B in F.

So the following generalizations hold relative to any one thesis
specified as parameter: Only all paired individuals that either are
(both) basic propositional phrases, are convariables of some ingredient of a thesis, or are analogous arguments or functors of respective ingredients of certain theses (which may be the same thesis)
are thetic direct homosemes; i.e., to anticipate, are thetics belonging
directly to the same semantic category. For the qualification 'direct'
simply indicates that the relation *TDH* of being thetic direct
homosemes is the base relation, in terms of which its ancestral
relation *TH* of being thetic homosemes (i.e., thetics of the same
semantic category) is inductively defined in XXXV below.

To anticipate further, the relation TDH (resp. TH) equals the more inclusive base
relation DH of being direct homosemes (resp. ancestral relation H of being homosemes: i.e., individuals of the same semantic category) restricted to ingredients of
theses, as distinguished from ingredients of propositions in general. Similarly, thetics
equal categorics in theses, as distinguished from categorics in general. (§ 11)

Analysis of XXXIV makes clear that pairs of individuals are thetic
direct homosemes if and only if the paired individuals either (1)
are (both) basic propositional phrases, each individually being
either a thesis, quantificate in a thesis, or argument of some ingredient of a thesis which ingredient is a parentheme of type '(– –)';
(2) are convariables of some ingredient of a thesis; (3) are homologous arguments, occupying the same relative position, of ingredients
of theses, which ingredients are parenthemes of the same type;
or (4) are the functors of ingredients of theses, which ingredients are
functions whose last parenthemes are of the same type. (Alternative 4 is incompatible with 1 and with 3, since no functor is a
thesis, quantificate, or argument.) (§ 6.1.8) Comparison with the
definition of 'thetic', in XXXIII above, shows further that all
paired individuals that are thetic direct homosemes are both thetic,
and that only any thetic is a thetic direct homoseme of itself.

If A is a thetic direct homoseme of B, then A is a thetic direct homoseme of A, and B is a thetic direct homoseme both of itself and of A. So the order in which thetic direct homosemes are mentioned is immaterial. But the reflexive and symmetrical relation TDH is not an equivalence relation. For its nontransitivity is instanced, whenever the defined constant of a definition is a functor of new semantic category, by any argument of the succeeding parentheme, as demonstrated by the following reasoning, which will become clear in the light of explanation XLIV below:

Suppose the defined constant of definition D is a functor of semantic category new in D, D being taken as parameter throughout the following deduction. Then the definiendum of D contains a parentheme of new type, of which no thesis preceding D contains a homotype, and every argument of which is a variable of generalization D related to at least one variable in the definiens of D. Hence an arbitrary argument A of any such parentheme is a thetic direct homoseme of some related variable B of D in the definiens of D. And B is required to be analogous, in an ingredient of D, to some argument or functor C of an ingredient of some thesis preceding D. So B is a thetic direct homoseme of C, just as A is a thetic direct homoseme of B. Yet A is not a thetic direct homoseme of C.

But the reflexivity and symmetry of TDH do equate its domain, converse domain, and field to each other, to those of the equivalence relation TH, to thetics, and to individuals that are thetic direct homosemes of themselves. At any stage, since the number of theses is finite, so is the number of thetics, and whether individuals are thetic, or are thetic direct homosemes, is therefore effectively decidable by inspection of a finite number of phrases. (§ 6.1.7)

T.E. XXXV. A ε homosemp(B, C), A ε homosemo(B, C)

For every A, B, and C: A is (a) *thetic homoseme of* (*thetic*) B *relative to* (*thesis*) C (*of this system*) if and only if (1) A is a thetic direct homoseme of itself relative to thesis C of this system, and so too is B; and (2) the following holds for every d: Suppose that, for every E, E is d only if E is a thetic direct homoseme of E relative to thesis C of this system; that, for every E and F, if E is a thetic direct homoseme of F relative to thesis C of this system, and F is d, then E is d; and that B is d; then A is d also.

—I.e., relative to thesis C, A and B are both thetic and, for every d such that only thetics are d and all thetic direct homosemes of any d are also d, A is d if B is d; in other words, as expressed distributively in the material mode, A is a thetic member of all subclasses of thetics that include thetic B as a member and are closed with respect to base relation TDH. (§ 1.8)

So the following generalizations hold relative to any one thesis specified as parameter: Since TDH is a symmetrical relation whose field equals thetics, only all paired thetics either of which inherits all properties possessed by the other, possessed only by thetics, and hereditary with respect to the base relation TDH are thetic homosemes. Indeed, whatever is exemplified by some thetic and is either closed or hereditary is both closed and hereditary with respect to TDH, and is exemplified only by thetics. So two of Lesniewski's requirements (as he acknowledges) are logically redundant, simply making explicit what is implicit in the remaining requirements of XXXV: namely, that all paired individuals that are thetic homosemes are both thetic, and that any thetic homoseme of any individual need inherit from that thetic ancestor only all subproperties of thetics; so that, in order to decide at any stage whether pairs of individuals are thetic homosemes, only properties peculiar to the finite number of thetics need be considered. (§ 6.1.7)

Since TH thus equals the ancestral of the symmetrical base relation TDH, only any ancestor or descendant (i.e., "member of all closed classes characteristic" or "inheritor of all hereditary properties") of an individual (thetic), with respect to TDH, is one of its thetic homosemes; i.e., is a thetic of its semantic category. And, since only all pairs of thetic homosemes are linked by the ancestral relation TH (i.e., by some finite power) of the base relation TDH, whether pairs of individuals are thetic homosemes is also effectively decidable at any stage. For paired individuals are thetic homosemes if and only if either they are the same thetic individual or one is a thetic direct homoseme, a thetic direct homoseme of a thetic direct homoseme,..., or a thetic direct homoseme...of a thetic direct homoseme of the other, for some finite number of intermediary links in the chain of thetic direct homosemes linking these individuals, which are necessarily phrases in theses but not inside quantifiers. Since the ancestral always includes both the base relation and the proper ancestral, and the base relation TDH is reflexive, what is suggested by the foregoing schemes can be made explicit in the following corollaries of XXXV, relative to the specified thesis: Since only all paired individuals either of which is a thetic direct homoseme of a thetic homoseme of the other are thetic homosemes, only all pairs of thetic direct homosemes, or of individuals either of which individuals is a thetic direct homoseme of a thetic homoseme of the other, are thetic homosemes. This latter corollary of Lesniewski's explicit "inductive" definition is even more useful, being a recursive characterization (§ 6.1.9) of the ancestral TH in terms of the base relation TDH, (§ 5.4) logically equivalent to the conjunction of the following basic, inductive, and extremal or minimal clauses:

(1) *All pairs of thetic direct homosemes are thetic homosemes.*

(2) *All paired individuals one of which is a thetic direct homoseme of a thetic homoseme of the other are thetic homosemes.*

(3) All pairs of thetic homosemes either are thetic direct homosemes or one of the paired individuals is a thetic direct homoseme of a thetic homoseme of the other; i.e., only pairs of individuals satisfying at least one of the two conditions enumerated above are thetic homosemes.

As the ancestral of the symmetrical and reflexive base relation TDH, TH is not only symmetrical and reflexive but, like any ancestral relation, is also transitive. So the relation TH of being thetic homosemes, unlike its nontransitive base relation TDH, is an equivalence relation, with respect to which only all equivalence classes (§ 1.8) are semantic categories *of thetics.* By virtue of the symmetry and reflexivity of both relations, the domain, converse domain, and field of TH are equal to each other, to those of TDH, and so also to thetics, to individuals being thetic direct homosemes of themselves, to individuals being thetic homosemes of themselves, to categorics in theses, to individuals that in theses belong each to some one semantic category, and to phrases in theses but not inside quantifiers.

The rationale of XXXVI–XXXIX below should become clear in retrospect, upon seeing how the expressions defined are used to formulate requirements for propositions, and to assure that any thesis T asserted according to Lesniewski's directives be a proposition, significant relative to the latest thesis (either T itself or some preceding thesis) introducing a constant or semantic category of an expression in T, (§ 6.1.9) and hence relative also to any later thesis.

T.E. XXXVI. A ε constp(B, C, D, E), A ε consto(B, C, D, E)

For every A, B, C, D, and E: *argument or functor* A *of an ingredient of* C *is suited to be a constant equisignificant to homoseme* D *of its analog* E, *relative to* (*thesis*) B (*of this system*), if and only if (1) D is a thetic homoseme of E relative to thesis B of this system; (2) for every F and G, if F is in G, and G is a thesis relative to thesis B of this system, then D is (individual but) not a variable of generalization F related to D; (3) A is an expression equiform to D; and (4) for certain F, G, and H, F is in C, H is in G, G is a thesis relative to thesis B of this system, and argument or functor A of F is analogous to E in H.

—I.e., relative to thesis B, argument or functor A of an ingredient of C has analog E in some ingredient of a thesis, and is equiform to non-variable thetic homoseme D of E. So A and its analog E alike either are homologous arguments of similar parenthemes or are the functors of functions whose last parenthemes are similar. If C is in a proposition, then A belongs to the semantic category of its non-variable homomorph D and its analog E and, if a non-variable term, not only is suited to but will be a constant equisignificant to D. If C is in a thesis (as when C itself is asserted as a thesis) then A is not only a homoseme but also a thetic homoseme of D and E. Since homosemes in theses are clearly *thetic* homosemes, corresponding consequences need not be explicitly drawn from now on.

T.E. XXXVII. A ε constp(B, C), A ε consto(B, C)

For every A, B, and C: A is (an *argument or functor of*) *an ingredient of* C (*and*) *suited to be* (a) *constant, relative to* (*thesis*) B (*of this system*), if and only if, for certain D and E, argument or functor A of an ingredient of C is suited to be a constant equisignificant to homoseme D of its analog E, relative to thesis B of this system.

—I.e., relative to thesis B, argument or functor A of an ingredient of C has an analog in some ingredient of a thesis, and is equiform to some non-variable thetic homoseme of that analog. So A is either an argument or functor of some ingredient of C and, if C is in a thesis or other proposition, belongs to the appropriate semantic category and, if a non-variable term, not only is suited to but will be of the constant significance indicated by its form together with its category.

T.E. XXXVIII. A ε quasihomosemp(B, C, D, E, F),
A ε quasihomosemo(B, C, D, E, F)

For every A, B, C, D, E, and F: *arguments or functors* A *and* B *of ingredients of* D *are quasihomosemes* (eligible by analogy to the semantic category) *of their respective analogs* E *and* F, *relative to* (*thesis*) C (*of this system*), if and only if (1) E is a thetic homoseme of F relative to thesis C of this system; (2) for certain G, H, and I, G is in D, H is in I, I is a thesis relative to thesis C of this system, and argument or functor A of G is analogous to E in H; and (3) for certain G, H, and I, G is in D, H is in I, I is a thesis relative to thesis C of this system, and argument or functor B of G is analogous to F in H.

—I.e., relative to thesis C, argument or functor A of an ingredient of D has analog E in some ingredient of a thesis, and argument or functor B of an ingredient of D has analog F in some ingredient of a thesis, and E and F are thetic homosemes. Hence A is either argument or functor of some ingredient of D, and so too is B. If D is in a thesis or other proposition, then A and B not only are eligible but belong to the semantic category of their respective analogs the homosemes E and F.

I say that A *and* B *are arguments or functors of ingredients of* D, *and are quasihomosemes* (eligible by analogy to the same semantic category), *relative to* (*thesis*) C (*of this system*), if and only if arguments or functors A and B of ingredients of D are quasihomosemes (eligible by analogy to the semantic category) of their respective analogs, relative to thesis C of this system; i.e., have respective analogs in ingredients of respective theses, which analogs are thetic homosemes relative to C. If D is in a thesis or other proposition, such quasihomosemes not only are eligible but belong to the same semantic category.

T.E. XXXIX. A ε fnctp(B, C, D, E), A ε fncto(B, C, D, E)

For every A, B, C, D, and E: *argument or functor* A *of an ingredient of* C *is* (a function) *eligible* (by analogy) *to the semantic category of*

its generate D *and its analog* E, *relative to* (*thesis*) B (*of this system*),
if and only if (1) D is a thetic homoseme of E relative to thesis B of
this system; (2) A is a generating function with respect to function
D; and (3) for certain F, G, and H, F is in C, G is in H, H is a thesis
relative to thesis B of this system, and argument or functor A of F
is analogous to E in G.

—I.e., relative to thesis B, argument or functor A of an ingredient of C has analog E in some ingredient of a thesis, and is a
generating function with respect to thetic homoseme D of E. So
function A is either argument or functor of some ingredient of C
and, if C is in a thesis or other proposition, not only is eligible but
belongs to the semantic category of its generate D and its analog E.

I say that A is (an) *argument or functor of an ingredient of* C, *and
is* (a function) *eligible* (by analogy) *to the appropriate semantic
category, relative to* (*thesis*) B (*of this system*), if and only if argument
or functor A of an ingredient of C is a function eligible by analogy
to the semantic category of some generate and some analog of A;
i.e., argument or functor A of an ingredient of C has an analog in
some ingredient of a thesis, and is a generating function with respect
to some thetic homoseme of its analog, relative to thesis B of this
system. So function A is either argument or functor of some ingredient of C and, if C is in a thesis or other proposition, not only is
eligible but belongs to the appropriate semantic category: that of
its generate and its analog.

At this point I interpolate the explanation of the term 'proposition' that Lesniewski appended to his *1931* article on definitions
(p. 300, n. 1). I number it XXXIX' in order not to disrupt the
numbered sequence of explanations for protothetic and ontology,
which it helps to clarify by elucidating how requirements, expressed
without use of the term 'proposition', are designed to assure that
all theses of his system be propositions. Certain of his requirements
should be self-explanatory, on semantic grounds; the rationale of
others should be clarified by my commentary, together with reference to the analogous requirements of Frege's[30] logical grammar
of *1893*. Although logical, philosophical, and terminological differences make it impossible to translate Frege's principles literally

into Lesniewski's terminology, and to apply them unmodified to Lesniewski's system, here as elsewhere the intention of Lesniewski's requirements is often illumined by reference to Frege.

T.E. XXXIX'. A ε propp(B)   For every A and B: A is (a) *proposition relative to* (*thesis*) B (§ 5.3) (*of this system*) if and only if the following eight conditions are fulfilled:

(1) B is a thesis of this system.

(2) Either (i) A is a universal generalization; (ii) for at least one C, A is a generating function with respect to C, and C is a basic propositional phrase relative to thesis B of this system; or (iii) the following holds, for at least one C: A is an expression equiform to C, C is a word and basic propositional phrase relative to B; for every D and E, if D is a thesis relative to B, and E is in D, then C is (individual but) not a variable of E related to C; and (see below) for every D, A is (individual but) not a variable of D related to A, nor a word inside D if D is a quantifier.

(3) For every C, if C is a term in A, then either (i) A is the same individual as C; (ii) for at least one D, C is a word inside D, and D is a universal quantifier in A; (iii) for certain D and E, D is in A, and C is a variable of generalization D bound by E; or (iv) C is an argument or functor of an ingredient of A and suited to be constant, relative to B.

(4) For every C and D, if C is a word inside D, and D is a universal quantifier in A, then, for certain E and F, E is in A, and F is a variable of generalization E bound by C.

(5) For every C, D, and E, if C is convariable with variable D of generalization E, and E is in A, then either C is the same individual as D or, for certain F and G, arguments or functors C and D of ingredients of A are quasihomosemes of their respective analogs F and G, relative to B.[84]

(6) For every C, if C is a universal generalization in A, then either C is the same individual as A or, for certain D, E, F, and G, D is a thesis relative to B, E is in D, F is in A, and G is a thetic homoseme of B, relative to B, and is analogous, as argument of parentheme E, to C in F.

(7) For every C and D, if C is a universal generalization in A, and D is the nucleus of C, then either D is a word or, for at least one E, D is a generating function with respect to E, and E is a basic propositional phrase relative to B.

(8) For every C, if C is a function in A, then either (i) C is the same individual as A; (ii) for at least one D, C is the nucleus of D, and D is a universal generalization in A; or (iii) for certain D and E, argument or functor C of an ingredient of A is eligible by analogy to the semantic category of its generate D and its analog E, relative to B.

So A is a proposition relative to thesis B if and only if (1) B is a thesis of this system relative to which the following seven of these eight conditions are fulfilled: (2) A is either a generalization, generating function with respect to some basic propositional phrase, or (see below) term neither variable nor inside a quantifier but equiform to some non-variable basic propositional phrase (i.e., word being such a phrase but not a variable of an ingredient of a thesis). (3) Any term merely part of A either is a variable of some ingredient of A, is a word inside a quantifier itself in A, or is an argument or functor of an ingredient of A and suited to be constant. (4) Any word inside a quantifier in A binds at least one variable of some ingredient of A. (5) All nonidentical convariables of any ingredient of A are arguments or functors of ingredients of A, and are quasi-homosemes, eligible by analogy to the same semantic category.[84] (6) Any generalization merely part of A is analogous, as argument of some ingredient of A, to a thetic homoseme of thesis B in some ingredient of a thesis. (7) The quantificate of any ingredient of A, if not a word, is a generating function with respect to some basic propositional phrase. (8) Any function merely part of A, if not the quantificate of some ingredient of A, is an argument or functor of an ingredient of A, and is eligible by analogy to the appropriate semantic category.

Following the pattern of XXXIII, I call *propositional (relative to thesis* B) only any individual that, relative to an individual thesis B of this system, is either a proposition, quantificate in a proposition, or individual analogous, as argument of an ingredient of a proposition, to a thetic homoseme of Axiom AP in an ingredient of a thesis, the alternatives being mutually exclusive. So any proposition or basic propositional phrase is a propositional phrase, and no propositional phrase is a functor. Lesniewski's directives are such that every thesis T of this system is an independent (§ 1.4) proposition, relative to the latest thesis (either T itself or some preceding thesis) introducing a semantic category of expression in T; and every proposition (§ 5.3) is in an independent proposition, and is a relatively "self-contained, closed, and complete" propositional phrase or "clause", even if merely part of a longer proposition, as for example the generalizations '$_⌊r⌋$ $⌈r⌉$', to the effect that "everything is the case", are parts of the following independent proposition: $φ (_⌊r⌋ ⌈r⌉ _⌊r⌋ ⌈r⌉)$. Indeed only any "closed" propositional expression, containing no variable of some generalization of which generalization that expression is merely part, is a proposition. The propositional variables 'r' in the foregoing example contribute, as variables of determinate category, to the significance of the propositions of which they are parts, but are not themselves propositions, since only constants may be propositions. Various other results concerning propositions and propositional phrases can be established by strong induction—for example, that all parenthemes in propositional functions have at least one argument, as do all parenthemes in Axiom AP: For Lesniewski's directives assure that all parenthemes in a thesis do, if so do all parenthemes in all preceding theses. And, relative to any one thesis, all parenthemes in propositions do, if so do all parenthemes in all preceding theses.

I call *categoric* (*relative to thesis* B) only any phrase that is in some proposition, relative to an individual thesis B of this system, but is not inside a quantifier. So the following generalizations hold, relative to any one thesis specified as parameter: Any propositional phrase is categoric; and Lesniewski's requirements for propositions are such that any categoric is either (1) a proposition, (2) a quantificate in some proposition, (3) a variable of some ingredient of a proposition, (4) an argument of some ingredient of a proposition, or (5) the functor of some ingredient of a proposition. To anticipate, only any categoric is an individual belonging to some (one) semantic category. Of the subcases enumerated above, only all those indicated as follows are mutually exclusive: Case 1 is incompatible with 2, 3, or 5; 2 with 4 or 5; and 4 with 5.

I call *homosemes* (*relative to thesis* B) only all paired individuals that, relative to an individual thesis B of this system, either are (both) propositional or, alternatively, are arguments or functors of ingredients of propositions and are quasihomosemes, eligible by analogy to the same semantic category; i.e., have analogs in ingredients of respective theses, which analogs are thetic homosemes. From the foregoing definitions, together with Lesniewski's directives, can be derived the following result, which, like the other subsequent remarks, holds relative to any one thesis specified as parameter: The relation H of being homosemes (i.e., members of the same semantic category) is an equivalence relation, with respect to which semantic categories will be defined as equivalence classes. On the pattern of XXXV above it equals, and so could instead be defined as, the ancestral of the base relation *DH* of being *direct homosemes* (belonging directly to the same semantic category), defined by analogy with XXXIV above as paired individuals that either are (both) propositional, are convariables of some ingredient of a proposition, or are analogous arguments or functors of respective ingredients of certain propositions (which may be the same proposition). Further analysis makes clear that pairs of individuals are direct homosemes if and only if the paired individuals either (1) are (both) propositional phrases, each individually being either a proposition, quantificate in a proposition, or analogous, as argument of some ingredient of a proposition, to some thetic homoseme of Axiom AP in some ingredient of a thesis; (2) are convariables of some ingredient of a proposition; (3) are homologous arguments, occupying the same relative position, of ingredients of propositions, which ingredients are parenthemes of the same type; or (4) are the functors of ingredients of propositions, which ingredients are functions whose last parenthemes are of the same type. As in XXXIV, alternative 4 is incompatible with 1 and with 3; and the reflexive and symmetrical base relation is not transitive, as instanced by any non-propositional argument in the definiendum of any definition of a functor of new semantic category. Comparison with the definition of 'categoric' above shows further that all paired individuals that are direct homosemes are both categoric, and that only any categoric is a direct homoseme of itself.

Thus, according to the pattern of XXXIV–XXXV above, homosemes (relative to thesis B) equal pairs of individuals (necessarily categoric) linked by the ancestral H of the base relation DH of being direct homosemes, relative to an individual thesis B of this system. Just as all pairs of thetic direct homosemes are thetic homosemes, and all paired individuals that are thetic homosemes are both thetic, so all pairs of direct homosemes are homosemes, and all paired individuals that are homosemes are both categoric. Since all theses are propositions, all thetics (resp. pairs of thetic direct homosemes, pairs of thetic homosemes) are categoric (resp. direct homosemes, homosemes), though only all categorics (resp. pairs of direct homosemes, pairs of homosemes) in (propositions that are also) theses are thetic (resp. thetic direct homosemes, thetic homosemes). And just as only any thetic (i.e., phrase in a thesis but not inside a quantifier) is a member, in a thesis, of some (one) semantic category, so only any categoric (i.e., phrase in a proposition but not inside a quantifier) is a member (necessarily in a proposition) of some (one) semantic category.

Thus the relationship between the reflexive and symmetrical base relation DH and its ancestral equivalence relation H parallels that between TDH and TH, discussed in XXXIV and XXXV above. So the following generalizations, which hold relative to any one thesis specified as parameter, parallel preceding generalizations in explanations XXXIV and XXXV, 'proposition' taking the place of 'thesis', 'categoric' of 'thetic', 'propositional' of 'basic propositional phrase', 'DH' of 'TDH', and 'H' of 'TH': Any property either closed or hereditary is both closed and hereditary (§ 1.8) with respect to DH, and is exemplified only by categorics; and one such property is that of being categoric itself. So only all paired individuals either of which inherits all properties (resp. subproperties of categorics) closed or hereditary (and hence both) with respect to DH and possessed by the other, which is categoric, are homosemes, both of which are categoric. Since all paired individuals that are homosemes are both categoric, and any homoseme of an individual need inherit from that categoric ancestor only all subproperties of categorics, only any ancestor or descendant (i.e., "member of all closed classes characteristic" or "inheritor of all hereditary properties") (§ 1.8) of an individual, with respect to DH, is a member of its semantic category. So paired individuals are homosemes if and only if either they are the same categoric individual or one is a direct homoseme, a direct homoseme of a direct homoseme,..., or a direct homoseme...of a direct homoseme of the other, for some finite number of intermediary links in the chain of direct homosemes linking these individuals, which are necessarily phrases in propositions but not inside quantifiers. Since only all paired individuals either of which is a direct homoseme of a homoseme of the other are homosemes, only all pairs of direct homosemes, or of individuals either of which individuals is a direct homoseme of a homoseme of the other, are homosemes; i.e., recursively characterized: (§ 5.4)

(1) *All pairs of direct homosemes are homosemes.*

(2) *All paired individuals one of which is a direct homoseme of a homoseme of the other are homosemes.*

(3) All pairs of homosemes either are direct homosemes or one of the paired individuals is a direct homoseme of a homoseme of the other; i.e., only pairs of individuals satisfying at least one of the two conditions enumerated above are homosemes.

So, by applying the basic, inductive, and extremal clauses of this recursive corollary of my explicit definition, it is always effectively decidable whether pairs of individuals are homosemes. (§ 5.4) For the recursive procedure for deciding category membership always terminates after a finite number of steps, (§ 6.1.7) by which it leads to the members of a certain finite subclass of categoric phrases: (§ 5.2) namely, the initial, founding members of the finite number of semantic categories already introduced into the system at that stage of development, which serve as basis for recursive determination of their semantic descendants among later arrivals, since only all homosemes are fellow members of the same semantic category.

For I call *semantic categories* (*relative to thesis* B) only all equivalence classes with respect to the equivalence relation H of being homosemes, relative to an individual thesis B of this system. Relative to the thesis specified as parameter, semantic categories, being equivalence classes (or properties), (§ 1.8) are mutually exclusive and jointly exhaustive of the field of H (i.e., exhaustive of categorics): Semantic categories that have a member in common have all their members in common, and hence coincide; and only any categoric belongs to (at least and so to exactly) one semantic category, which can therefore be identified as *the* category of any (one and hence of every) (§ 1.7) phrase of that category. Membership in any semantic category is both closed and hereditary with respect to each of the symmetrical relations TDH, TH, DH, and H. According to relativity scheme RS of XXXII above, instances of which will henceforth not be explicitly stated, if A is a thesis relative to B, then all semantic categories (resp. categorics, pairs of direct homosemes, pairs of homosemes, thetics, pairs of thetic direct homosemes, pairs of thetic homosemes) relative to A are categories (resp. categorics, direct homosemes, homosemes, thetics, thetic direct homosemes, thetic homosemes) relative to B also. By virtue of the symmetry and reflexivity of both relations, the domain, converse domain, and field of H are equal to each other, to those of DH, and so also to categorics, to individuals being direct homosemes of themselves, to individuals being homosemes of themselves, to individuals belonging to some (one) semantic category, and to phrases in propositions but not inside quantifiers.

Suppose ingredient A of B is of semantic category c, relative to an individual thesis B of this system, and no thesis preceding B in this system contains a member of the same category. Then and only then I call (*semantic category*) c *new in* (*thesis*) B (resp. *introduced by* B, *founded by* A). Axiom AP (§ 6.2.2) for example both is the introductory thesis and, together with the other propositional phrases in AP, is a founding member of the semantic category of propositions. AP is also the thesis introducing the category of connectors of two propositional arguments, founded by the binary connectors in AP. As founding member and first thesis, AP belongs to the category of propositions relative to any thesis whatever. For only all homosemes of any (one and hence every) (§ 1.7) proposition, such as AP or any other thesis, are propositional relative to any one thesis specified as parameter. (§ 5.2) Any category not introduced by some one axiom is introduced by some one definition, and is founded by some phrase (§ 1.4) in its definiendum. Phrases in propositions might be described as honorable candidates for category membership, since they alone may meet the admission requirements. Non-phrases, such as punctuators, parenthemes, quantifiers, and sub-quantifiers, are permanently excluded; so are all outsiders not in propositions, such as isolated phrases; and even phrases *in* propositions may be disqualified. But, provided it does not violate the membership requirements by appearing inside a quantifier, between lower corners, or in some other improper place, any phrase is eligible for admission into the semantic category appropriate to its position in a proposition. The title 'categoric' singles out any candidate that satisfies the requirements and succeeds to membership in the category founded by its semantic ancestors.

The following generalizations, which also hold relative to any one thesis specified as parameter, help to explain Lesniewski's use of distinctive forms of brackets as contextual indices (§ 6.1.8) of

semantic category: (§ 5.2) If functions in propositions are homogeneous, then their functors are homosemes, and so too are homologous arguments of their terminally homologous parenthemes.
That all terminally homologous parenthemes of categoric functions
are of the same type thus contextually indicates, in canonic language
L, not only that those functions are of the same genus, but also that
their functors belong to the same semantic category, and that so do
arguments occupying the same relative position inside such parenthemes. The type of the last parentheme of any categoric function,
in particular, indicates the semantic category of the functor and
that of each respective argument of this function. Since the type of a
parentheme, given the number of its arguments, is indicated by the
form of its initial (and hence of its symmetrical terminal) bracket,
brackets of distinctive forms serve in language L as contextual
indices of semantic category. Functors or homologous arguments of
categoric functions of the same number of arguments are direct
homosemes if and only if either (1) they are convariable or (2) the
last parenthemes of those functions have initial (and hence terminal)
brackets of the same form, and so are of the same type. Consequently,
if a functor or argument of a function having a given number of
arguments is not variable, its semantic category is uniquely indicated by the form of such a bracket; and, if it is variable, by the
category of a convariable or by the form of such a bracket or by
both. The semantic category contextually indicated by any convariable is the same category indicated by type of parentheme.
For Lesniewski's directives assure that any thesis be a proposition
satisfying requirement XXXIX'.5, which precludes terms therein
analogous to arguments or functors of *different* categories from
being convariables of the *same* category.[84]

    The need for such a requirement should be made clear by
the following examples, together with explanations XLIV and
XLVII–XLVIII below. Suppose this requirement were omitted.
Then generalization A below and its alphabetic variant B (§ 6.1.8)
would by definition be "propositions", relative to Axiom AP, despite
their manifest absurdity. To omit also the analogous requirement
XLIV.7 would, as illustrated in XLIV, be even more disastrous: C
below (as well as the unexceptionable D and E) could then be

subjoined to AP as a definition. In consequence, the semantic category of propositions would almost from the first coincide with that of binary connectors. So standard contradictions 'Λ' and disjunctors '$\multimap$' would be "defined propositional-*and*-binary-connector constants" that, miscast each in the other's role, would not be definitionally eliminable from nonsensical "propositions" (relative to E) such as F and G, whose lack of meaning would reveal itself in

(A) $\llcorner r \lrcorner \ulcorner r(rr) \urcorner$

(B) $\llcorner \phi \lrcorner \ulcorner \phi(\phi \phi) \urcorner$

(C) $\phi \left(\llcorner r \lrcorner \ulcorner r(rr) \urcorner \text{ Nnsns} \right)$

(D) $\phi (\llcorner r \lrcorner \ulcorner r \urcorner \Lambda)$

(E) $\llcorner rs \lrcorner \ulcorner \phi \left(\phi \left(\phi (rs) \Lambda \right) \multimap (rs) \right) \urcorner$

(F) $\Lambda(\Lambda \; \Lambda)$

(G) $\multimap(\multimap \; \multimap)$

(H) $\llcorner \Lambda \lrcorner \ulcorner \Lambda \urcorner$

(I) $\llcorner r \lrcorner \ulcorner r \urcorner$

(J) $\llcorner \Lambda r \lrcorner \ulcorner \Lambda(rr) \urcorner$

(K) $\llcorner fr \lrcorner \ulcorner f(rr) \urcorner$

the attempt to stammer out paraphrases such as this illustrative gibberish: "Everything is the case that everything is the case everything is the case. If and only if not if and only if not if and only if not." But, by excluding such absurdities, such requirements prevent fusion of categories, intended to be distinct, through illegitimate admission of improper common members; and so help preserve the desired "purity" of semantic categories, completeness of definition,[34] consequent eliminability of defined constants from all propositional contexts, and consistent determinacy of meaning of all propositions in canonic language L.

In order to maintain these virtues, I myself have added to Lesniewski's requirement XXXIX'.2(iii) the final restriction that phrase A, if a term (rather than a function or generalization), be neither variable nor inside a quantifier. For in his definition (appended to his treatment in *1931* of a system of Lukasiewicz which lacks the explicit quantifiers (§ 3.5.2) of Lesniewski's own system) Lesniewski apparently overlooked the possibility that, in his own "contextualist" system, terms equiform to propositional (or other) constants may be used as variables, even of different categories. (§ 6.1.8) In formulating his requirements, presumably he was thinking of isolated terms, and intended to admit as propositions appropriate independent constants, such as standard contradictions 'Λ' or tautologies 'V', but to exclude indeterminates such as 'x' in isolation. He surely did not intend to let functor variables, or terms inside quantifiers binding variables, be called "propositions". Yet, without the added restriction, his definition would admit as "propositions" (relative to any prior definition D of a standard contradiction, and to any later thesis) all the terms 'Λ' in generalizations H and J above, though not the terms 'r' in J, nor the terms 'f' and 'r' in the merely alphabetic variants I and K, respectively.

I call *junction* (resp. *combination, relative to thesis* B) only any function whose arguments all belong to the same semantic category (resp. to the same semantic category as that function itself), relative to an individual thesis B of this system. I call *connection* (*relative to thesis* B) only any function that, like all its arguments, belongs to the category of propositions, and hence is a propositional combination, relative to an individual thesis B of this system. I call *junctor* (resp. *combinator, connector*) *of* B (*relative to thesis* C) only any functor of junction (resp. combination, connection) B, relative to an individual thesis C of this system. I call simply *junctor* (resp. *combinator, connector, relative to thesis* B) only any homoseme, relative to an individual thesis B of this system, of the functor of a junction (resp. combination, connection) relative to B.

I say that individual A is *of degree* n (resp. n-*ary*—singulary, binary, ternary, quaternary, quinary, etc.—*relative to thesis* B) if and only if, relative to an individual thesis B of this system, either (1) A belongs to a semantic category of which no member is a func-

tor, and n equals zero, or (2) A belongs to the same semantic category as the functor of some function having n arguments, and n is a
positive integer. I say that individual A is *of level* n (*relative to thesis*
B) if and only if, relative to an individual thesis B of this system,
either (1) A belongs to a semantic category of which no member is a
functor, and n equals zero, or (2) A belongs to the same semantic
category as the functor of some function whose one or more arguments of highest level are of level n–1, and n is a positive integer
(greater than zero). The degree (resp. level) of any (one and hence
every) (§ 1.7) member of a certain semantic category may loosely
and elliptically be called "the degree (resp. level) of that category".
For all members of the same category are of the same degree (resp.
level); though not all individuals of the same degree (resp. level)
need be of the same semantic category, since for example even individuals of degree and level zero may be either propositional or
nominal. It is essential to distinguish between indications of place
and indications of degree, since an m-adic function may be an n-ary
functor, for numerically different m and n. The monadic function

$$\text{'Cnv} \left(\underset{2}{\cap} \, \underset{2}{(PQ)} \right) \text{'}$$

in the sample many-link function SMF in XIX above, for instance,
is the binary functor of dyadic function SMF.

I call individuals *equisignificant constants* (*relative to thesis* B)
if and only if, relative to an individual thesis B of this system, they
are homosemes containing the same number of words, neither
contains a variable of some generalization of which it is merely part,
homologous but non-equiform words in the two are inside quantifiers
or are variables of corresponding generalizations (i.e., generalizations
whose first and hence last words are homologous), any words in
either homoseme that are respectively homologous to (words in the
other which words are) convariables of some generalization are
convariables of the corresponding generalization, and no word that
in either homoseme is homologous to a (word in the other which
word is a) variable of some generalization G is a variable of a generalization corresponding to another generalization merely part of G.
So, relative to any one thesis specified as parameter, equisignificant

constants are "closed" phrases of the same semantic category and of the same form, except perhaps for alphabetic variation of variables and permutation of terms inside the quantifiers of ingredient generalizations (see T.E. XLVIII below); and, if terms, they are non-variable. I call *constant* (*relative to thesis* B) only any constant equisignificant to itself, relative to an individual thesis B of this system; i.e., only any categoric that is "closed" in the sense that it contains no variable of a generalization of which generalization it is itself merely part. So, relative to any one thesis specified as parameter, terms in particular are constant if and only if they are categoric but not variable: i.e., are in propositions but neither inside nor bound by a term inside a quantifier. It can be demonstrated that only every propositional constant is a proposition; and that every dependent propositional constant is an argument, and every non-propositional constant is either an argument or functor, of some function itself in a proposition. I call *constant significance* (*relative to thesis* B) only any equivalence property (§ 1.8) with respect to the equivalence relation of being equisignificant constants, relative to an individual thesis B of this system. Hence, relative to the thesis specified as parameter, only all equisignificant constants are of the same constant significance, and only any constant is of unique constant significance. Consequently one may speak of *the* significance of any constant in canonic language L, wherein any constant is univocal.

Suppose A is a constant *term* in and relative to thesis B of this system, and no thesis preceding B in this system contains a constant equisignificant to A. Then and only then I call *constant* (resp. *term*) A *new in* (*thesis*) B, since it differs in significance from every constant already in the system; i.e., differs either in form or in semantic category, or in both: in form from any other of the same category, in category from any other of the same form. I call *constant* (resp. *term*) *introduced by* (*thesis*) B (*relative to thesis* C) only any constant equisignificant, relative to an individual thesis C of this system, to some term new in thesis B of this system. Any constant is introduced into canonic language L by the axiom or definition containing a new term of the same constant significance; i.e., by the first thesis containing an equisignificant constant term.

Only any coimplicator, for instance, is an undefined constant introduced by Axiom AP. I call *directly introduced in terms of* (the one or more individuals that are) c only any constant (term) introduced by a thesis itself containing a term either (1) of the same constant significance as individual c or (2) of constant significance c. (§ 1.7) I call *introduced in terms of* (the one or more individuals that are) c only any individual having all properties that are possessed by all c and are closed with respect to being directly introduced in terms of, there being at least one c; i.e., only any member of the closure of c, which exist, with respect to this relation. (See D93 of LVI° below.) For example, if A is directly introduced in terms of (individuals being either) B or C, B is directly introduced in terms of D, and C is directly introduced in terms of E, then A is introduced in terms of (individuals being either) D or E.

The expressions defined in the four auxiliary explanations XL–XLIII below are later used to formulate Lesniewski's requirements for definitions.

T.E. XL. A ε varp(B, C, D, E, F), A ε varo(B, C, D, E, F)

For every A, B, C, D, E, and F: A is (a) *variable of* (generalization) D *related to analog* F *of homoseme* E *of* B (and so suited to belong to the semantic category of B), *relative to* (*thesis*) C (*of this system*), if and only if (1) E is a thetic homoseme of B relative to thesis C of this system; (2) for certain G, H, and I, G is in D, I is in H, H is a thesis relative to thesis C of this system, and argument or functor F of G is analogous to E in I; (3) F is in the provisory coimplicans of the nucleus of D; and (4) A is convariable with variable F of generalization D.

—I.e., variable A of generalization D is related to ingredient F of the provisory coimplicans of the nucleus (i.e., quantificate) of generalization D, and argument or functor F of some ingredient of D is analogous to thetic homoseme E of B in some ingredient of a thesis, relative to thesis C of this system. (Certain of these individuals here as elsewhere may be the same.) Suppose that generalization D is a thesis following or identical with C, so that C is a thesis relative to D. Then, relative to D or any later thesis, since A is a thetic homoseme of F, F of E, and E of B, A is a thetic homoseme of B; so any variable of D related to an analog of a homoseme of B not only is suited to but will belong to the semantic category of B.

T.E. XLI. A ε prntmp(B, C, D, E), A ε propprntmo(B, C, D, E) (§ 7.0)   For every A, B, C, D, and E: *parentheme* A *of the provisory coimplicate of the nucleus of* (*generalization*) C is *suited to be similar to parentheme* E *of propositional function* D, *relative to* (*thesis*) B (*of this system*), if and only if (1) D is a thetic homoseme of B relative to thesis B of this system; (2) E is a parentheme of function D; (3) A is a parentheme of the provisory coimplicate of the nucleus of C; (4) arguments of A and arguments of E are equinumerous; and (5) for every F and G, if F is an argument of A, G is an argument of E, and arguments of A that precede F are equinumerous to arguments of E that precede G, then, for certain H and I, F is a variable of generalization C related to analog I of homoseme H of G, and so suited to belong to the semantic category of G, relative to thesis B of this system.

—I.e., relative to thesis B, parentheme A of the provisory coimplicate of the nucleus (i.e., quantificate) of generalization C has the same number of arguments as parentheme E of propositional function D, and every argument of A is a variable of C related to an analog of a homoseme of the homologous argument of E, and so suited to belong to the semantic category of its homolog. That parentheme E has at least one argument is a corollary of the generalization (provable as indicated in XXXIX' above) that any parentheme in a propositional function has at least one argument. It follows that every argument of parentheme A is a variable of C, and hence that C is a generalization, whose nucleus is the same individual as its quantificate. Suppose that generalization C is a thesis following or identical with B, so that B is a thesis relative to C. Then, relative to C or any later thesis, C itself, its nucleus, and the provisory coimplicans and coimplicate of its nucleus alike are basic propositional phrases; and homologous arguments of parenthemes A and E are thetic homosemes; so A and E, since their arguments are the same in number, and arguments occupying the same relative positions will be of the same semantic category, are suited to be of the same type.

T.E. XLII. A $\varepsilon_1$prntmp(B, C, D, E), A $\varepsilon_1$propprntmo(B, C, D, E)

For every A, B, C, D, and E: *parentheme* A *of the provisory coimplicate of the nucleus of (generalization)* C *is suited to be similar to the last parentheme* E *of propositional function* D, *relative to (thesis)* B (*of this system*), if and only if (1) parentheme A of the provisory coimplicate of the nucleus of generalization C is suited to be similar to parentheme E of propositional function D, relative to thesis B of this system, and (2) the last word in D is in E.

T.E. XLIII. A $\varepsilon_2$prntmp(B, C, D, E, F, G),

A $\varepsilon_2$propprntmo(B, C, D, E, F, G)

For every A, B, C, D, E, F, and G: *parentheme* A *of the provisory coimplicate of the nucleus of (generalization)* C *is suited to be similar to the parentheme* E, *of propositional function* D, *immediately preceding a parentheme* F *similar to (parentheme)* G, *relative to (thesis)* B (*of this system*), if and only if (1) parentheme A of the provisory coimplicate of the nucleus of generalization C is suited to be similar to parentheme E of propositional function D, relative to thesis B of this system, (2) F is a parentheme of D, (3) the last word preceding F is in E, and (4) G is a parentheme similar to F.

—I.e., relative to thesis B, parentheme A of the provisory coimplicate of the nucleus (i.e., quantificate) of generalization C is suited to be similar to the parentheme E, of propositional function D, containing the last word preceding a parentheme F of D similar to parentheme G.

Lesniewski's first directive for (propositive) definition is based on explanation XLIV below, just as his second directive for (nominative) definition is based on LVI°. (§ 7.0) These directives are designed to assure that any definition D in canonic language L introduce a single new constant term at one stroke in a general propositional context, uniquely determine its semantic category, assign it definite significance in terms of constants already significant in the system, and at the same time make it eliminable from any propositional context, in favor of constants in terms of which it is defined; that any closed expression whose nucleus is equiform to the definiens of D be a proposition already significant, relative to the latest thesis introducing a constant in the definiens and to any later thesis such as D; and that D itself, though as definition of a new constant it is not a proposition relative to any preceding thesis, be a proposition relative to itself and to any later thesis. (§ 6.1.9) Certain of Lesniewski's requirements should be self-explanatory, on semantic grounds; the rationale of others should be clarified by my commentary, together with reference to explanation XXXIX' above and to Frege's requirements for definitions,[34] which Lesniewski adapted (§ 3.5.1) and sought to perfect. (§ 6.1.6)

T.E. XLIV. A ε defp(B), A ε $_1$defo(B)   For every A and B: A is *legitimate as propositive* (§ 7.0) *definition immediately after* (*thesis*) B (*of this system*) if and only if the following eighteen conditions are fulfilled:

(1) The first word in the nucleus of A is (individual but) not a variable of A related to itself.

(2) The first word in the provisory coimplicate of the nucleus of A is (individual but) not a variable of A related to itself.

(3) The first word in the provisory coimplicate of the nucleus of A is (individual but) not an ingredient of A suited to be constant, *relative to thesis B* of this system.

(4) For every C, if C is a term in the provisory coimplicans of the nucleus of A, then either (i) for at least one D, C is a word inside D, and D is a universal quantifier in A; (ii) for certain D and E, D is in A, and C is a variable of generalization D bound by E; or (iii) C is an argument or functor of an ingredient of A and suited to be constant, relative to thesis B of this system.

(5) For every C and D, if C is a word inside D, and D is a universal quantifier in A, then, for certain E and F, E is in A, and F is a variable of generalization E bound by C.

(6) For every C, D, and E, if C is a word inside the universal quantifier of A, D is an argument of E, and E is a parentheme of the nucleus of A, then, for at least one F, F is in D and is a variable of generalization A bound by C.

(7) For every C, D, and E, if C and D are both in the provisory coimplicans of the nucleus of A, and are convariables of generalization E, and E is in A, then either C and D are the same individual or, for certain F and G, arguments or functors C and D of ingredients of A are quasihomosemes of their respective analogs F and G, relative to thesis B of this system.[84]

(8) For every C, if C is a universal generalization in A but not identical with A then, for certain D, E, F, and G, E is a thesis relative to thesis B of this system, F is in E, G is in A, and D is a thetic homoseme of B, relative to B, and is analogous, as argument of parentheme F, to argument C of parentheme G.

(9) For every C and D, if C is a universal generalization in A, and D is the nucleus of C, then either D is a word or, for at least one E, D is a generating function with respect to E, and E is a basic propositional phrase relative to thesis B of this system.

(10) For every C, if C is a function in the provisory coimplicans of the nucleus of A, then either (i) for at least one D, C is the nucleus of D, and D is a universal generalization in A, or (ii) for certain D and E, argument or functor C of an ingredient of A is eligible by analogy to the semantic category of its generate D and its analog E, relative to thesis B of this system.

(11) For every C, if C is a parentheme of the provisory coimplicate of the nucleus of A then, for at least one D, D is an argument of C.

(12) For every C and D, if C is a parentheme of the provisory coimplicate of the nucleus of A, and D is an argument of C, then, for at least one E, D is a variable of generalization A bound by E.

(13) For every C and D, if C and D are equiform (expressions and are both) terms in the provisory coimplicate of the nucleus of A, then C and D are the same individual.

(14) For every C and D, if C and D are similar parenthemes (and are both parenthemes) of the provisory coimplicate of the nucleus of A, then C and D are the same individual.

(15) For every C, D, and E, if parentheme C of the provisory coimplicate of the nucleus of generalization A is suited to be similar to parentheme E of propositional function D, relative to thesis B of this system, and contains the last word in the provisory coimplicate of the nucleus of A, then C is a parentheme similar to E.

(16) For every C, D, E, F, and G, if parentheme C of the provisory coimplicate of the nucleus of generalization A is suited to be similar to the parentheme E, of propositional function D, immediately preceding a parentheme F similar to parentheme G, relative to thesis B of this system, and contains the last word preceding G, and G is in A, then C is a parentheme similar to E.

(17) For every C, D, and E, if C is a parentheme of the provisory coimplicate of the nucleus of A, contains the last word in the provisory coimplicate of the nucleus of A, and is similar to parentheme E, and E is in D, and D is a thesis relative to thesis B of this system, then, for certain F and G, parentheme C of the provisory coimplicate of the nucleus of generalization A is suited to be similar to the last parentheme G of propositional function F, relative to B.

(18) For every C, D, E, and F, if C is a parentheme of the provisory coimplicate of the nucleus of A, contains the last word preceding D, and is similar to parentheme F, and D is a parentheme in A, F is in E, and E is a thesis relative to thesis B of this system, then, for certain G, H, and I, parentheme C of the provisory coimplicate of the nucleus of generalization A is suited to be similar to the parentheme H, of propositional function G, immediately preceding a parentheme I similar to D, relative to B.

I call only any provisory coimplicans (resp. coimplicate) of the nucleus of A simply (a and hence the) *provisory definiens* (resp. *definiendum*) *of* A. So A is legitimate as propositive definition immediately after thesis B of this system if and only if B is a thesis[85] of this system relative to which the following conditions are fulfilled: (1) The first word in the nucleus of A is (individual but) not a

variable of A; and (2–3) the first word in the provisory definiendum
of A is (individual but) neither a variable of A nor an ingredient of
A suited to be constant (*relative to B*). (4) Any term in the provisory
definiens of A either is a variable of some ingredient of A, is a word
inside a quantifier itself in A, or is an argument or functor of an
ingredient of A and suited to be constant. (5) Any word inside a
quantifier itself in A binds at least one variable of some ingredient
of A; and (6) any word inside the universal quantifier of A binds
at least one variable of A in each argument of the parentheme
of the nucleus of A: i.e., in both the provisory definiens and definiendum of A. (7) All nonidentical convariables of any ingredient of A,
if in the provisory definiens of A, are arguments or functors of ingredients of A, and are quasihomosemes, eligible by analogy to the
same semantic category.[84] (8) Any generalization merely part of A
is analogous, as argument of some ingredient of A, to a thetic
homoseme of B in (i.e., to a propositional argument of) some ingredient of a thesis. (9) The quantificate of any ingredient of A, if not
a word, is a generating function with respect to some basic propositional phrase. (10) Any function in the provisory definiens of A, if not
the quantificate of some ingredient of A, is an argument or functor
of an ingredient of A, and is eligible by analogy to the appropriate
semantic category. (11–14) Any parentheme of the provisory definiendum of A, which (definiendum) contains no two equiform terms
and has no two similar parenthemes, has at least one argument;
and any such argument is a variable of A. (15, 17) Suppose P is the
last parentheme of the provisory definiendum of A. Then P, if
suited to be, is similar to the last parentheme P' of some propositional function; if not, P is a parentheme of new type, no thesis
(*relative to B*) containing a similar parentheme. (16, 18) Suppose
parentheme P of the provisory definiendum of A immediately
precedes parentheme Q in A. Then P, if suited to be, is similar to the
parentheme P', of some propositional function, immediately preceding a parentheme Q' similar to Q; if not, P is a parentheme of
new type, no thesis (*relative to B*) containing a similar parentheme.

Requirements XLIV.15–.18 concern parenthemes of the provisory definiendum whose arguments are equinumerous to, and suited
to belong to the semantic category of homologous, arguments of

parenthemes already in the system. The basic, inductive, and extremal clauses of these requirements are designed recursively to assure that brackets of such corresponding parenthemes be of the same form, in order that terminally homologous parenthemes be of the same type. The preceding requirement XLIV.14 that the provisory definiendum have at most one parentheme of given type is essential to assure proper application of the inductive clause. The rationale of XLIV.14–.18 and other requirements will subsequently be further explained.

In order to avoid proleptic use of expressions not yet defined, I give illustrations and define additional terminology now, before explaining the rationale of certain of Lesniewski's requirements for definitions. The following numbered examples, according as their numerals are prefixed by 'D' or by 'S', either (1) are expressions that, in the order listed, might be subjoined to Axiom AP as propositive definitions, each being legitimate immediately after its direct predecessor if all preceding expressions were asserted as theses, or (2) are schemes representing individual specifications that would be legitimate as propositive definitions if asserted in appropriate order. Since these examples are intended only as illustrations, I freely use terms from earlier examples, instead of using only primitive notation later translatable into defined terms—a practice by which Lesniewski often succeeded in logically simplifying his definitions.

D1. $\phi\left(\llcorner r \lrcorner \ulcorner r \urcorner \Lambda\right)$

D2. $\phi\left(\llcorner r \lrcorner \ulcorner \phi(rr) \urcorner V\right)$

D3. $\llcorner r \lrcorner \ulcorner \phi\left(r \dashv (r)\right) \urcorner$

D4. $\llcorner r \lrcorner \ulcorner \phi\left(\phi(r\Lambda) \vdash (r)\right) \urcorner$

D5. $\llcorner r \lrcorner \ulcorner \phi\left(\phi(rr) \vdash\dashv (r)\right) \urcorner$

D6. $\llcorner r \lrcorner \ulcorner \phi\left(\vdash \left(\phi \ (rr)\right) - (r)\right) \urcorner$

D7. $_\llcorner rs_\lrcorner \ulcorner \phi \Big(\vdash \big(\phi\,(rs)\big) \multimap (rs) \Big) \urcorner$

D8. $_\llcorner rs_\lrcorner \ulcorner \phi \Big(_\llcorner f_\lrcorner \ulcorner \phi \big(r\,\phi\,(f(r)f(s))\big) \urcorner \varphi\,(rs) \Big) \urcorner$

D9. $_\llcorner rs_\lrcorner \ulcorner \phi \Big(\vdash \big(\varphi\,(rs)\big) \multimapdotbothB (rs) \Big) \urcorner$

D10. $_\llcorner rs_\lrcorner \ulcorner \phi \Big(\varphi \big(\vdash (r) \vdash (s)\big) \delta\,(rs) \Big) \urcorner$

D11. $_\llcorner rs_\lrcorner \ulcorner \phi \Big(\phi \big(\phi\,(rs)\,\phi\,(rs)\,\big) \multimapinv (rs) \Big) \urcorner$

D12. $_\llcorner rs_\lrcorner \ulcorner \phi \Big(\vdash \big(\multimapinv(rs)\big) \circ (rs) \Big) \urcorner$

D13. $_\llcorner rs_\lrcorner \ulcorner \phi \Big(\varphi \big(r \vdash (s)\big) \multimap (rs) \Big) \urcorner$

D14. $_\llcorner rs_\lrcorner \ulcorner \phi \big(\multimap (sr) \multimap (rs)\big) \urcorner$

D15. $_\llcorner rs_\lrcorner \ulcorner \phi \Big(\phi \big(r\,\varphi\,(rs)\big) \multimapinv (rs) \Big) \urcorner$

D16. $_\llcorner rs_\lrcorner \ulcorner \phi \big(\multimapinv(sr) \multimapinv (rs)\big) \urcorner$

D17. $_\llcorner rs_\lrcorner \ulcorner \phi \Big(\multimapinv \big(\vdash (r)s\big) \multimapinv (rs)\big) \urcorner$

D18. $_\llcorner rs_\lrcorner \ulcorner \phi \Big(\phi \big(r\,\phi\,(ss)\big) \varphi\,(rs) \Big) \urcorner$

D19. $_\llcorner rs_\lrcorner \ulcorner \phi \big(\varphi\,(sr) \varphi\,(rs)\big) \urcorner$

D20. $_\llcorner rs_\lrcorner \ulcorner \phi \Big(\vdash \big(\varphi\,(rs)\big) \multimapdotbothB (rs) \Big) \urcorner$

D21. $\llcorner rs \lrcorner \ulcorner \phi \left(\diamond\text{-}(sr) \diamond\text{-} (rs) \right) \urcorner$

D22. $\llcorner frs \lrcorner \ulcorner \phi \left(f(rs) \text{'}(fs) (r) \right) \urcorner$

D23. $\llcorner rs \lrcorner \ulcorner \phi \left(\text{'}(\diamond s)(r) \diamond (\!(s)\!)(r) \right) \urcorner$

D24. $\llcorner fh \lrcorner \ulcorner \phi \left(\llcorner r \lrcorner \ulcorner \phi \left(f(r)h(r) \right) \urcorner \subset (\!fh\!) \right) \urcorner$

D25. $\llcorner fh \lrcorner \ulcorner \phi \left(\llcorner r \lrcorner \ulcorner \phi \left(f(r)h(r) \right) \urcorner \equiv (\!fh\!) \right) \urcorner$

D26. $\llcorner fh \lrcorner \ulcorner \phi \left(\llcorner rs \lrcorner \ulcorner \phi \left(f(rs)h(rs) \right) \urcorner \subset (\!fh\!) \right) \urcorner$

D27. $\llcorner fh \lrcorner \ulcorner \phi \left(\llcorner rs \lrcorner \ulcorner \phi \left(f(rs)h(rs) \right) \urcorner \equiv (\!fh\!) \right) \urcorner$

D28. $\llcorner fr \lrcorner \ulcorner \phi \left(f(\vdash (r)) \ \text{inv} \ \langle f \rangle (r) \right) \urcorner$

D29. $\llcorner fr \lrcorner \ulcorner \phi \left(\vdash (f(r)) \sim \langle f \rangle (r) \right) \urcorner$

D30. $\llcorner fr \lrcorner \ulcorner \phi \left(\sim \langle \text{inv} \ \langle f \rangle \rangle (r) \ \text{dl} \ \langle f \rangle (r) \right) \urcorner$

D31. $\llcorner frs \lrcorner \ulcorner \phi \left(f(\vdash (r) \vdash (s)) \ \text{inv} \ \langle f \rangle (rs) \right) \urcorner$

D32. $\llcorner frs \lrcorner \ulcorner \phi \left(\vdash (f(rs)) \sim \langle f \rangle (rs) \right) \urcorner$

D33. $\llcorner frs \lrcorner \ulcorner \phi \left(\sim \langle \text{inv} \ \langle f \rangle \rangle (rs) \ \text{dl} \ \langle f \rangle (rs) \right) \urcorner$

D34. $\llcorner frs \lrcorner \ulcorner \phi \left(f(sr) \ \text{cnv} \ \langle f \rangle (rs) \right) \urcorner$

D35. $\llcorner frs \lrcorner \ulcorner \phi \Big(f(\vdash (s)r) \text{ intrv } \langle f \rangle (rs) \Big) \urcorner$

D36. $\llcorner frs \lrcorner \ulcorner \phi \Big(f(s \vdash (r)) \text{ cntrv } \langle f \rangle (rs) \Big) \urcorner$

D37. $\llcorner f \lrcorner \ulcorner \phi \big(\equiv (f \text{ cnv } \langle f \rangle) \text{ cnvsym } (f) \big) \urcorner$

D38. $\llcorner f \lrcorner \ulcorner \phi \big(\equiv (f \text{ inv } \langle f \rangle) \text{ invsym } (f) \big) \urcorner$

D39. $\llcorner f \lrcorner \ulcorner \phi \Big(\subset \big(f \sim \langle \text{cnv } \langle f \rangle \rangle \big) \text{ asym } (f) \Big) \urcorner$

D40. $\llcorner f \lrcorner \ulcorner \phi \big(\llcorner r \lrcorner \ulcorner f(r) \urcorner \text{ V } (f) \big) \urcorner$

D41. $\llcorner f \lrcorner \ulcorner \phi \big(\llcorner r \lrcorner \ulcorner \vdash (f(r)) \urcorner \wedge (f) \big) \urcorner$

D42. $\llcorner f \lrcorner \ulcorner \phi \big(\llcorner rs \lrcorner \ulcorner f(rs) \urcorner \text{ V } (f) \big) \urcorner$

D43. $\llcorner f \lrcorner \ulcorner \phi \big(\llcorner rs \lrcorner \ulcorner \vdash (f(rs)) \urcorner \wedge (f) \big) \urcorner$

D44. $\llcorner f \lrcorner \ulcorner \phi \big(\llcorner r \lrcorner \ulcorner \phi (r \ f(rr)) \urcorner \text{ idmp } (f) \big) \urcorner$

D45. $\llcorner f \lrcorner \ulcorner \phi \big(\llcorner r \lrcorner \ulcorner f(rr) \urcorner \text{ rflx } (f) \big) \urcorner$

D46. $\llcorner f \lrcorner \ulcorner \phi \Big(\llcorner rs \lrcorner \ulcorner \phi \big(f(rs) \ \varphi \ (f(rr)f(ss)) \big) \urcorner \text{ rfl}(f) \Big) \urcorner$

D47. $\llcorner f \lrcorner \ulcorner \phi \big(\llcorner r \lrcorner \ulcorner \vdash (f(rr)) \urcorner \text{ irfl } (f) \big) \urcorner$

D48. $\llcorner f \lrcorner \ulcorner \phi \Big(\llcorner rsu \lrcorner \ulcorner \phi \big(\varphi (f(rs)f(su)) \ f(ru) \big) \urcorner \text{ trns } (f) \Big) \urcorner$

D49. $\llcorner f \lrcorner \ulcorner \phi \Big(\llcorner rsu \lrcorner \ulcorner \phi \Big(f\big(f(rs)u\big)\ f\big(r\ f(su)\big) \Big) \urcorner\ asc\ (f) \Big) \urcorner$

D50. $\llcorner fh \lrcorner \ulcorner \phi \Big(\llcorner rsu \lrcorner \ulcorner \phi \Big(f\big(r\ h(su)\big)\ h\big(f(rs)f(ru)\big) \Big) \urcorner\ dstrin\ (fh) \Big) \urcorner$

D51. $\llcorner fh \lrcorner \ulcorner \phi \Big(\llcorner rsu \lrcorner \ulcorner \phi \Big(f\big(h(rs)u\big)\ h\big(f(ru)f(su)\big) \Big) \urcorner\ dstrex\ (fh) \Big) \urcorner$

D52. $\llcorner f \lrcorner \ulcorner \phi \Big(\llcorner rs \lrcorner \ulcorner \phi \Big(\phi\,(rs)\ \phi\ \big(f(r)f(s)\big) \Big) \urcorner\ extnsnl\ (f) \Big) \urcorner$

D53. $\llcorner f \lrcorner \ulcorner \phi \Big(\llcorner hk \lrcorner \ulcorner \phi \Big(\llcorner r \lrcorner \ulcorner \phi \big(h(r)k(r)\big) \urcorner \phi \ \big(f(h)f(k)\big) \Big) \urcorner\ extnsnl\ (f) \Big) \urcorner$

D54. $\llcorner f \lrcorner \ulcorner \phi \Big(\llcorner hk \lrcorner \ulcorner \phi \Big(\llcorner rs \lrcorner \ulcorner \phi \big(h(rs)k(rs)\big) \urcorner \phi \ \big(f(h)f(k)\big) \Big) \urcorner extnsnl\ (f) \Big) \urcorner$

S55. $\llcorner r_1 \ldots r_m r_n \lrcorner \ulcorner \phi \Big(\wp \big(\wp\,(r_1 \ldots r_m)r_n \big) \ \wp\ (r_1 \ldots r_m r_n) \Big) \urcorner$

S56. $\llcorner r_1 \ldots r_m r_n \lrcorner \ulcorner \phi \Big(\div \big(\div (r_1 \ldots r_m)r_n \big) \div (r_1 \ldots r_m r_n) \Big) \urcorner$

S57. $\llcorner r_1 r_2 \ldots r_m r_n \lrcorner \ulcorner \phi \Big(\wp \big(\div (r_1 r_2 \ldots r_m) \div (r_2 \ldots r_m r_n) \div (r_n r_1) \big)$
$\div (r_1 r_2 \ldots r_m r_n) \Big) \urcorner$

S58. $\llcorner r_1 \ldots r_m r_n \lrcorner \ulcorner \phi \Big(\wp \big(\div (r_1 \ldots r_m) \div (r_m r_n) \big) \div (r_1 \ldots r_m r_n) \Big) \urcorner$

S59. $\llcorner r_1 \ldots r_m r_n \lrcorner \ulcorner \phi \Big(\wp \big(\phi (r_1 \ldots r_m) \phi (r_m r_n) \big) \phi (r_1 \ldots r_m r_n) \Big) \urcorner$

S60. $\llcorner f r_1 r_2 \ldots r_n \lrcorner \ulcorner \phi \Big(\vdash \big(f(r_1 r_2 \ldots r_n) \big) \sim \langle f \rangle_{nn} (r_1 r_2 \ldots r_n) \Big) \urcorner$

S61. $\llcorner f r_1 r_2 \ldots r_n \lrcorner \ulcorner \phi \Big(f\big(\vdash (r_1) \vdash (r_2) \ldots \vdash (r_n) \big)\ inv\ \langle f \rangle_{nn} (r_1 r_2 \ldots r_n) \Big) \urcorner$

S62. $_\llcorner fr_1r_2\ldots r_{n\lrcorner}\ ^\ulcorner\phi\Big(\sim\underset{n}{\big\langle}inv\ \underset{nn}{\big\langle}\underset{n}{f}\big\rangle\big\rangle(r_1r_2\ldots r_n)\ dl\ \underset{n}{\big\langle}\underset{n}{f}\big\rangle(r_1r_2\ldots r_n)\Big)^\urcorner$

S63. $_\llcorner f_1\ldots f_n rs_{\lrcorner}\ ^\ulcorner\phi\Big(\varphi\big(f_1(rs)\ldots f_n(rs)\big)\cap\langle f_1\ldots f_n\rangle(rs)\Big)^\urcorner$

S64. $_\llcorner f_1\ldots f_m r_1r_2\ldots r_{n\lrcorner}\ ^\ulcorner\phi\Big(\varphi\big(f_1(r_1r_2\ldots r_n)\ldots f_m(r_1r_2\ldots r_n)\big)$

$\cap\underset{n}{\langle}f_1\ldots f_m\underset{n}{\rangle}(r_1\ldots r_n)\Big)^\urcorner$

S65. $_\llcorner f_1\ldots f_m rs_{\lrcorner}\ ^\ulcorner\phi\Big(\hookleftarrow\big(f_1(rs)\ldots f_m(rs)\big)\cup\langle f_1\ldots f_m\rangle(rs)\Big)^\urcorner$

S66. $_\llcorner f_1\ldots f_m r_1r_2\ldots r_{n\lrcorner}\ ^\ulcorner\phi\Big(\hookleftarrow\big(f_1(r_1r_2\ldots r_n)\ldots f_m(r_1r_2\ldots r_n)\big)$

$\cup\underset{n}{\langle}f_1\ldots f_m\underset{n}{\rangle}(r_1r_2\ldots r_n)\Big)^\urcorner$

S67. $_\llcorner r_1r_2\ldots r_{n\lrcorner}\ ^\ulcorner\phi\Big(\cap\underset{n}{\langle}\hookleftarrow\hookrightarrow\underset{n}{\rangle}(r_1r_2\ldots r_n)\hookrightarrow(r_1r_2\ldots r_n)\Big)^\urcorner$

S68. $_\llcorner f_1\ldots f_{m\lrcorner}\ ^\ulcorner\phi\Big(_\llcorner r_1r_2\ldots r_{n\lrcorner}\ ^\ulcorner\phi\big(f_1(r_1r_2\ldots r_n)\ldots f_m(r_1r_2\ldots r_n)\big)^\urcorner$

$\subset\underset{n}{(}f_1\ldots f_m\underset{n}{\rangle}\Big)^\urcorner$

S69. $_\llcorner f_1\ldots f_{m\lrcorner}\ ^\ulcorner\phi\Big(_\llcorner r_1r_2\ldots r_{n\lrcorner}\ ^\ulcorner\phi\big(f_1(r_1r_2\ldots r_n)\ldots f_m(r_1r_2\ldots r_n)\big)^\urcorner$

$\equiv\underset{n}{(}f_1\ldots f_m\underset{n}{\rangle}\Big)^\urcorner$

S70. $_\llcorner f_{\lrcorner}\ ^\ulcorner\phi\Big(\equiv\underset{n}{(}f\ inv\ \underset{nn}{\langle}\underset{n}{f}\rangle\ invsym\ \underset{nn}{(}\underset{n}{f})\Big)^\urcorner$

S71. $_\llcorner f_{\lrcorner}\ ^\ulcorner\phi\Big(_\llcorner r_1r_2\ldots r_{n\lrcorner}\ ^\ulcorner f(r_1r_2\ldots r_n)^\urcorner\ V\ \underset{nn}{(}\underset{n}{f})\Big)^\urcorner$

S72. $_\llcorner f_{\lrcorner}\ ^\ulcorner\phi\Big(_\llcorner r_1r_2\ldots r_{n\lrcorner}\ ^\ulcorner\vdash\big(f(r_1r_2\ldots r_n)\big)^\urcorner\ \Lambda\ \underset{nn}{(}\underset{n}{f})\Big)^\urcorner$

The terms proleptically elucidated as follows will be useful for subsequent explanations in § 7 and § 8 below.

Were the expressions mentioned below asserted, in the order listed above, as theses of this system of prototethic, I should call only any constant introduced by

AP   a *coimplicator;* and, similarly:
D1   ,, *standard contradiction;*
D2   ,, *standard tautology;*
D3   ,, *affirmator;*
D4   ,, *negator;*
D5   ,, *tautologous singulary connector;*
D6   ,, *contradictory singulary connector;*
D7   ,, *disjunctor;*
D8   ,, *conjunctor;*
D9   ,, *exclusor;*
D10 ,, *conegator;*
D11 ,, *tautologous (binary) connector;*
D12 ,, *contradictory (binary) connector;*
D13 ,, *distinctor;*
D14 ,, *contradistinctor;*
D15 ,, *implicator;*
D16 ,, *counterimplicator;*
D17 ,, *alternator;*
D18 ,, *antecedent affirmator;*
D19 ,, *consequent affirmator;*
D20 ,, *antecedent negator;*
D21 ,, *consequent negator.*

I call only any function whose functor is a

coimplicator	a *coimplication;* and, similarly:
affirmator	,, *affirmation;*
negator	,, *negation;*
tautologous singulary connector	,, *tautologous connection of one argument;*
contradictory singulary connector	,, *contradictory connection of one argument;*
disjunctor	,, *disjunction;*
conjunctor	,, *conjunction;*
exclusor	,, *exclusion;*
conegator	,, *conegation;*
tautologous binary connector	,, *tautologous connection (of two arguments);*
contradictory binary connector	,, *contradictory connection (of two arguments);*
distinctor	,, *distinction;*
contradistinctor	,, *contradistinction;*
implicator	,, *implication;*
counterimplicator	,, *counterimplication;*
alternator	,, *alternation;*
antecedent affirmator	,, *antecedent affirmation;*

consequent affirmator   ,, *consequent affirmation;*
antecedent negator   ,, *antecedent negation;*
consequent negator   ,, *consequent negation.*

I call only any argument of
coimplication B a *coimplicant of* B; and, similarly:

affirmation   ,, ,, *affirmate of*   ,, ;
negation   ,, ,, *negate of*   ,, ;
disjunction   ,, ,, *disjunct of*   ,, ;
conjunction   ,, ,, *conjunct of*   ,, ;
exclusion   ,, ,, *exclude of*   ,, ;
conegation   ,, ,, *conegate of*   ,, ;
alternation   ,, ,, *alternant of*   ,, .

I call only any first of the two arguments of implication (resp. coimplication) B (a and hence the) *implicans* (resp. *coimplicans*) *of* B; and call only any second of the two arguments of implication (resp. coimplication) B (a and hence the) *implicate* (resp. *coimplicate*) *of* B.

To facilitate expression of the ideographic principles (§ 8) of Lesniewski's notation for propositional, singulary connector, and binary connector constants, (§ 3.8) it is useful to define special names for these elementary constants, and for arguments and functors of the corresponding connections, according to a uniform mnemonic scheme. But it is not necessary, or even desirable, to define special names for all constants. For a constant may be adequately characterized simply by specifying either its introductory thesis, an equisignificant constant, or both its form and its semantic category. Where ambiguity does not matter, or is eliminated by context, I apply names of familiar constants loosely to analogous constants (maybe of the same form but) of different semantic category. Thus I speak, for example, of nominal as distinguished from propositional negation, conjunction, alternation, etc.; and paraphrase systematically analogous constants of various degrees and levels (§ 6.1.8) by systematically ambiguous homonyms (§ 5.1.1) of ordinary language, such as these: not, and, or, is, includes, comprises, is identical with, equals, coincides.

In particular, to preserve the systematic analogy underlying and sustaining such systematic ambiguity in use of homonyms, in this generalized sense I call *conjunction* only any connection true if and only if each of its arguments is true (see S55 above); call *alternation* only any connection true if and only if at least one of its two or more arguments is true (see S56 above); call *conegation* only any connection that is true if and only if each of its two or more arguments is false, and that is therefore equivalent to a negation of an alternation of (homomorphs of) its arguments; call *implication* only any connection true if and only if each of its two or more arguments is true if any (one and hence every) (§ 1.7) preceding argument is true, each argument implying any following argument (see S58 above); call *coimplication* only any connection true if and only if all of its two or more arguments have the same value, all being true or all being false, so that any two coimply each other (see S59 above); call *exclusion* only any connection true if and only if at most one of its two or more arguments is true, excluding all the others, which are false (see S57 above); and call *disjunction* only any connection true if and only if its two or more arguments are disjunctive, exactly (i.e., at least and at most) one being true, all the others being false (see S67 above). Since conjunction, alternation, coimplication, exclusion, and disjunction of two arguments are logically associative and symmetrical (or "commutative"), the two or more arguments of any such connection may be permuted at will without altering its value.

The import of the following, quite general definitions should be clarified by reference to the explanations and schematic diagrams in IL and LVII° below. Suppose that for some proposition P, relative to an individual thesis C of this system, expression A′, of the same form and semantic category as A, and expression B′, of the same form and semantic category as B, either (1) alike are coimplicants of the nucleus of P or (2) are the functors of homogeneous functions containing the first word in respective coimplicants (resp. predicates of coimplicants) of the nucleus of P, wherein all homologous arguments of whatever terminally homologous parenthemes of those coimplicants (resp. predicates) follow those functors are convariables of P. If P is true, then and only then I call A and B *equivalent* (resp. *coextensive, interchangeable*—whichever seems traditionally most appropriate to the case in question—, *relative to thesis* C). If P is not only true but is a thesis[47] of this system of logic (resp. of canonic language L), then and only then I reinforce such descriptions by a modifier like *'logically'* (resp. *'provably'*, *'demonstrably'*). I call *value* (resp. *force, extent, extension*—whichever seems most appropriate—, *relative to thesis* B) only any equivalence property (§ 1.8) with respect to equivalence relative to an individual thesis B of this system. Again, I call *logically* (resp. *demonstrably, provably*) of the same value (force, extent, extension, relative to B) only all individuals logically equivalent relative to an individual thesis B of this system of logic (resp. language L). Similarly, suppose that for some proposition P, relative to an individual thesis C of this system, expression A', of the same form and semantic category as A, precedes expression B', of the same form and semantic category as B, and A' and B' either (1) alike are implicants of the nucleus of P or (2) are the functors of homogeneous functions containing the first word in respective implicants (resp. predicates of implicants) of the nucleus of P, wherein all homologous arguments of whatever terminally homologous parenthemes of these implicants (resp. predicates) follow those functors are convariables of P. If P is true, then and only then I say that (*relative to thesis* C) A *implies* (resp. *is contained in, is of greater force than, is stronger than*—whichever seems most appropriate) B, or, equivalently, B *is of lesser force* (resp. *is weaker*) *than* B. If P is not only true but is a thesis[47] of this system of logic (resp. of canonic language L), then and only then I again reinforce the indicated descriptions by a modifier like *'logically'* (resp. *'provably'*, *'demonstrably'*), or say that A *entails* B (*relative to thesis* C).

To assert a thesis according to the directives of this system is an act of choice. I call *propositive* (§ 7.0) *definition* (*of this system of logic*) only any individual not only legitimate as propositive definition, immediately after some thesis of this system, but also actually asserted and subjoined to this system as a new thesis immediately thereafter, according to the directive for propositive definition.

Similarly, to anticipate, I call nominative (§ 7.0) definition (of this system) only any individual not only legitimate as nominative definition, immediately after some thesis of this system, but also asserted as a new thesis immediately thereafter, according to the directive for nominative definition. I call simply definition (of this system) only any propositive or nominative definition of this system.

I call only any coimplicans (resp. coimplicate) of the nucleus of definition D (a and hence the) *definiens* (resp. *definiendum*) *of* D. I call only any constant new in definition D (a and hence the) *defined constant* (resp. *term*) *of* D. I call only any constant introduced by (and hence equisignificant to the defined constant of) definition D, relative to some thesis of this system, simply *defined by* (definition) D; resp. individual *of which* D *is* (a and hence the) *definition*. The defined constant of any definition is itself a term defined by D—indeed, the first (§ 1.3) term defined by D. I call only whatever is defined by some individual (definition) simply *defined*. So *having* must be distinguished from merely *containing* a defined term: For, whereas any defined term of D is a defined term in D, a defined term *in* D need not be the defined term *of* D. For instance, no defined term in the definiens of a definition is the defined term of that definition; and a non-definition has no defined term, however many defined terms it may contain.

Suppose that D, being legitimate as propositive definition immediately after some thesis, is asserted as a thesis immediately thereafter. Then the first word of the nucleus, not being variable, is a coimplicator, and the nucleus of definition D is a coimplication, whose coimplicate (resp. coimplicans) is identical with its provisory coimplicate (resp. coimplicans) the provisory definiendum (resp. definiens) of D, which, since D is a definition, is simply the definiendum (resp. definiens) of D, the first word in which definiendum is the defined constant of D. Since any propositional constant is equivalent either to a standard tautology 'V' or to a standard contradiction 'Λ', there is little point in defining further propositional terms. In the consequently rare case when D is the definition of a propositional constant such as 'V' or 'Λ', D is simply a coimplication which, not being a generalization, satisfies requirements XLIV.6 and XLIV.11–.18 vacuously, and its coimplicate (the definiendum) is simply the defined term of D. In all other cases, D is a universal generalization; its nucleus is therefore the same individual as its quantificate, whose coimplicate is a propositional function fulfilling these requirements, and whose first word is the defined constant of D.

So D is a propositive definition of this system if and only if thesis

D of this system fulfills the following three sets of conditions, the first of which makes clear that the nucleus of D is a coimplication:

(1) The first word in the coimplicate of the nucleus of D (i.e., the defined term) is a constant new in thesis D. Any word inside a quantifier itself in D binds at least one variable of some ingredient of D; and any word inside the universal quantifier of D itself binds at least one variable of D in the provisory definiens and exactly one in the provisory definiendum of D. Any parentheme of the provisory definiendum of D, which (definiendum) contains no two terms of the same form nor two parenthemes of the same type, has at least one argument; and any such argument is a variable of D related to one or more variables of D in the provisory definiens of D. (So the only non-variable term in the provisory definiendum of D is its first word, the term to be defined; and any generalization merely part of D is in the provisory definiens—not in the provisory definiendum of D, any parentheme in which is inside no parentheme and hence is a parentheme *of* the provisory definiendum of D.)

(2) The following additional conditions are fulfilled relative to the thesis of this system immediately preceding thesis D: Any term in the provisory definiens of D, if neither variable nor inside a quantifier, is an argument or functor of an ingredient of D and suited to be constant. All nonidentical convariables in the provisory definiens of D are arguments or functors of ingredients of D, and are quasihomosemes, eligible by analogy to the same semantic category.[84] Any generalization merely part of A is analogous, as argument of some ingredient of D, to a propositional argument of some ingredient of a thesis; its quantificate, if not a word, is a generating function with respect to some basic propositional phrase; and any function in the provisory definiens of D, if not the quantificate of some ingredient of D, is an argument or functor of an ingredient of D, and is eligible by analogy to the appropriate semantic category.

(3) Finally, the following conditions are fulfilled relative to thesis D itself, though not necessarily relative to any preceding thesis: Suppose P is the last parentheme of the provisory definiendum of D. Then, if P' is the last parentheme of any propositional function relative to the thesis of this system immediately preceding D, and every argument of P belongs to the same semantic category as the

homologous argument of P' (in which case arguments of P and of P' are equinumerous), the initial brackets of P and of P' are of the same form (as are the symmetrical terminal brackets, so that P and P' are of the same type); otherwise the brackets of P differ in form from those of any parentheme having the same number of arguments in any preceding thesis (so that P is a parentheme of new type, no preceding thesis containing a parentheme of the same type). Suppose instead that parentheme P of the provisory definiendum of D immediately precedes parentheme Q in D. Then, if parentheme P' of any propositional function, relative to the thesis of this system immediately preceding D, immediately precedes a parentheme Q' of the same function and of the same type as Q, and every argument of P belongs to the same semantic category as the homologous argument of P', the initial brackets of P and of P' are of the same form (so that P and P' are of the same type); otherwise the brackets of P differ in form from those of any parentheme having the same number of arguments in any preceding thesis (so that P is a parentheme of new type, no preceding thesis containing a parentheme of the same type).

An expression might be called legitimate as propositive definition immediately after thesis B if and only if it *would* be a propositive definition, fulfilling the three sets of conditions above, *were* it asserted as a thesis immediately after thesis B. But Lesniewski's requirements have the advantage of being rigorously formulated without use of subjunctive conditionals, and so being expressible, at a later stage, in extensional language L itself.

By virtue of the requirements regulating formation of brackets in the definiendum of any definition, the following generalizations hold, relative to any one thesis specified as parameter, for any function F in a proposition: Parentheme P of the definiendum of D is of the same type as parentheme P' of F if and only if (1) F too is a propositional function, (2) every argument of P belongs to the same semantic category as the homologous argument of P', and (3) any parentheme immediately following P in D is of the same type as the parentheme of F immediately following P'. So the definiendum of D belongs to the same genus as F if and only if (1) F too is a propositional function, (2) all terminally homologous parenthemes of the two functions have the same number of arguments, and (3) all homologous arguments of such parenthemes belong to the same semantic category. The functors of such homogeneous and categoric functions are also homosemes.

I call A *eliminable from* B *in favor of* (the one or more individuals that are) d (*relative to thesis* C) if and only if, relative to an individual thesis C of this system, A is a constant term in B, and B is logically equivalent to some individual which contains no constant equisignificant to A and all constant terms in which are d. I call simply *eliminable from* B (*relative to thesis* C) only any individual (i.e., constant) eliminable from B, relative to a thesis C of this system, in favor of constants introduced by theses preceding the thesis introducing that individual. I call *directly defined in terms of* (the one or more individuals that are) d only any constant the definiens of whose definition contains a term either (1) of the same constant significance as individual d or (2) of the constant significance d. (§ 1.7) I call *defined in terms of* (the one or more individuals that are) d only any individual having all properties that are possessed by all d and are closed with respect to the relation of being directly defined in terms of, there being at least one d; i.e., only any member of the closure of d, which exist, with respect to this relation. (See D93 of LVI° below.) For example, if A is directly defined in terms of (individuals being either) B or C, B is directly defined in terms of D, and C is directly defined in terms of E, then A is defined in terms of (individuals being either) D or E.

In canonic language L any definition D (being a thesis whose nucleus is a coimplication) makes its definiendum logically equivalent to its definiens, relative to D and any later thesis, and so makes any constant defined by D (including the defined constant of D itself) eliminable from every propositional context, in favor of terms constant relative to the latest thesis introducing a constant term itself in the definiens of D; i.e., in favor of constants already significant in the system; and ultimately in favor of undefined constants relative to the latest axiom introducing a constant term in D. (§ 6.1.9) Any constant eliminable from every propositional context in favor of d, but not defined in terms of d, can be defined in terms of d by rearranging the order of definitions and theses of the system. For example, constants defined by D13 and D14 above would clearly be interdefinable, since if constant ' ᴐ ' were first defined (by interchanging it with '-ᴐ ', and 'r' with 's', in the definiendum of D13) then '-ᴐ ' could be defined in terms of ' ᴐ' by merely interchanging definiens and definiendum of D14.

The rationale of certain of Lesniewski's rules of definition, if not yet clear, may be clarified by the following remarks and examples, intended to show how these rules are designed to preserve consistent determinacy of meaning, "purity" of semantic categories, completeness of definition, (§ 6.1.9) univocality of defined constants and propositions containing defined constants, and consequent eliminability of defined constants from all propositional contexts. As the examples illustrate, Lesniewski's requirements are not merely patent inventions to suppress formal contradiction but, rather, are integral parts of his positive logical grammar, designed to maintain uniqueness of semantic category and univocality of significance, to assure that expressions play only the roles for which they are introduced and exercise only their delegated capacities, to prevent fusion of what he intended to be distinct semantic categories through illegitimate admission of impure common members, and *thereby* to preclude contradiction.

Clearly an expression violating any of the first four requirements, even if it consistently satisfied all the others, would fail to define— i.e., introduce, assign univocal significance in, and make eliminable from all propositional contexts—a single new constant. Recursive or conditional characterizations violating requirement XLIV.1 or XLIV.4 (by not establishing an equivalence, or by containing in the provisory "definiens" one or more constants of the same significance as the new constant in the provisory "definiendum") therefore cannot be asserted as "partial definitions" in canonic language L, for reasons explained in § 6.1.9 above. Also excluded are pseudo-definitions, (§ 6.1.9) which begin with particular instead of universal quantifiers, and which violate requirements XLIV.2–.3 by not even introducing a new constant, but containing in its place a variable bound by a term inside the initial particular quantifier.

The need for the requirement (XLIV.2–.3 together with XLIV.12 and XLIV.17–.18) that the term to be defined be the *first* word in the provisory definiendum may be indicated as follows. Were this requirement omitted, expression A below might then be asserted as legitimate propositive definition immediately after Axiom AP of protothetic, whereupon its instance B would follow by substitution.

(A) $\llcorner$fs$\lrcorner$ $\ulcorner\phi\left(\phi\left(\llcorner r\lrcorner \ulcorner r\urcorner f(s\,s)\right) f(?!\,s)\right)\urcorner$

(B) $\phi\left(\phi\left(\llcorner r\lrcorner \ulcorner r\urcorner \phi(?!\ ?!)\right) \phi(?!\ ?!)\right)$

(C) $\llcorner r\lrcorner \ulcorner r\urcorner$

(A') $\llcorner f\lrcorner$ $\ulcorner\phi\left(\phi\left(\llcorner r\lrcorner \ulcorner r\urcorner f(\llcorner r\lrcorner \ulcorner r\urcorner)\right) f(!\,?)\right)\urcorner$

(B') $\phi\left(\phi\left(\llcorner r\lrcorner \ulcorner r\urcorner \vdash\dashv (\llcorner r\lrcorner \ulcorner r\urcorner)\right) \vdash\dashv (!\,?)\right)$

(B'') $\phi\left(\phi\left(\llcorner r\lrcorner \ulcorner r\urcorner \phi(\llcorner r\lrcorner \ulcorner r\urcorner \llcorner r\lrcorner \ulcorner r\urcorner)\right) \phi(!\,? \ !\,?)\right)$

Contradiction C, to the effect that "everything is the case", which entails any proposition and its negation alike, would then follow by successive detachments, since the coimplicate of B and that of the coimplicans of B are both tautologous, being instances of a thesis '$\llcorner u\lrcorner$ $\ulcorner \phi$ (uu)$\urcorner$'. Nor could contradiction C be excluded merely by barring "impredicative" (§ 5.4) substitution of a propositional constant such as '?!' above for the propositional variables of its own definition. For C could as readily be derived from expression A' (asserted as propositive definition immediately after D3 above) by substituting, instead, tautologous singulary connectors '$\vdash\dashv$' defined by D5 to obtain instance B', and then eliminating them to derive the definitional translation B'', from which C would result as from B.

Together with Lesniewski's other requirements, XLIV.6 entails that (1) any variable of a proposed definition in its provisory definiendum be related to at least one convariable in its provisory definiens, and that (2) any in its provisory definiens be related to

exactly one in its provisory definiendum. There is no need to assert
any definition violating condition one, since the logical force of its
nucleus, or of its provisory definiendum, would not be altered by
reforming it to satisfy Lesniewski's requirements: Each offending
variable could either (1) simply be deleted or (2) be rehabilitated by
incorporating a tautologous connection of one or more related
variables as conjunct or coimplicant in the definiens of a corresponding legitimate definition. For example, expression D here might

(D) $\llcorner p \lrcorner \ulcorner \phi \left(\llcorner r \lrcorner \ulcorner r \urcorner \wedge (p) \right) \urcorner$

(E) $\llcorner p \lrcorner \ulcorner \phi \left(\phi \left(\llcorner r \lrcorner \ulcorner r \urcorner \phi (pp) \right) \wedge (p) \right) \urcorner$

better be replaced by some logical equivalent, such as expression E
or D1 above, that would, unlike D itself, be legitimate as propositive
definition immediately after Axiom AP or some other thesis. And
condition two above is essential not only for completeness of definition (§ 6.1.9) but also for consistency, as illustrated by the
following prototlectical analog of the contradiction that Lesniewski
proved in Chwistek's propositional calculus. (§ 3.9) For only XLIV.6
precludes assertion of expression F here as legitimate propositive

(F) $\llcorner p \lrcorner \ulcorner \phi \left(\vdash (p) \text{ Arbamb} \right) \urcorner$

(G) $\phi \left(\vdash (\text{Arbamb}) \text{ Arbamb} \right)$

(H) $\varphi \left(\vdash (\text{Arbamb}) \text{ Arbamb} \right)$

definition (immediately after a definition equiform to D4 above),
whose substitution instance G would yield contradiction H by
classical truth-functional inference. Even apart from the resulting
contradiction, constants introduced by F would have no definite
meaning, as illustrated by the paraphrase "For every p, arbitrary
ambiguity is the case if and only if not p", in contrast to a legitimate
definition

$$\text{`}\phi \left(\llcorner p \lrcorner \ulcorner \vdash (p) \urcorner \Lambda_1 \right)\text{'}$$

paraphrased by "Nothing is the case if and only if, for every p, it is not the case that p". Indeed, translating the nucleus of F into conjoined implications, distributing the universal quantifier through the resulting conjunction, and applying classical rules of transposition and interchange of quantifiers would yield a logical falsehood,

$$`\lozenge\big(\vdash(\llcorner\mathrm{p}\lrcorner\ \ulcorner\mathrm{p}\urcorner)\ \llcorner\mathrm{p}\lrcorner\ \ulcorner\vdash(\mathrm{p})\urcorner\big)`,$$

to the effect that "if not everything is the case, then nothing is".

In conjunction with the other requirements, XLIV.7 assures that convariables of any ingredient of a proposed definition D be quasihomosemes, eligible by analogy to the same semantic category. This requirement is essential to preclude admitting into the same semantic category (relative to D) convariables respectively analogous to arguments or functors differing in category (relative to the thesis immediately preceding D). The respective categories, which should be distinct, would then coalesce,[84] as a result of illegitimately admitting a common member, and this confusion of semantic categories would manifest itself in analogs of Russell's contradiction such as the following. Suppose requirement XLIV.7 were omitted. Expression I below might then be asserted as

$$\text{(I)} \quad \llcorner\mathrm{p}\lrcorner\ \ulcorner\lozenge\big(\vdash(\mathrm{p(p)})\ \mathrm{Absrd\ (p)}\big)\urcorner$$

$$\text{(J)} \quad \lozenge\big(\vdash(\mathrm{Absrd\ (Absrd)})\ \mathrm{Absrd\ (Absrd)}\big)$$

$$\text{(K)} \quad \varphi\big(\vdash(\mathrm{Absrd\ (Absrd)})\ \mathrm{Absrd\ (Absrd)}\big)$$

legitimate propositive definition immediately after a definition equiform to D4 above, whereupon the convariables 'p' of generalization I would become members of the same semantic category. So, by analogy, would the argument and functor of the provisory definiendum of I. Consequently the semantic category of propositions and that of singulary connectors would coincide; the senseless substitution instance J and contradiction K would follow, as in the preceding example; and, in addition, constants introduced by I would not be eliminable from nonsensical "propositions" (relative to I) such as J and K and their coimplicants, since constants introduced by I to play the role of singulary connectors would have no definite meaning miscast as "propositional constants" in H and J, as shown by the unintelligible paraphrases of I, J, and K: "For every p, it is not p that p if and only if it is absurd that p. So it is not absurd that it is absurd that if and only if it is absurd that it is absurd that. Hence it is not absurd that it is absurd that but yet it is absurd that it is absurd that."

The requirement XLIV.13 that no provisory definiendum of a proposed definition contain two terms of the same form is also essential to assure that definitions be completely general, that propositions containing defined constants be determinate in meaning, and that defined constants be eliminable from all propositional contexts. (§ 6.1.9) For only XLIV.13 precludes assertion of expression L below as a legitimate propositive definition imme-

$$(\text{L}) \qquad \llcorner r \lrcorner \ulcorner \phi \left(r \text{ Ditto } (r \ r) \right) \urcorner$$

$$(\text{M}) \qquad \phi \left(\text{Ditto} \left(\Lambda \vdash (\Lambda) \right) \text{Ditto} \left(\Lambda \vdash (\Lambda) \right) \right)$$

diately after Axiom AP, and subsequent derivation of "tautology" M as a thesis, relative to which M and its coimplicants alike would be "propositions". Yet constant connectors 'Ditto' introduced by thesis L would not be eliminable from M, not having been defined with complete generality, (§ 6.1.9) for arbitrary arguments of appropriate category, (§ 6.1.2) but only partially, for equiform arguments, and hence having no definite meaning miscast as connectors of non-equiform arguments. Their partial indeterminacy of meaning is illustrated by the dubious paraphrases: (L) "For every r, r if and only if r, repeat, r." (M) "Everything is the case, repeat, not everything is the case, if and only if everything is the case, repeat, not everything is the case." These "repetitions" are as pointless as they are absurd: No useful purpose would be served by introducing a binary functor to do the work that a singulary functor could do as well—indeed, better—without either redundancy in meaningful cases or loss of meaning in other cases. One variable in the definiendum of a definition suffices to represent all convariables in the definiens, just as one term inside a quantifier suffices to bind all equiform variables of a generalization. So duplication would be as superfluous here as there. Even in meaningful cases, such a pseudo-binary functor would only play the role of a singulary functor in disguise, as illustrated by a legitimate counterpart of expression L, equiform to D3 above and paraphrased by "For every p, p if and only if it is the case that p." Analogous remarks apply to other functors in effect of degree n but masquerading as functors of degree greater than n.

Lesniewski added requirements XLIV.14–.18 to his adaptation of Frege's[34] rules of definition (§ 3.5.1) in order to preserve the intended "purity" of semantic categories and to maintain his hierarchy. As XLIV.7 helps maintain order in the definiens, so they help maintain order in the definiendum of any generalization, however many new semantic categories are introduced into the system, being designed to preserve seniority of old members, and harmony between old and new, throughout the strata of canonic and hierarchic language L. Abrogation of these principles of his grammar, even if it occasioned no outright contradiction, and in this respect proved less disastrous than the partial relaxation of Frege's simple type restrictions, (§ 6.1.6) would confound his categories, undermine his hierarchy, and manifest itself in loss of meaning.

The requirement XLIV.14 that no provisory definiendum contain two parenthemes of the same type is essential to sustain XLIV.15–.18 in differentiating the links in many-link functions, and to help assure that propositions be determinate in meaning and that defined constants be eliminable from any propositional context. Were XLIV.14 omitted, expression N here might be asserted as

$$(N) \quad \llcorner rs \lrcorner \ulcorner \phi \left(\phi(rs) \ \phi(s)(r) \right) \urcorner$$

$$(O) \quad \phi \left(\phi (\llcorner r \lrcorner \ulcorner r \urcorner) \ \phi (\llcorner r \lrcorner \ulcorner r \urcorner) \right)$$

propositive definition immediately after Axiom AP. The singulary connector being functor of the provisory definiendum of N would then belong to the same semantic category as its own functor ' ϕ ', relative to N itself and any later thesis; in consequence, the category of singulary connectors would coalesce and thereafter coincide with that of functors of singulary connectors of the same genus. Even if no contradiction ensued, the "tautologous" instance O of a thesis

$$'\llcorner\mathrm{fr}\lrcorner\ulcorner\phi\left(\mathrm{f(r)}\ \mathrm{f(r)}\right)\urcorner'$$

would follow as a nonsensical "thesis". Relative to N, O and the coimplicants of O would be "propositions", wherein the constants ' ϕ ', introduced to be eliminable functors of connectors, would appear instead in the guise of ineliminable singulary connectors, and the functions ' $\phi\left(\llcorner\mathrm{r}\lrcorner\ulcorner\mathrm{r}\urcorner\right)$ ' would likewise be demoted, from being first-level singulary connectors, to the level zero of their own propositional arguments. The degradation and loss of meaning brought about by this leveling of categories is illustrated by paraphrasing either "propositional" coimplicant of O by "If and only if everything is so, then", as contrasted with the unexceptionable propositions resulting from a legitimate definition equiform to D23 above and paraphrased by "If and only if everything is so, then everything is so".

Thanks to observance of requirements XLIV.15–.18 in particular, the following generalization holds, relative to any one thesis specified as parameter: All categoric functions of the same genus belong to the same semantic category; so do their functors; and so do homologous arguments of their terminally homologous parenthemes, which parenthemes are of the same type. Were XLIV.15–.18 omitted, expression P or Q below might be asserted as legitimate propositive definition immediately after a thesis equiform to D23 above. Yet constants 'V' and ' $\sim$ ' introduced by P and Q, respectively, would then belong to categories other than those appropriate and intended, 'V' becoming a singulary connector and ' $\sim$ ' becoming a homoseme of the defined constant of D23. The arguments 'f' in the provisory definienda of P and of Q alike would belong to the category of the convariable singulary connectors and, at the same time, to

the category of the analogous propositional arguments in the provisory definienda of D4 and of D23, respectively. As a result, the
category of propositions would coincide with the category of singulary connectors and of homosemes of the defined term of P, relative
to P and any later thesis. Upon assertion of Q expressions such as
R, S, T, and U, which make sense neither in language L nor as
paraphrased in English, and from which "defined constants" are
not eliminable, would be not only "propositions", like their coim-

$$(P) \quad \lfloor f \rfloor \ulcorner \phi \left(\lfloor r \rfloor \ulcorner f(r) \urcorner V(f) \right) \urcorner$$

$$(Q) \quad \lfloor fr \rfloor \ulcorner \phi \left(\vdash (f(r)) \sim (\!(f)\!)(r) \right) \urcorner$$

$$(R) \quad \phi \, (\vdash \vdash)$$

$$(S) \quad \phi \left(V(V) \, V(V) \right)$$

$$(T) \quad \phi \left(\vdash (\vdash) \, \vdash (\vdash) \right)$$

$$(U) \quad \lfloor p \rfloor \ulcorner \phi \left(p(p) \, p(p) \right) \urcorner$$

plicants, but also "tautologous instances" of a thesis '$\lfloor r \rfloor \ulcorner \phi \, (rr) \urcorner$'.
Worse still, as U above suggests, the earlier analog I of Russell's
famous "definition" would become legitimate as propositive definition immediately thereafter, and analog J of Russell's contradiction
would follow in consequence of thus violating Lesniewski's grammar.

Lesniewski's directives for distributing the universal quantifier,
for detachment, and for substitution are based on explanations
XLV–XLVIII below, in connection with which I use the stylistic
variants 'is derivable from', 'is deducible from', 'is a result of',
'results from', and 'logically follows (from)' interchangeably with
'is a consequence of', and conversely use 'yields' interchangeably
with 'yields as a consequence'.

I call A *result of distributing the quantifier of* B *through* c if and only if any word inside the quantifier of A is equiform to some expression in (i.e., word inside) the quantifier of B, the nuclei of A and of B are both c, the nuclei of analogous arguments of the nuclei of A and of B are equiform, and the following conditions are also fulfilled: Suppose argument A′ of the parentheme of the nucleus of A is analogous to argument B′ of the parentheme of the nucleus of B. Then any variable of B in B′ is equiform to a word inside the quantifier either of A or of A′; any word inside the quantifier of B′ is equiform to an expression in (i.e., word inside) the quantifier of A′; any word inside the quantifier of A′ is equiform to a word inside the quantifier of B′ or to a variable of B in B′; and any expression that is in (and hence is a word inside) the quantifier of A′, and is equiform to a word inside the quantifier of A, is equiform to an expression in (i.e., word inside) the quantifier of B′. (Clearly any word inside the quantifier of A′ is therefore equiform to a word inside the quantifier either of B′ or of B.) The operation of distributing the quantifier through a connection of two arguments may be represented by the following scheme:

$$\llcorner xy \ldots \lrcorner \ulcorner F(PQ) \urcorner \ / \ \llcorner \ldots \lrcorner \ulcorner F(\llcorner x \ldots \lrcorner \ulcorner P \urcorner \llcorner y \ldots \lrcorner \ulcorner Q \urcorner) \urcorner.$$

In the familiar manner of speaking about individual expressions in terms of their forms in abstraction from their occurrences, the operation may be loosely described as follows: Typically, it consists in actually distributing the quantifier of B by generalizing the arguments of the nucleus of B, if they are not already generalizations, translating one or more terms from inside the quantifier of B into the respective interiors of the quantifiers of the resulting generalizations, so as to bind the same variables they bound before, but now in the shorter contexts, provided that in the process these terms do not illicitly capture and bind variables formerly bound by terms inside the quantifiers (if any) of the original arguments of the nucleus of B. But, trivially, the operation may consist in leaving B and arguments of the nucleus of B unchanged, or in merely duplicating B, except perhaps for permuting terms inside the quantifier of B or of any argument of the nucleus of B, as illustrated in

XLV below. Lesniewski's directive for distributing the universal quantifier through a coimplication is based on XLV and, together with his other directives and Axiom AP, makes it possible to derive universally valid classical rules for distributing the quantifier through other connections, such as implication, conjunction, and alternation, as well as rules for "reiterating" expressions and for permuting terms inside quantifiers. (§ 6.2.1)

T.E. XLV. A ε consqrprtqntf(B)   For every A and B:
A is (a) *consequence of* B *by distribution of the* (*universal*) *quantifier* (*through a provisory coimplication*) if and only if the following seven conditions are fulfilled:

(1) The nucleus of the provisory coimplicans of the nucleus of A is an expression equiform to the nucleus of the provisory coimplicans of the nucleus of B.

(2) The nucleus of the provisory coimplicate of the nucleus of A is an expression equiform to the nucleus of the provisory coimplicate of the nucleus of B.

(3) For every C, if C is a word inside the universal quantifier of A then, for at least one D, D is an expression equiform to C and is in the universal quantifier of B.

(4) For every C, D, E, F, G, and H, suppose F is a parentheme of the nucleus of A, G is a parentheme of the nucleus of B, argument C of F is analogous to argument D of G, and E is in D and is a variable of generalization B bound by H; then, for at least one I, I is an expression equiform to E, and either is a word inside the universal quantifier of generalization A or is a word inside the universal quantifier of generalization C.

(5) For every C, D, E, F, and G, suppose F is a parentheme of the nucleus of A, G is a parentheme of the nucleus of B, argument C of F is analogous to argument D of G, and E is a word inside the universal quantifier of generalization D; then, for at least one H, H is an expression equiform to E, and is in the universal quantifier of generalization C.

(6) For every C, D, E, F, and G, suppose F is a parentheme of the nucleus of A, G is a parentheme of the nucleus of B, argument C of F is analogous to argument D of G, and E is a word inside the universal quantifier of generalization C; then, for at least one H, H is an expression equiform to E, is in D, and either is a word inside the universal quantifier of generalization D or, for at least one I, is a variable of generalization B bound by I.

(7) For every C, D, E, F, G, and H, suppose F is a parentheme of the nucleus of A, G is a parentheme of the nucleus of B, argument C of F is analogous to argument D of G, E is an expression equiform to H and is in the universal quantifier of generalization C, and H is a word inside the universal quantifier of generalization A; then, for at least one I, I is an expression equiform to E, and is in the universal quantifier of generalization D.

So only any result of distributing the universal quantifier of B through a function whose parentheme is of type '(– –)' and whose functor is a term of form ' ϕ ' (and which will therefore be a coimplication, *provided* its functor is categoric but not variable) is a consequence of B by distribution of the universal quantifier through a "provisory coimplication", which I call, for short, *consequence of* B

$$\llcorner fpqr \lrcorner \ulcorner \phi \Big(f(\phi(pq)r) \, f(\phi(qp)r) \Big) \urcorner$$

$$\llcorner frpq \lrcorner \ulcorner \phi \Big(f(\phi(pq)r) \, f(\phi(qp)r) \Big) \urcorner$$

$$\llcorner rpq \lrcorner \ulcorner \phi \Big(\llcorner f \lrcorner \ulcorner f(\phi(pq)r) \urcorner \, \llcorner f \lrcorner \ulcorner f(\phi(qp)r) \urcorner \Big) \urcorner$$

$$\llcorner qp \lrcorner \ulcorner \phi \Big(\llcorner fr \lrcorner \ulcorner f(\phi(pq)r) \urcorner \, \llcorner rf \lrcorner \ulcorner f(\phi(qp)r) \urcorner \Big) \urcorner$$

$$\llcorner pq \lrcorner \ulcorner \phi \Big(\llcorner rf \lrcorner \ulcorner f(\phi(pq)r) \urcorner \, \llcorner fr \lrcorner \ulcorner f(\phi(qp)r) \urcorner \Big) \urcorner$$

$$\phi \Big(\llcorner fpqr \lrcorner \ulcorner f(\phi(pq)r) \urcorner \, \llcorner rqpf \lrcorner \ulcorner f(\phi(qp)r) \urcorner \Big)$$

$$\phi \Big(\llcorner fpqr \lrcorner \ulcorner f(\phi(pq)r) \urcorner \, \llcorner fpqr \lrcorner \ulcorner f(\phi(qp)r) \urcorner \Big)$$

$$\phi \Big(\llcorner fpqr \lrcorner \ulcorner f(\phi(pq)r) \urcorner \, \llcorner fpqr \lrcorner \ulcorner f(\phi(qp)r) \urcorner \Big)$$

by partition of the quantifier. For example, each of the expressions listed below is a consequence, by partition of the quantifier, both of itself and of any expression preceding it in the list. As certain of these examples illustrate, such a consequence may be merely a "reiteration"; i.e., a homomorph or equisignificant proposition derived by permuting terms inside quantifiers. (§ 6.2.1) For not only any expression derived from a "provisory coimplication" B by actually partitioning its quantifier, but also any homomorph of B, including B itself, is a consequence of B by partition of the quantifier, whether or not B is a generalization having a quantifier, and whether or not the nucleus of B and that of its derivative are meaningful coimplications. (§ 7.0) Thus each of the following expressions yields both itself and the corresponding expression beneath it by partition of the quantifier:

$$\phi(\phi\phi),\ \phi(rs),\ {}_\llcorner\phi_\lrcorner\ {}^\ulcorner\phi(\phi\phi)^\urcorner,\ {}_\llcorner\phi rst_\lrcorner\ {}^\ulcorner\phi(rs)^\urcorner,$$

$$ {}_\llcorner\phi_\lrcorner\ {}^\ulcorner\phi({}_\llcorner\phi p_\lrcorner\ {}^\ulcorner q^\urcorner\ {}_\llcorner r_\lrcorner\ {}^\ulcorner s^\urcorner)^\urcorner$$

$$\phi(\phi\phi),\ \phi(rs),\ \phi\big({}_\llcorner\phi_\lrcorner\ {}^\ulcorner\phi^\urcorner\ {}_\llcorner\phi_\lrcorner\ {}^\ulcorner\phi^\urcorner\big),\ {}_\llcorner t\phi_\lrcorner\ {}^\ulcorner\phi\big({}_\llcorner r_\lrcorner\ {}^\ulcorner r^\urcorner\ {}_\llcorner s_\lrcorner\ {}^\ulcorner s^\urcorner\big)^\urcorner,$$

$$\phi\big({}_\llcorner\phi p_\lrcorner\ {}^\ulcorner q^\urcorner\ {}_\llcorner r_\lrcorner\ {}^\ulcorner s^\urcorner\big).$$

But, relative to the thesis specified as parameter, any consequence of a proposition (such as a thesis) by partition of the quantifier is itself a proposition, (§ 7.0) whose nucleus is a coimplication; and propositions mutually derivable from one another by partition of the quantifier are equisignificant, either being equiform or else differing only trivially in the order of terms of the same forms inside certain universal quantifiers. The following valid inference, if formalized in language L, would exemplify derivation of a consequence by distribution of the universal quantifier through coimplication: Since, for every x and y, x is greater than y if and only if y is smaller than x, it follows that, for every y, all x are greater than y if and only if y is smaller than all x.

Lesniewski's directive for detachment (of the provisory coimplicate), based on explanation XLVI below, may be represented by the following scheme: P, φ (PQ)/Q. Together with Axiom AP and his other directives, this directive makes it possible to derive the classical rules of detachment for implication, and for generalizations whose nuclei are implications or coimplications.

T.E. XLVI. A ε cnsqcqvl(B, C)   For every A, B, and C:
A is (a) *consequence of* B *and* C *by detachment (of the provisory coim-*

plicate) if and only if (1) C is an expression equiform to the provisory coimplicans of B, and (2) A is an expression equiform to the provisory coimplicate of B.

—I.e., C and A are homomorphs of the provisory coimplicans and coimplicate of B respectively. B need not be a coimplication, since its functor ' ϕ ' may be variable if B is not a proposition. (§ 7.0) But, relative to the thesis specified as parameter, *provided* that B is a proposition (such as a thesis), the functor of B is a coimplicator, B is a coimplication, and any consequence of B and C by detachment is also a proposition, like C and the coimplicants of B. The following valid inference, if formalized in language L, would exemplify detachment of the provisory coimplicate: Since Moscow is east of Warsaw if and only if Warsaw is west of Moscow, and Moscow is east of Warsaw, it follows that Warsaw is west of Moscow.

Lesniewski's directive for substitution, universally valid for variables and substituent expressions for any semantic category, incidentally incorporates the usual rules for alphabetic variation and reiteration of independent generalizations, in that it permits revision by "relettering" their variables or permuting binders inside the same universal quantifier. It is based on explanations XLVII and XLVIII below. The rationale of requirement XLVII.6 may be clarified by reference to Frege (*1893*, § 48; also Quine, *1951*, §§ 12–15), and that of requirements XLVII.9–.14 by reference to XXXIX' above.

T.E. XLVII. A ε cnsqsbstp(B, C, d), A ε cnsqsbsto(B, C, d)

For every A, B, C, and d: A is (a) *consequence of* C *by substitution of* (one or more) d, *relative to* (*expression*) B, if and only if the following fourteen conditions are fulfilled:

(1) The nucleus of A is the complex of the one or more expressions that are d.

(2) There are exactly as many d as words inside the subquantifier of generalization C.

(3) For every E and F, if E is d, F is a word inside the subquantifier of C, and there are exactly as many d that precede E as words inside the subquantifier of C that precede F, then, for at least one G, F is a variable of C bound by G or is an expression equiform to E.

(4) For every E and F, if E is d, F is a word inside the subquantifier of C, and there are exactly as many d that precede E as words inside the subquantifier

of C that precede F, then E is either a term, universal generalization, function, or expression equiform to F.

(5) For every E, F, G, and H, if F and G are both d, E and H are convariables of C, there are exactly as many d that precede F as words inside the subquantifier of C that precede E, and exactly as many d that precede G as words inside the subquantifier of C that precede H, then F is an expression equiform to G.

(6) For every E, F, G, H, I, J, K, and L, if J is in the nucleus of C, E is a word inside the universal quantifier of generalization J, F is a variable of C bound by K and is in J, G and H are both d, there are exactly as many d that precede G as words inside the subquantifier of C that precede E, there are exactly as many d that precede H as words inside the subquantifier of C that precede F, L is in A, and I is a variable of generalization L bound by G, then I is (individual but) not in H.

(7) For every E and F, if E is an expression equiform to F and is in C, and F is a word inside the universal quantifier of generalization A, then either (i) for at least one G, E is a word inside G, and G is a universal quantifier in C, or (ii) for certain G and H, G is in C, and E is a variable of generalization G bound by H.

(8) B is an expression.

(9) For every E, if E is a term in A, then either (i) E is an argument or functor of an ingredient of A and suited to be constant, relative to thesis B of this system; (ii) for at least one F, E is a word inside F, and F is a universal quantifier in A; or (iii) for certain F and G, F is in A, and E is a variable of generalization F bound by G.

(10) For every E and F, if F is a word inside E, and E is a universal quantifier in A, then, for certain G and H, G is in A, and H is a variable of generalization G bound by F.

(11) For every E, F, and G, if F and G are convariables of generalization E, and E is in A, then either F and G are the same individual or, for certain H and I, arguments or functors F and G of ingredients of A are quasihomosemes of their respective analogs H and I, relative to thesis B of this system.[84]

(12) For every E, if E is a universal generalization in A but (an individual) not identical with A then, for certain F, G, H, and I, G is a thesis relative to thesis B of this system, H is in G, I is in A, and F is a thetic homoseme of B, relative to B, and is analogous, as argument of parentheme H, to argument E of parentheme I.

(13) For every E and F, if F is a universal generalization in A, and E is the nucleus of F, then either E is a word or, for at least one G, E is a generating function with respect to G, and G is a basic propositional phrase relative to thesis B of this system.

(14) For every E, if E is a function in A, then either (i) E is the same individual as A; (ii) for at least one F, E is the nucleus of F, and F is a universal generalization in A; or (iii) for certain F and G, argument or functor E of an ingredient of A is eligible by analogy to the semantic category of its generate F and its analog G, relative to thesis B of this system.

Since the one or more individuals that are d are equinumerous to words inside the subquantifier (i.e., in the quantificate) of generalization C, only any d initially homologous to a word inside the sub-

quantifier of C is the d homologous to that word in the quantificate
of C. So A is a consequence of C by substitution of one or more d,
relative to expression B, if and only if the following *requirements
governing substitution* of d are fulfilled: (1–2) The nucleus of A is the
complex of the one or more expressions that are d, which are equinumerous to words in the quantificate of generalization C. (3) Any
word in the quantificate of C not equiform to the homologous d
is a variable of C; (4) any d not equiform to the homologous word
in the quantificate of C is a phrase; and (5) the d homologous to
(any words in the quantificate of C that are) convariables of C are
equiform. (6) If E is a variable of C and is in generalization G,
itself in the quantificate of C, F is a word inside the quantifier of G,
and E′ and F′ are the d respectively homologous to words E and F
in the quantificate of C, then E′ contains no variable (of a generalization itself in A) bound by F′. I.e., if G is a generalization in the
quantificate of C (and so merely part of C), then no d homologous to a
(word in the quantificate of C which word is a) variable of C in G
contains a variable (of a generalization in A) bound by the d homologous to a word (in the quantificate of C which word is) inside the
quantifier of G. (7) Any homomorph in C of a word inside the quantifier of A either is a word inside a quantifier itself in C or, alternatively, is a variable of some ingredient of C. (8) B is an expression
relative to which are fulfilled the following *additional requirements to
assure that if C is a proposition, relative to B, so is the result A of
substitution*: (9) Any term in A either is a variable of some ingredient of A, is a word inside a quantifier itself in A, or is an argument
or functor of an ingredient of A and suited to be constant. (10) Any
word inside a quantifier itself in A binds at least one variable of
some ingredient of A. (11) All nonidentical convariables of any
ingredient of A are arguments or functors of ingredients of A, and
are quasihomosemes, eligible by analogy to the same semantic
category.[84] (12) Any generalization merely part of A is analogous, as
argument of some ingredient of A, to a thetic homoseme of B in
(i.e., to a propositional argument of) some ingredient of a thesis.
(13) The quantificate of any ingredient of A, if not a word, is a
generating function with respect to some basic propositional phrase.
(14) Any function merely part of A, if not the quantificate of some

ingredient of A, is an argument or functor of an ingredient of A, and is eligible by analogy to the appropriate semantic category.

Reference to XXXIX′ above makes clear that A is a consequence of C by substitution of d, relative to expression B, if and only if requirements XLVII.1–.7 governing substitution of d are satisfied, B is an expression, and if C is a proposition relative to thesis B then so is A. According to XLVII.3–.5, only phrases may be substituted for variables of generalization C, and only for variables of C, not for variables of generalizations merely part of C; and phrases substituted for related and hence equiform variables of C must also be equiform. As illustrated below, XLVII.7 permits the quantifier of A to enclose more terms than the quantifier of C, if phrases substituted for variables of C contain additional variables; and also permits terms inside the quantifier to be permuted at will. XLVII.6 requires that no d homologous to a variable of C contain a variable bound by the d homologous to a word inside the quantifier of some part of C. This requirement is essential to prevent the homolog of a variable of C, bound by a term inside the quantifier of C itself, not merely of some part of C containing that variable, from being illicitly captured and bound by a homomorph inside the quantifier of the corresponding part of A. The following valid inference, if formalized in language L, would exemplify substitution: Since nothing equals everything, it is not true that money equals everything; i.e., since, for every x, it is not true that, for every y, x equals y, it follows that it is not true that, for every y, money equals y. But only XLVII.6 precludes a variable free in the quantificate of the premiss from being illicitly captured and bound by an internal quantifier, as in *fallaciously* inferring the following false conclusion from the same true premiss: it is not true that everything equals itself; i.e., it is not true that, for every y, y equals y. Similarly, in Lesniewski's "contextualist" system, in which variables and constants may be of the same form, but are clearly differentiated in and by context, (§ 6.1.8) only requirement XLVII.7 precludes using 'Λ' (§ 1.7) as a variable to infer, from a thesis to the effect that any nonentity is and is not itself, a false conclusion to the effect that any individual is and is not, in the following *fallacious* way: Since whatever is a nonentity is both itself and not itself, it follows that whatever is itself is both itself and not itself; i.e., since, for every x, x is Λ only if x is both x and not x, it follows that, for every Λ, Λ is Λ only if Λ is both Λ and not Λ—this conclusion, in language L, being a merely alphabetic variant of the following: for every x, x is x only if x is both x and not x.

I say that S is *substituted in* A *for* V *in* B if and only if, for certain C and d, relative to C, A is a consequence of B by substitution of (one or more) d, and S is a d homologous but not equiform to word V in the quantificate of C. The following scheme represents a pattern for definitions, to be obtained by specifying the appropriate number of arguments: I say that A is a *consequence of* B *by substitution of* s_1 *for* $v_1, \ldots,$ s_n *for* v_n (*relative to expression* C) if and only if, relative to an individual (expression) C, A is a consequence of B by substitution of d, and any d not equiform to the homologous word in the quantificate of B is either s_1 or...or s_n, and the homologous d is respectively either v_1 or...or v_n, s_1 being substituted for $v_1, \ldots,$ s_n for v_n. That a certain line in a derivation is a consequence of T by substitution, say, of expressions of form 'r' for expressions of form 'p', and similarly 's' for 'q', may be indicated at its right by a bracketed metalinguistic index containing specimens of the corresponding forms, such as either of the following:

$$[\text{T}:r/p;s/q], \left[\text{T}:\frac{r}{p};\frac{s}{q}\right].$$

The "fractional" representation indicates analogy with the arithmetical operation of "canceling by dividing out factors", as in the equation

$$\text{'pq} \cdot \frac{r}{p} \cdot \frac{s}{q} = rs\text{'}.$$

Analogous notation may also be used to indicate which variables of *particular* generalizations (as defined in X above) correspond to what phrases in the instances from which such generalizations are derived, as represented by the following scheme, wherein B is supposed to be a consequence of A by substitution of certain d, relative to a specified thesis, and the d homologous to any (word in the quantificate of A that is a) variable of A is supposed to be constant:

(A)　　$\llcorner v_1 \ldots v_n \lrcorner$　　$\ulcorner \ldots v_1 \ldots v_n \ldots \urcorner$

B)　　　　　　　　　$\ldots c_1 \ldots c_n \ldots$　　　　$[A : c_1/v_1 ; \ldots ; c_n/v_n]$

(C)　　$\perp v_1 \ldots v_n \perp$　$\ulcorner \ldots v_1 \ldots v_n \ldots \urcorner$　　$[B : v_1/c_1 ; \ldots ; v_n/c_n]$

T.E. XLVIII. A ε cnsqsbstp(B, C), A ε cnsqsbsto(B, C)

For every A, B, and C: A is (a) *consequence of* C *by substitution, relative to* (*expression*) B if and only if, for at least one d, A is a consequence of C by substitution of (one or more) d, relative to expression B.

Relative to any one thesis specified as parameter, any consequence of a proposition by substitution is itself a proposition. I call *alphabetic variant* or *revision of* B (resp. *consequence of* B *by alphabetic variation* or *revision, relative to expression* C) only any consequence of B by substitution of (one or more) d, relative to an individual C, such that every d homologous but not equiform to a (word in the quantificate of B which word is a) variable of B is itself variable; i.e., any consequence derived by substituting one or more variables of different form for certain variables of B, and substituting only variables, but no constant. I call *reiteration of* B (resp. *consequence of* B *by reiteration*) only any consequence of B by distribution of the quantifier from which consequence B itself is derivable by distribution of the quantifier; i.e., only any expression equiform to B except that terms inside universal quantifiers may be permuted. I call (*substitution*) *instance of* B (resp. *consequence of* B *by instantiation, relative to expression* C) only any consequence of B by substitution, relative to an individual (expression) C, which consequence is not merely a reiteration or alphabetic variant of B. So any consequence of B by substitution is derivable by either reiteration, alphabetic variation, or instantiation, the alternatives being mutually exclusive. Relative to Axiom AP, for example, each of the propositions below, including A itself, is a consequence of A by substitution: A and B are mere homomorphs of A, derivable by reiteration; C is an alphabetic variant of A; and D, E, and F are substitution instances of A, E being derivable from D by reiteration, and F having no variable. That A, B, and F are derivable from A, not only by substititution, but also by distribution of the quantifier illustrates that certain lines in a derivation may be justifiable in alternative ways. Relative to any one thesis specified as parameter, propositions mutually derivable by substitution, each from any other, are equisignificant, being merely alphabetic variants, such as A and C, or reiterations of one another, such as A and B, or D and E.

(A) $\llcorner r \lrcorner \ulcorner \phi(rr) \urcorner$

(B) $\llcorner r \lrcorner \ulcorner \phi(rr) \urcorner$ [A]

(C) $\llcorner s \lrcorner \ulcorner \phi(ss) \urcorner$ [A:s/r]

(D) $\llcorner rs \lrcorner \ulcorner \phi(\phi(rs)\ \phi(rs))\urcorner$ [A:ϕ(rs)/r]

(E) $\llcorner sr \lrcorner \ulcorner \phi(\phi(rs)\ \phi(rs))\urcorner$ [A:ϕ(rs)/r]

(F) $\phi(\llcorner r \lrcorner \ulcorner r \urcorner \llcorner r \lrcorner \ulcorner r \urcorner)$ [A:$\llcorner r \lrcorner \ulcorner r \urcorner$/r]

Lesniewski's first directive of extensionality is based on explanation IL, just as his second directive of extensionality, peculiar to ontology, is based on LVII° below. (§ 7.0) Once a new semantic category is introduced, Lesniewski's directives (as exact verbal formulations of what might more loosely be represented by "axiom schemes") (§ 6.1.7) authorize assertion of an extensionality thesis for (expressions of) that category. (Requirements IL.5 and LVII°.6 prohibit its assertion before introduction of that category.) Reference to XXXIX' above, together with my commentary, should clarify how Lesniewski's requirements are designed to assure that, relative to the latest thesis preceding T and introducing a semantic category of expressions in T, any thesis T of extensionality be a proposition (§ 7.0) of the canonic form represented by the scheme in IL below.

T.E. IL. A ε extnsnlp(B), A $\varepsilon_1$extnsnlo(B)   For every A and B: A is *legitimate as propositive* (§ 7.0) *thesis of extensionality immediately after* (*thesis*) B (*of this system*) if and only if the following nine conditions are fulfilled:

(1) For certain C and D, C and D are both words inside the universal quantifier of generalization A, and C precedes D.

(2) For every C and D, if C is a word inside D, and D is a universal quantifier in A, then, for certain E and F, E is in A, and F is a variable of generalization E bound by C and is (individual but) not an expression equiform to the first word in the nucleus of A.

(3) For at least one C, the first word in the provisory coimplicans of the complex of expressions that are words and are inside the subquantifier of the provisory coimplicans of the nucleus of A is a variable of generalization A related to the complex of the (at least one) expression that is a word itself inside C, and C is a parentheme of the provisory coimplicans of the nucleus of the provisory coimplicate of the nucleus of A.

(4) For at least one C, the first word in the provisory coimplicate of the nucleus of the provisory coimplicans of the nucleus of A is a variable of generalization A related to the complex of the (at least one) expression that is a word itself inside C, and C is a parentheme of the provisory coimplicate of the nucleus of the provisory coimplicate of the nucleus of A.

(5) For every C, if C is a function in A, then either (i) for at least one D, C is the nucleus of D, and D is a universal generalization in A, or (ii) for certain D and E, argument or functor C of an ingredient of A is eligible by analogy to the semantic category of its generate D and its analog E, relative to thesis B of this system.

(6) For every C, D, E, and F, if E is a parentheme of the provisory coimplicans of the nucleus of the provisory coimplicans of the nucleus of A, F is a parentheme of the provisory coimplicate of the nucleus of the provisory coimplicans of the nucleus of A, and argument C of E is analogous to argument D of F, then C and D are convariables of the provisory coimplicans of the nucleus of A.

(7) For every C, D, and E, if C is in A, and D and E are convariables of generalization C, then, for certain F and G, arguments or functors D and E of ingredients of A are quasihomosemes of their respective analogs F and G, relative to thesis B of this system.[84]

(8) For every C and D, if C and D are convariables of the provisory coimplicans of the nucleus of A then, for certain E and F, E and F are both in A, and argument C of parentheme E is analogous to argument D of parentheme F.

(9) For every C, D, and E, if C is the functor of function D, D is an argument of E, and E is a parentheme of the nucleus of the provisory coimplicate of the nucleus of A, then C is a variable of the provisory coimplicate of the nucleus of A bound by the complex of the (at least one) expression that is a word itself inside the universal quantifier of the provisory coimplicate of the nucleus of A.

So A is legitimate as propositive thesis of extensionality immediately after thesis B of this system if and only if the following nine conditions are fulfilled: (1) At least one word inside precedes another word inside the universal quantifier of generalization A, which quantifier therefore encloses at least two different words. (2) Any word inside a quantifier itself in A binds at least one variable of some ingredient of A, which variable is not equiform to the first word in the nucleus of A. (3) The first word in the provisory coimplicans of the quantificate of the provisory coimplicans of the nucleus of A is a variable of A related to the interior of some parentheme of the provisory coimplicans of the nucleus of the provisory coimplicate of the nucleus of A; and (4) the first word in the provisory coimplicate of the nucleus of the provisory coimplicans of the nucleus of A is a variable of A related to the interior of some parentheme of the provisory coimplicate of the nucleus of the provisory coimplicate of the nucleus of A. (5) Any function in A, if not the quantificate of some ingredient of A, is an argument or functor of an ingredient of A, and is eligible by analogy to the appropriate semantic category, relative to thesis B of this system. (6) All analogous arguments of parenthemes of the provisory coimplicans and of the provisory coimplicate, respectively, of the nucleus of the provisory coimplicans of the nucleus of A are convariables of the provisory coimplicans of the nucleus of A; (7) all convariables of any ingredient of A are arguments or functors of ingredients of A, and are quasihomosemes, eligible by analogy to the same semantic category,[84] relative to thesis B of this system; and (8) all convariables of the provisory coimplicans of the nucleus of A are analogous arguments of respective ingredients of A. (9) The functor of any argument of any parentheme of the nucleus of the provisory coimplicate of the nucleus of A is a variable of the provisory coimplicate of the nucleus of A bound by the interior of the universal quantifier of the provisory coimplicate of the nucleus of A.

Since no term of the form ' ϕ ' of the first word in the nucleus of such an A is a variable of an ingredient of A, every term of this form in proposition A (relative to B) is a coimplicator, and the provisory coimplicans (resp. coimplicate) of any ingredient of A is the same individual as the coimplicans (resp. coimplicate) of that ingredient coimplication. Since A and the coimplicants of its nucleus are all universal generalizations whose nuclei (i.e., quantificates) are coimplications, the canonic skeleton of A is schematically represented by the following diagram, wherein the blanks have yet to be filled according to further requirements:

$$\llcorner \lrcorner \ulcorner \phi \left(\llcorner \lrcorner \ulcorner \phi (\ ) \urcorner \llcorner \lrcorner \ulcorner \phi (\ ) \urcorner \right) \urcorner .$$

So A is legitimate as propositive thesis of extensionality immediately after thesis B of this system if and only if the following *requirements for propositive theses of extensionality* are fulfilled: A and the coimplicants of its quantificate are all universal generalizations whose quantificates are coimplications. Calling the coimplicans of the quantificate of A *CnQA* for short, consider the two coimplicants of the quantificate of CnQA: Both are functions of whose one or more parenthemes the one or more arguments are all variables of CnQA, bound by their respective homomorphs inside the universal quantifier of CnQA. Indeed, only all analogous arguments of these parenthemes are convariables of CnQA. Calling the coimplicate of the quantificate of A *CtQA* for short, consider the two coimplicants of the quantificate of CtQA: They are simple monadic functions whose functors are convariables of CtQA, bound by the single homomorph that is the interior of the universal quantifier of CtQA. The sole term that is the interior of the sole parentheme of each coimplicant is a variable of A related to the first word in the analogous coimplicant of the quantificate of CnQA, and is bound by the homomorph inside the universal quantifier of A, which quantifier thus encloses exactly two terms, each term binding both convariables of the equiform pair. So the representative diagram above may be schematically elaborated as follows, where arcs indicate bondage and relation of convariables, dashes represent variables or their binders, solidi demarcate the first word from the complex of the one or more parenthemes of a function, groups of three dots indicate possible ellipses, and dashes between such groups in quantificates represent the one or more arguments:

Finally, B is a thesis[85] of this system, relative to which are fulfilled the following *additional requirements to assure that any extensionality thesis A be a proposition*, relative to the latest thesis (either B or some preceding thesis) introducing a semantic category of expressions in A: Any word inside a quantifier itself in A binds at least one variable (of some ingredient of A) not of the form ' ϕ ' of the first word in the quantificate of A. All convariables of any ingredient of A are arguments or functors of ingredients of A, and are quasihomosemes, eligible by analogy to the same semantic category.[84] Any function in A, if not the quantificate of some ingredient of A, is an argument or functor of an ingredient of A, and is eligible by analogy to the appropriate semantic category.

I call *propositive thesis of extensionality* (*of this system of logic*) only any individual not only legitimate as propositive thesis of extensionality, immediately after some thesis of this system, but also actually asserted and subjoined to the system as a new thesis immediately thereafter, according to Lesniewski's first directive of extensionality. Since the two generalizations merely part of any propositive extensionality thesis A are the coimplicants of the quantificate of generalization A, the quantificate of every generalization itself in A is a coimplication, and every term in A either is a variable of some ingredient of A, is a word inside a quantifier itself in A and binds exactly two convariables of some ingredient of A, or is a coimplicator not only suited to be but actually constant, relative to Axiom AP and hence to any later thesis. So A is a proposition, relative to the latest thesis preceding A and introducing a semantic category of expressions in A. Proposition A below, for example, would be legitimate and assertible as propositive extensionality thesis immediately after a definition equiform to D37 of XLIV above and, according to a consequence of D54, would be logically equivalent to a proposition of form

$$`\lfloor f \rfloor \ulcorner \text{extnsnl} (\overset{_2}{f}) \urcorner`.$$

Being completely general, an extensionality thesis establishes the extensionality of every expression of the relevant category, and yields as special case any instance, such as B or C below, of itself or of a logical equivalent such as the proposition above or E below.

Together with his axioms and other directives, Lesniewski's directives of extensionality make any defined constant eliminable from any propositional context, in favor of constants in terms of which it is defined. If constant C' defined by definition D is analogous, as argument or functor of an ingredient of proposition P,

(A) $\llcorner$hk$\lrcorner$ $\ulcorner$ϕ$\left(\llcorner rs \lrcorner \ulcorner ϕ\left(h(rs)\ k(rs)\right)\urcorner \llcorner f \lrcorner \ulcorner ϕ\left(f(h)f(k)\right)\urcorner\right)\urcorner$

(B) $\llcorner$k$\lrcorner$ $\ulcorner$ϕ$\left(\llcorner rs \lrcorner \ulcorner ϕ\left(\multimap(rs)\ k(rs)\right)\urcorner \llcorner f \lrcorner \ulcorner ϕ\left(f(\multimap)f(k)\right)\urcorner\right)\urcorner$ [A :$\multimap$/h]

(C)   ϕ$\left(\llcorner rs \lrcorner \ulcorner ϕ\left(\multimap(rs) \vdash \langle ϕ\rangle\ (rs)\right)\urcorner \llcorner f \lrcorner \ulcorner ϕ\left(f(\multimap)f(\vdash \langle ϕ\rangle)\right)\urcorner\right)$

$$[B : \vdash \langle ϕ\rangle/k]$$

to the defined constant of D in an ingredient of D, then C′ is eliminable from P by virtue of its definition D, together with appropriate substitution instances of the extensionality thesis, of form

$$\text{`}\llcorner frs \lrcorner \ulcorner ϕ\left(ϕ\,(rs)\ ϕ\left(f(r)f(s)\right)\right)\urcorner\text{',}$$

that is derivable from Axiom AP without aid of the directives of extensionality. (§ 6.2) Suppose, however, that C′ is not in an analogous position; i.e., that C′ is not a functor, like the equisignificant defined constant of its definition D, but instead is an argument in P, as in the proposition 'cnvsym($\multimap$)', the disjunctor ' $\multimap$' having been defined by a definition equiform to D below, or D7 of XLIV above, and the functor 'cnvsym' by a definition equiform to D37 of XLIV. Then C′ can be eliminated from P only with the aid of an extensionality thesis asserted according to one of the directives of extensionality—in this case a thesis equiform to A above, which would be legitimate as propositive thesis of extensionality immediately after a thesis equiform to D37. From A can be derived a logical equivalent E, which in turn yields a consequence F. Nucleate G of the converse of the nucleus of F is also provable, since a homomorph of the implicans of the quantificate of F is derivable, with complete generality, from a homomorph of the implicate, by substituting 'h' for 'k' and detaching the consequent of the result, the antecedent being provable as a thesis. So the nucleate H of a corresponding coimplication, and substitution instances of H such as I, follow and establish the logical equivalence of 'cnvsym($\multimap$)' to a proposition containing defined constant ' $\multimap$'

only as functor, analogous to the defined constant of its definition D. A further elimination, carried out in the way already mentioned, yields coimplication J, and establishes the logical equivalence of 'cnvsym($\multimap$)' to a proposition containing no constant '$\multimap$' of the

(D) $\llcorner rs \lrcorner \ulcorner \phi \left(\vdash (\phi (rs)) \multimap (rs) \right) \urcorner$

(E) $\llcorner fhk \lrcorner \ulcorner \phi \left(\llcorner rs \lrcorner \ulcorner \phi \left(h(rs)\ k(rs) \right) \urcorner \phi \left(f(h)\ f(k) \right) \right) \urcorner$

(F) $\llcorner fh \lrcorner \ulcorner \phi \left(f(h)\ \llcorner k \lrcorner \ulcorner \phi \left(\llcorner rs \lrcorner \ulcorner \phi \left(h(rs)\ k(rs) \right) \urcorner f(k) \right) \urcorner \right) \urcorner$

(G) $\llcorner fh \lrcorner \ulcorner \phi \left(\llcorner k \lrcorner \ulcorner \phi \left(\llcorner rs \lrcorner \ulcorner \phi \left(h(rs)\ k(rs) \right) \urcorner f(k) \right) \urcorner f(h) \right) \urcorner$

(H) $\llcorner fh \lrcorner \ulcorner \phi \left(f(h)\ \llcorner k \lrcorner \ulcorner \phi \left(\llcorner rs \lrcorner \ulcorner \phi \left(h(rs)\ k(rs) \right) \urcorner f(k) \right) \urcorner \right) \urcorner$

(I) $\phi \left(cnvsym(\multimap)\ \llcorner k \lrcorner \ulcorner \phi \left(\llcorner rs \lrcorner \ulcorner \phi \left(\multimap (rs)\ k(rs) \right) \urcorner cnvsym(k) \right) \urcorner \right)$

(J) $\phi \left(cnvsym(\multimap)\ \llcorner k \lrcorner \ulcorner \phi \left(\llcorner rs \lrcorner \ulcorner \phi \left(\vdash (\phi (rs)) k(rs) \right) \urcorner cnvsym(k) \right) \urcorner \right)$

(K) $\llcorner k \lrcorner \ulcorner \phi \left(\llcorner rs \lrcorner \ulcorner \phi \left(\vdash (\phi (rs)) k(rs) \right) \urcorner \llcorner rs \lrcorner \ulcorner \phi \left(k(rs)\ k(sr) \right) \urcorner \right) \urcorner$

same significance at all. Elimination of the further defined constant 'cnvsym' in turn would yield a logical equivalent K; and successive elimination of the remaining defined constants would ultimately yield a logically equivalent proposition, in primitive notation, containing no defined constant at all.

In general, from an extensionality thesis represented by the following scheme—

$\llcorner hk \lrcorner \ulcorner \phi \left(\llcorner \dots x \dots \lrcorner \ulcorner \phi (h/ \dots x \dots k/ \dots x \dots) \urcorner \llcorner f \lrcorner \ulcorner \phi (f/h\ f/k) \urcorner \right) \urcorner$

—can thus be derived a corresponding thesis represented by the following scheme:

$$\llcorner\mathrm{fh}\lrcorner\ulcorner\phi\Big(\mathrm{f/h}\llcorner\mathrm{k}\lrcorner\ulcorner\phi\big(\llcorner\ldots\mathrm{x}\ldots\lrcorner\ulcorner\phi(\mathrm{h}/\ldots\mathrm{x}\ldots\mathrm{k}/\ldots\mathrm{x}\ldots)\urcorner\ \mathrm{f/k}\big)\urcorner\Big)\urcorner.$$

Suppose a proposition or propositional phrase contains as an argument a constant equisignificant to a defined functor. For any such propositional context this thesis yields a logical equivalent containing equisignificant constants only as functors, eliminable by means of their definitional equivalences together with appropriate instances of an extensionality thesis derivable from Axiom AP. Thus, in extensional language L, any proposition P containing a defined constant C′ is definitionally translatable into a logically equivalent proposition containing no constant equisignificant to or defined in terms of C′. For it is always possible to prove a thesis represented by the following scheme, in which C′ is schematically represented by 'H', P by 'F/H', and a logical equivalent of the definiens of the definition of C′ by the provisory coimplicans '...x...', according to the scheme '$\llcorner\ldots\mathrm{x}\ldots\lrcorner\ulcorner\phi(\ldots\mathrm{x}\ldots\mathrm{H}/\ldots\mathrm{x}\ldots)\urcorner$' of the definition of C′:

$$\phi\Big(\mathrm{F/H}\llcorner\mathrm{k}\lrcorner\ulcorner\phi\big(\llcorner\ldots\mathrm{x}\ldots\lrcorner\ulcorner\phi(\ldots\mathrm{x}\ldots\mathrm{k}/\ldots\mathrm{x}\ldots)\urcorner\ \mathrm{F/k}\big)\urcorner\Big).$$

7.2 The first five directives for this system of logic

These five directives, which incorporate the complete directives for this system of protothetic, (§ 7.0) can now be formulated as follows:

Suppose that individual A is the last thesis actually subjoined to this system of logic; then expression B may be asserted and subjoined to this system as a new thesis if (and as a new thesis of protothetic only if) at least one of the following five conditions is fulfilled:

(1) *Individual B is legitimate as propositive definition immediately after thesis A of this system.*

(2) *For at least one C, individual C is a thesis relative to thesis A of this system, and individual B is a consequence of C by distribution of the universal quantifier through a provisory coimplication.*

(3) *For certain C and D, individuals C and D are both theses relative to thesis A of this system, and B is a consequence of C and D by detachment of the provisory coimplicate.*

(4) *For at least one C, individual C is a thesis relative to thesis A of this system, and individual B is a consequence of C by substitution, relative to A.*

(5) *Individual B is legitimate as propositive thesis of extensionality immediately after thesis A of this system.*

—I.e., individual B is legitimate as propositive definition or propositive thesis of extensionality immediately after thesis A of this system; or, relative to thesis A of this system, is a consequence of some thesis either by distribution of the universal quantifier through a provisory coimplication or by substitution, or is a consequence of two theses by detachment of the provisory coimplicate.

For purposes of reference, the prescription above may be treated as a conjunction of five separate *directives*: (1) *for propositive definition* (the *first* as distinguished from the second *directive of definition*); (2) *for distributing the universal quantifier* (through a provisory coimplication—i.e., *for partition of the quantifier*); (3) *for detaching the provisory coimplicate* (resp. *for detachment*); (4) *for substitution;* and (5) *for propositive* (*theses of*) *extensionality* (the *first* as distinguished from the second *directive of extensionality*). In proofs, the directive according to which any thesis T other than an axiom is subjoined to the system, the status of T as thesis, and any preceding theses from which T is derived are indicated in the margins by the metalinguistic indices mentioned in § 6.1.9 and XLVII of § 7.1 above. On the basis of Lesniewski's directives, it can be proved by strong induction that any thesis T of this system is an independent proposition, relative to T itself and any later thesis and, if T is not an axiom or definition introducing a new constant or semantic category, even relative to the latest thesis preceding T and introducing a constant or semantic category of expression in T.

7.3 Terminological explanations peculiar to ontology

Lesniewski specified that any effective protothetical basis for ontology was to consist of the axiom of the system of protothetic in question (in this system Axiom AP) (§ 6.2.2) together with a finite number of individual theses meeting his requirements, actually

(§ 6.1.7) subjoined to the axiom of protothetic according to his directives, and preceding the first thesis asserted as axiom of ontology (in this system Axiom AO). (§ 6.2.3) His requirements for this effective protothetical basis are self-explanatory: In any axiom of ontology all terms neither variable, inside quantifiers, nor peculiar to ontology (in AO coimplicators, negators, and conjunctors) must be constants introduced by effective basic theses of protothetic (*efthp*) before the construction of ontology is begun by asserting an axiom of ontology. For otherwise the new axiom would be meaningless. And any parentheme not suited to be similar to any parentheme in any preceding thesis must be of new type, no preceding thesis containing a parentheme of the same type. (So in AO the brackets '{' and '}' enclosing nominal arguments must be of new forms.) For parenthemes in axioms too, like those in definitions, must satisfy requirements 'designed to preserve "purity" of semantic categories and maintain consistent determinacy of meaning.

Since the following explanations are partially clarified by their protothetical prototypes, *mutatis mutandis*, I restrict my comments to a minimum and discuss only *new* aspects.

T.E. XXXII°. A ε tho(B) (§ 7.0, § 6.1.5) For every A and B:

A is (a) *thesis relative to* (*thesis*) B (*of this system*) *of ontology* if and only if (1) A is an effective basic thesis of this system of protothetic or is a thesis of this system of ontology, (2) B is a thesis of this system of ontology, and (3) A is an individual preceding B or identical with B.

So only any thesis relative to thesis B of this system of ontology either is an effective basic thesis of this system of protothetic or is a thesis of this system of ontology, and precedes or is identical with B, which is a thesis of this system of ontology. Hence every effective basic thesis of this system of protothetic is a thesis relative to every thesis of this system of ontology, and every thesis of this system of ontology is a thesis relative to itself and to any later thesis of this system of ontology.

(T.E. XXIII°–IL°. See § 7.0 and § 7.1 above.)

I call *nominal* (*relative to thesis* B) only any homoseme, relative to an individual thesis B of this system of ontology, of the tenth word in Axiom AO; (§ 6.2.3) and call *noun* (*relative to thesis* B) only any term both nominal and constant relative to an individual thesis B of this system of ontology. So only any member of the semantic category of nouns, introduced by AO and founded by arguments of parenthemes of type '{- -}' in AO, is nominal, and only any nominal constant term is a noun, relative to any one thesis specified as parameter. I call *nomination* (*relative to thesis* B) only any nominal combination relative to an individual thesis B of this system of ontology. I call *predication* (*relative to thesis* B) only any function which is propositional, relative to an individual thesis B of this system of ontology, and whose arguments are all nominal relative to B. So only any nominal (resp. propositional) junction of one or more nominal arguments is a nomination (resp. predication) relative to any one thesis specified as parameter, and any nominator or predicator is a junctor. I call *description* (*relative to thesis* B) only any nomination or predication relative to an individual thesis B of this system of ontology. So only any nominal or propositional junction of one or more nominal arguments is a description, and only any nominal (resp. propositional) description is a nomination (resp. predication), relative to any one thesis specified as parameter. I call only any functor of nomination (resp. predication, description) B, relative to an individual thesis C of this system of ontology, (a and hence the) *nominator* (resp. *predicator, descriptor*) *of* (*function*) B (*relative to thesis* C). I call simply *predicator* or *verbial* (resp. *nominator, descriptor, relative to thesis* B) only any homoseme, relative to an individual thesis B of this system of ontology, of the functor of any (§ 1.7) predication (resp. nomination, description) relative to thesis B. So only any nominator or predicator is a descriptor, relative to any one thesis specified as parameter. I call *adverbial* (*relative to thesis* B) only any homoseme, relative to an individual thesis B of this system of ontology, of the functor of a verbial combination relative to thesis B ("auxiliary verbs" included). Hence any connector, nominator, or adverbial functor is a combinator, relative to any one thesis specified as parameter. I call *verb* (resp. *adverb*, *relative to thesis* B) only any term both verbial (resp. adverbial) and constant relative to an individual thesis B of this system of ontology. So only any noun (resp. verb, adverb) is a nominal (resp. verbial, adverbial) constant term, relative to any one thesis specified as parameter. I call only any first (resp. second) of the two arguments of dyadic predication B, relative to an individual thesis C of this system of ontology, (a and hence the) *subject* (resp. *object* or *predicate*— whichever is traditionally more appropriate to the case in question) of (*predication*) B (*relative to thesis* C). I call *singular predicator* (*relative to thesis* B) only any epsilon that, relative to an individual thesis B of this system, is a nonvariable binary predicator; i.e., is a constant introduced by Axiom AO and equisignificant to the epsilons in AO. I call *singular predication* (*relative to thesis* B) only any individual (predication) whose functor is a singular predicator, relative to an individual thesis B of this system of ontology.

T.E. L°. A ε cnjnct(B)   For every A and B:

A is (a) *provisory conjunct of* (*dyadic function*) B if and only if (1) the functor of function B is an expression equiform to the twenty-first word in Axiom AO (§ 6.2.3, § 7.0) of this system of ontology; and (2) for at least one C, C is a parentheme of function B, and A either is the antecedent of C or is the consequent of C.

So only any antecedent or consequent of a parentheme of function B, whose functor is a term of form ' φ ', is a provisory conjunct of dyadic function B; and is a conjunct of conjunction B, *provided* that B is propositional and its functor ' φ ' is not variable. The qualification 'provisory', here and in the following two explanations, is accounted for by such provisos, (§ 7.0) as in XXXI above.

T.E. LI°. A ε Sbjct(B)   For every A and B:

A is (the) *provisory subject of* (*function*) B if and only if (1) the functor of function B is an expression equiform to the eighth word in Axiom AO of this system of ontology; and (2) for certain C and D, C is a parentheme of function B, D is in AO, and argument A of C is analogous to the tenth word of AO, in D; i.e., to the first argument of the parentheme of dyadic function B, a function of form 'ε{Ab}'.

T.E. LII°. A ε Prdct(B)   For every A and B:
A is (the) *provisory predicate of* (*function*) B if and only if (1) the
functor of function B is an expression equiform to the eighth word in
Axiom AO of this system of ontology; and (2) for certain C and D,
C is a parentheme of function B, D is in AO, and argument A of C
is analogous to the eleventh word of AO, in D; i.e., to the second
argument of the parentheme of dyadic function B, a function of form
'ε{Ab}'.

So only any first (resp. second) of the two arguments of the sole
parentheme, of type '{– –}', of function B, whose functor is an
epsilon, is (a and hence the) provisory subject (resp. provisory predicate) of the dyadic function B; and is the same individual as
the subject (resp. predicate) of singular predication B, *provided*
that B is propositional and its functor epsilon is not variable.

T.E. LIII°. A ε nomprntmo(B, C, D, E) (§ 7.0)
For every A, B, C, D, and E: *parentheme A of the provisory predicate*
of the provisory coimplicate of the nucleus of (*generalization*) C *is*
suited to be similar to parentheme E of nominal function D, relative
to (*thesis*) B (*of this system of ontology*), if and only if (1) D is a thetic
homoseme of the tenth word in Axiom AO (§ 6.2.3) relative to
thesis B of this system of ontology; (2) E is a parentheme of function
D; (3) A is a parentheme of the provisory predicate of the provisory
coimplicate of the nucleus of C; (4) arguments of A and arguments
of E are equinumerous; and (5) for every F and G, if F is an argument of A, G is an argument of E, and arguments of A that
precede F are equinumerous to arguments of E that precede G,
then, for certain H and I, F is a variable of generalization C related to
analog I of homoseme H of G, and so suited to belong to the semantic
category of G, relative to thesis B of this system of ontology.

—I.e., relative to thesis B, parentheme A of the provisory predicate of the provisory coimplicate of the nucleus (i.e., quantificate)
of generalization C has the same number of arguments as parentheme E of nominal function D, and every argument of A is a
variable of C related to an analog of a homoseme of the homologous
argument of E, and so suited to belong to the semantic category
of its homolog. Suppose that generalization C is a thesis following

or identical with B, so that B is a thesis relative to C. Then, relative to C or any later thesis, C itself, its nucleus, and the provisory coimplicans and coimplicate of its nucleus alike are basic propositional phrases; the provisory predicate of the provisory coimplicate is nominal; and homologous arguments of parenthemes A and E are thetic homosemes; so A and E, since their arguments are the same in number, and arguments occupying the same relative position will be of the same semantic category, are suited to be of the same type.

T.E. LIV°. A ε ₁nomprntmo(B, C, D, E)

For every A, B, C, D, and E: *parentheme* A *of the provisory predicate of the provisory coimplicate of the nucleus of* (*generalization*) C *is suited to be similar to the last parentheme* E *of nominal function* D, *relative to* (*thesis*) B (*of this system of ontology*), if and only if (1) parentheme A of the provisory predicate of the provisory coimplicate of the nucleus of generalization C is suited to be similar to parentheme E of nominal function D, relative to thesis B of this system of ontology, and (2) the last word in D is in E.

T.E. LV°. A ε ₂nomprntmo(B, C, D, E, F, G)

For every A, B, C, D, E, F, and G: *parentheme* A *of the provisory predicate of the provisory coimplicate of the nucleus of* (*generalization*) C *is suited to be similar to the parentheme* E, *of nominal function* D, *immediately preceding a parentheme* F *similar to* (*parentheme*) G, *relative to* (*thesis*) B (*of this system of ontology*), if and only if (1) parentheme A of the provisory predicate of the provisory coimplicate of the nucleus of generalization C is suited to be similar to parentheme E of nominal function D, relative to thesis B of this system of ontology, (2) F is a parentheme of D, (3) the last word preceding F is in E, and (4) G is a parentheme similar to F.

—I.e., relative to thesis B, parentheme A of the provisory predicate of the provisory coimplicate of the nucleus of generalization C is suited to be similar to the parentheme E, of nominal function D, containing the last word preceding a parentheme of D similar to parentheme G.

Lesniewski's second directive for (nominative) definition is based on explanation LVI° below, just as his first directive for (propositive) definition is based on XLIV above, (§ 7.0) the prefatory remarks to which apply here too.

T.E. LVI°. A ε ₂defo(B)   For every A and B:

A is *legitimate as nominative* (§ 7.0) *definition immediately after* (*thesis*) B (*of this system of ontology*) if and only if the following twenty-one conditions are fulfilled:

(1) The first word in the nucleus of A is (individual but) not a variable of A related to itself.

(2) The first word in the provisory coimplicans of the nucleus of A is (individual but) not a variable of A related to itself.

(3) The first word in the provisory coimplicate of the nucleus of A is (individual but) not a variable of A related to itself.

(4) The first word in the provisory predicate of the provisory coimplicate of the nucleus of A is (individual but) not a variable of A related to itself.

(5) The first word in the provisory predicate of the provisory coimplicate of the nucleus of A is (individual but) not an ingredient of A suited to be constant, *relative to thesis B* of this system of ontology.

(6) For every C, if C is a term in the provisory coimplicans of the nucleus of A, then either (i) for at least one D, C is a word inside D, and D is a universal quantifier in A; (ii) for certain D and E, D is in A, and C is a variable of generalization D bound by E; or (iii) C is an argument or functor of an ingredient of A and suited to be constant, relative to thesis B of this system of ontology.

(7) For every C and D, if C is a word inside D, and D is a universal quantifier in A, then, for certain E and F, E is in A, and F is a variable of generalization E bound by C.

(8) For every C, D, and E, if C is a word inside the universal quantifier of A, D is an argument of E, and E is a parentheme of the nucleus of A, then, for at least one F, F is in D and is a variable of generalization A bound by C.

(9) For every C, D, and E, if C and D are both in the provisory coimplicans of the nucleus of A, and are convariables of generalization E, and E is in A, then either C and D are the same individual or, for certain F and G, arguments or functors C and D of ingredients of A are quasihomosemes of their respective analogs F and G, relative to thesis B of this system of ontology.[84]

(10) For every C, if C is a universal generalization in A but not identical with A then, for certain D, E, F, and G, E is a thesis relative to thesis B of this system of ontology, F is in E, G is in A, and D is a thetic homoseme of B, relative to B, and is analogous, as argument of parentheme F, to argument C of parentheme G.

(11) For every C and D, if C is a universal generalization in A, and D is the nucleus of C, then either D is a word or, for at least one E, D is a generating function with respect to E, and E is a basic propositional phrase relative to thesis B of this system of ontology.

(12) For every C, if C is a function in the provisory coimplicans of the nucleus of A, then either (i) for at least one D, C is the nucleus of D, and D is a universal generalization in A, or (ii) for certain D and E, argument or functor C of an ingredient of A is eligible by analogy to the semantic category of its generate D and its analog E, relative to thesis B of this system of ontology.

(13) For at least one C, the provisory subject of function C is a variable of generalization A related to the provisory subject of the provisory coimplicate of the nucleus of A, and C either is the provisory coimplicans of the nucleus of A or is a provisory conjunct of the provisory coimplicans of the nucleus of A.

(14) For every C, if C is a parentheme of the provisory predicate of the provisory coimplicate of the nucleus of A then, for at least one D, D is an argument of C.

(15) For every C and D, if C is a parentheme of the provisory predicate of the provisory coimplicate of the nucleus of A, and D is an argument of C, then, for at least one E, D is a variable of generalization A bound by E.

(16) For every C and D, if C and D are equiform expressions, and each is a term in the provisory coimplicate of the nucleus of A but is not the first word in the provisory coimplicate of the nucleus of A, then C and D are the same individual.

(17) For every C and D, if C and D are similar parenthemes (and are both parenthemes) of the provisory predicate of the provisory coimplicate of the nucleus of A, then C and D are the same individual.

(18) For every C, D, and E, if parentheme C of the provisory predicate of the provisory coimplicate of the nucleus of generalization A is suited to be similar to parentheme E of nominal function D, relative to thesis B of this system of ontology, and contains the last word in the provisory predicate of the provisory coimplicate of the nucleus of A, then C is a parentheme similar to E.

(19) For every C, D, E, F, and G, if parentheme C of the provisory predicate of the provisory coimplicate of the nucleus of generalization A is suited to be similar to parentheme E, of nominal function D, immediately preceding a parentheme F similar to parentheme G, relative to thesis B of this system of ontology, and contains the last word preceding G, and G is in A, then C is a parentheme similar to E.

(20) For every C, D, and E, if C is a parentheme of the provisory predicate of the provisory coimplicate of the nucleus of A, contains the last word in the provisory predicate of the provisory coimplicate of the nucleus of A, and is similar to parentheme E, and E is in D, and D is a thesis relative to thesis B of this system of ontology, then, for certain F and G, parentheme C of the provisory predicate of the provisory coimplicate of the nucleus of generalization A is suited to be similar to the last parentheme G of nominal function F, relative to B.

(21) For every C, D, E, and F, if C is a parentheme of the provisory predicate of the provisory coimplicate of the nucleus of A, contains the last word preceding D, and is similar to parentheme F, and D is a parentheme in A, F is in E, and E is a thesis relative to thesis B of this system of ontology, then, for certain G, H, and I, parentheme C of the provisory predicate of the provisory coimplicate of the nucleus of generalization A is suited to be similar to the parentheme H, of nominal function G, immediately preceding a parentheme I similar to D, relative to B.

So A is legitimate as nominative definition immediately after thesis B of this system of ontology if and only if B is a thesis[85] of this system of ontology relative to which the following conditions are fulfilled: (1–3) The first word in the nucleus (resp. provisory definiens, provisory definiendum) of A is (individual but) not a variable of generalization A; and (4–5) the first word in the provisory predicate of the provisory definiendum of A is (individual but) neither a variable of generalization A nor an ingredient of A suited to be constant (*relative to B*). (6) Any term in the provisory definiens of A either is a variable of some ingredient of A, is a word inside a quantifier itself in A, or is an argument or functor of an ingredient of A and suited to be constant. (7) Any word inside a quantifier itself in A binds at least one variable of some ingredient of A; and (8) any word inside the universal quantifier of generalization A binds at least one variable of A in each argument of the parentheme of the nucleus of A: i.e., in both the provisory definiens and definiendum of A. (9) All nonidentical convariables of any ingredient of A, if in the provisory definiens of A, are arguments or functors of ingredients of A, and are quasihomosemes, eligible by analogy to the same semantic category.[84] (10) Any generalization merely part of A is analogous, as argument of some ingredient of A, to a thetic homoseme of B in (i.e., to a propositional argument of) some ingredient of a thesis. (11) The quantificate of any ingredient of A, if not a word, is a generating function with respect to some basic propositional phrase. (12) Any function in the provisory definiens of A, if not the quantificate of some ingredient of A, is an argument or functor of some ingredient of A, and is eligible by analogy to the appropriate semantic category. (13) The provisory subject of the provisory definiens, or of at least one provisory conjunct of the provisory definiens, of A is a variable of generalization A related to the provisory subject of the provisory definiendum of A. (14–17) The provisory definiendum of A contains no two terms that are equiform and that both follow its first word; any parentheme of its provisory predicate, which (predicate) has no two similar parenthemes, has at least one argument; and any such argument is a variable of generalization A. (18, 20) Suppose P is the last parentheme of the provisory predicate of the provisory definiendum of A.

Then P, if suited to be, is similar to the last parentheme P′ of some nominal function; if not, P is a parentheme of new type, no thesis (*relative to B*) containing a similar parentheme. (19, 21) Suppose parentheme P of the provisory predicate of the provisory definiendum of A immediately precedes parentheme Q in A. Then P, if suited to be, is similar to the parentheme P′, of some nominal function, immediately preceding a parentheme Q′ similar to Q; if not, P is a parentheme of new type, no thesis (*relative to B*) containing a similar parentheme.

I call *nominative definition* (*of this system of ontology*) only any individual not only legitimate as nominative definition, immediately after some thesis of this system of ontology, but also asserted as a new thesis of this system immediately thereafter, according to the directive for nominative definition. I call simply *definition* (*of this system of logic*) only any propositive or nominative definition of this system.

Most of Lesniewski's requirements for nominative definition parallel their prototypes for propositive definition (*mutatis mutandis*) both in form and justification. For example, LVI°.17–.21 share the purpose and rationale of XLIV.14–.18, explained and illustrated in XLIV above. The one essentially new requirement, peculiar to nominative as distinguished from propositive definition, is (LVI°.13) that the definiens of a nominative definition either be or have as conjunct a singular predication whose subject is a variable (of the definition) related to the subject of the singular predication that is the definiendum. The import of LVI°.13 may be seen in §§ 3.3, 6.1.9, and 6.2.3 above. The logical reason for this requirement should be clear: Since a definition should not require ad hoc justification of its consistency, it should not assume without proof that (as expressed by Frege[34] in the material mode) a "concept may be treated as an object". (§ 6.1.6) More explicitly, since the definiendum of a nominative definition, being a singular predication paraphrasable by "the sole so-and-so is such-and-such", logically implies uniqueness of so-and-so, the definiens must also, in order logically to guarantee equivalence without begging the question. If this requirement (LVI°.13) were omitted, expression A below might be asserted as nominative definition immediately after Axiom AO. The paradoxical

"equivalence" B would then follow by substitution, entailing contradiction C by classical truth-functional inference, as in the propositive variant of Russell's contradiction (§ 3.3.4) that would be
obtained by putting '{p}' for '(p)', and '{Absrd}' for '(Absrd)',
throughout examples I, J, and K of XLIV above, in violation of
XLIV.7. Faults analogous to those illustrated in XLIV are excluded
from propositive definitions of ontology by the same requirements

$$\text{(A)} \quad {}_{\llcorner}x_{\lrcorner} \,{}^{\ulcorner}\phi\left(\vdash (\varepsilon\{x\,x\})\varepsilon\{x\,\underset{1}{\Lambda}\}\right)^{\urcorner}$$

$$\text{(B)} \quad \phi\left(\vdash (\varepsilon\{\underset{1}{\Lambda}\,\underset{1}{\Lambda}\})\,\varepsilon\{\underset{1}{\Lambda}\,\underset{1}{\Lambda}\}\right)$$

$$\text{(C)} \quad \varphi\left(\vdash (\varepsilon\{\underset{1}{\Lambda}\,\underset{1}{\Lambda}\})\,\varepsilon\{\underset{1}{\Lambda}\,\underset{1}{\Lambda}\}\right)$$

of XLIV that preclude their protothetical prototypes. Expression
A above is meaningful—unlike the propositive variants of Russell's
contradiction—but is logically false. (§ 3.3.4) Its valid counterpart
A′ here, on the other hand, would be legitimate as nominative

$$\text{(A′)} \quad {}_{\llcorner}A_{\lrcorner} \,{}^{\ulcorner}\phi\left(\varphi\left(\varepsilon\{AA\} \vdash (\varepsilon\{AA\})\right)\varepsilon\{A\,\underset{1}{\Lambda}\}\right)^{\urcorner}$$

$$\text{(B′)} \quad \phi\left({}_{\llcorner}A_{\lrcorner} \,{}^{\ulcorner}\vdash \left(\varphi\left(\varepsilon\{AA\} \vdash (\varepsilon\{AA\})\right)\right)^{\urcorner}\,{}_{\llcorner}A_{\lrcorner}\,{}^{\ulcorner}\vdash (\varepsilon\{A\,\underset{1}{\Lambda}\})^{\urcorner}\right)$$

$$\text{(C′)} \quad {}_{\llcorner}A_{\lrcorner}\,{}^{\ulcorner}\vdash (\varepsilon\{A\,\underset{1}{\Lambda}\})^{\urcorner}$$

definition (immediately after Axiom AO); and so too (later) would
be the results of replacing the definiens of A′ by logical equivalents,
such as '$\varepsilon\{A \sim (A)\}$' or '$\varepsilon\{A \sim (V)\}$', containing terms defined
by definitions of certain forms listed below. But the antecedent of
consequence B′ of A′ is logically equivalent to a substitution in-
stance '${}_{\llcorner}A_{\lrcorner}\,{}^{\ulcorner}\phi(\varepsilon\{AA\}\,\varepsilon\{AA\})^{\urcorner}$' of a thesis '${}_{\llcorner}r_{\lrcorner}\,{}^{\ulcorner}\phi(rr)^{\urcorner}$'. Consequently A′ or an equivalent would entail no paradox or contradic-
tion. Instead it would yield the natural consequence C′ that nothing
whatever is a nonentity, (§ 1.7) as defined by definition A′.

It is characteristic that Von Neumann and Quine, who later adopted requirements
reminiscent of LVI°.13, made no attempt to justify their expedients against contradiction on other than pragmatic grounds. (See Quine, *1951*, § 24.)

The following numbered examples, (§ 1.7) according as their numerals are prefixed by 'D' or by 'S', either (1) are expressions that, in the order listed, might be subjoined to Axiom AO as nominative definitions, each being legitimate immediately after its direct predecessor, if all preceding expressions were asserted as theses, or (2) are schemes representing individual specifications that would be legitimate as nominative definitions if asserted in appropriate order. As in XLIV above, I freely draw upon terms from preceding examples for purposes of illustration.

D73. $\llcorner AB \lrcorner$ $\ulcorner \phi \left(\phi \left(\varepsilon \left\{ AB \right\} \varepsilon \left\{ BA \right\} \right) \varepsilon \left\{ A \text{ Id } (B) \right\} \right) \urcorner$

D74. $\llcorner Ab \lrcorner$ $\ulcorner \phi \left(\phi \left(\varepsilon \left\{ AA \right\} \vdash \left(\varepsilon \left\{ Ab \right\} \right) \right) \varepsilon \left\{ A \sim (b) \right\} \right) \urcorner$

D75. $\llcorner A \lrcorner$ $\ulcorner \phi \left(\varepsilon \left\{ AA \right\} \varepsilon \left\{ A \text{ V} \right\} \right) \urcorner$

D76. $\llcorner A \lrcorner$ $\ulcorner \phi \left(\varepsilon \left\{ A \sim (V) \right\} \varepsilon \left\{ A \wedge \right\} \right) \urcorner$

D77. $\llcorner Abc \lrcorner$ $\ulcorner \phi \left(\phi \left(\varepsilon \left\{ Ab \right\} \varepsilon \left\{ Ac \right\} \right) \varepsilon \left\{ A \cap (bc) \right\} \right) \urcorner$

D78. $\llcorner Abc \lrcorner$ $\ulcorner \phi \left(\varepsilon \left\{ A \cap (b \sim (c)) \right\} \varepsilon \left\{ A - (bc) \right\} \right) \urcorner$

D79. $\llcorner Abc \lrcorner$ $\ulcorner \phi \left(\phi \left(\varepsilon \left\{ AA \right\} \varphi \left(\varepsilon \left\{ Ab \right\} \varepsilon \left\{ Ac \right\} \right) \right) \varepsilon \left\{ A \cup (bc) \right\} \right) \urcorner$

D80. $\llcorner Abc \lrcorner$ $\ulcorner \phi \left(\varepsilon \left\{ A \cup (\sim (b)c) \right\} \varepsilon \left\{ A \supset (bc) \right\} \right) \urcorner$

D81. $\llcorner Abc \lrcorner$ $\ulcorner \phi \left(\varepsilon \left\{ A \cap (\supset (bc) \supset (cb)) \right\} \varepsilon \left\{ A \backsim (bc) \right\} \right) \urcorner$

D82. $\llcorner ABf \lrcorner$ $\ulcorner \phi \left(\phi \left(\varepsilon \left\{ AA \right\} \varepsilon \left\{ B \text{ f } (A) \right\} \right) \varepsilon \left\{ A \text{ cnv } [f] (B) \right\} \right) \urcorner$

D83. $\llcorner Abf \lrcorner$ $\ulcorner \phi \left(\varepsilon \left\{ A \sim (f(b)) \right\} \varepsilon \left\{ A \sim [f] (b) \right\} \right) \urcorner$

D84. $\llcorner Abfh \lrcorner$ $\ulcorner \phi \left(\varepsilon \left\{ A \cap (f(b)h(b)) \right\} \varepsilon \left\{ A \cap [fh] (b) \right\} \right) \urcorner$

D85. $\llcorner$Abfh$\lrcorner$ $\ulcorner \phi \big(\varepsilon \{A \cup (f(b)h(b))\} \; \varepsilon \{A \cup [fh](b)\} \big) \urcorner$

D86. $\llcorner$Abfh$\lrcorner$ $\ulcorner \phi \big(\varepsilon \{A \cap [f \sim [h]](b)\} \; \varepsilon \{A - [fh](b)\} \big) \urcorner$

D87. $\llcorner$Abfh$\lrcorner$ $\ulcorner \phi \big(\varepsilon \{A \cup [\sim [f]h](b)\} \; \varepsilon \{A \supset [fh](b)\} \big) \urcorner$

D88. $\llcorner$Abfh$\lrcorner$ $\ulcorner \phi \big(\varepsilon \{A \cap [\supset [fh] \supset [hf]](b)\} \; \varepsilon \{A \infty [fh](b)\} \big) \urcorner$

D89. $\llcorner$Abf$\lrcorner$ $\ulcorner \phi \big(\phi(\varepsilon \{AA\}f\{Ab\}) \; \varepsilon \{A \; '[f](b)\} \big) \urcorner$

D90. $\llcorner$Abf$\lrcorner$ $\ulcorner \phi \Big(\phi \big(\varepsilon \{AA\} \vdash (\llcorner C \lrcorner \ulcorner \phi\!\!\!\!\!\!-\; (\varepsilon \{Af(C)\} \; \varepsilon \{Cb\}) \urcorner) \big)$

$\varepsilon \{A \text{ "}[f](b)\} \Big) \urcorner$

D91. $\llcorner$Af$\lrcorner$ $\ulcorner \phi \Big(\varepsilon \big\{A \text{ "} \big[\cup [f \; cnv \; [f]]\big] (V)\big\} \; \varepsilon \{A \; mem \; \{f\}\} \Big) \urcorner$

D92. $\llcorner$Abfh$\lrcorner$ $\ulcorner \phi \Big(\phi \big(\varepsilon \{AA\} \vdash (\llcorner C \lrcorner \ulcorner \phi\!\!\!\!\!\!-(\varepsilon \{A \; f(C)\} \; \varepsilon \{C \; h(b)\}) \urcorner) \big)$

$\varepsilon \{A \mid [fh](b)\} \Big) \urcorner$

D93. $\llcorner$Abf$\lrcorner$ $\ulcorner \phi \Big(\phi \big(\varepsilon \{AA\} \llcorner c \lrcorner \ulcorner \phi \big(\phi(\subset \{bc\} \subset \{\text{"}[f](c)c\}) \; \varepsilon \{Ac\}) \urcorner \big)$

$\varepsilon \{A \; clsr \; [f](b)\} \Big) \urcorner$

D94. $\llcorner$ABf$\lrcorner$ $\ulcorner \phi \big(\phi(\varepsilon \{A \; clsr \; [f](B)\} \; \varepsilon \{B \; mem \; \{f\}\}) \varepsilon \{A \; anc \; [f](B)\} \big) \urcorner$

D95. $\llcorner$ABf$\lrcorner$ $\ulcorner \phi \big(\varepsilon \{A \mid [f \; anc \; [f]](B)\} \; \varepsilon \{A \; prdc \; [f](B)\} \big) \urcorner$

D96. $\llcorner$ABf$\lrcorner$ $\ulcorner \phi \Big(\varepsilon \big\{A \cup \big[anc \; [f] \; anc \; [cnv \; [f]]\big] (B)\big\}$

$\varepsilon \{A \; fam \; [f](B)\} \Big) \urcorner$

D97. $\llcorner ABCf \lrcorner \ulcorner \phi \left(\varepsilon \left\{ A \cap \left(anc \left[f \right] (B) \, anc \left[cnv \left[f \right] \right] (C) \right) \right\} \right.$

$\left. \varepsilon \left\{ A \underset{2}{\text{inter}} \left[f \right] (BC) \right\} \right) \urcorner$

D98. $\llcorner Afghb \lrcorner \ulcorner \phi \left(\varepsilon \left\{ A \mid \left[\mid \left[fg \right] h \right] (b) \right\} \, \varepsilon \left\{ A \mid \left[fgh \right] (b) \right\} \right) \urcorner$

S99. $\llcorner Ab_1 b_2 \ldots b_n \lrcorner \ulcorner \phi \left(\phi \left(\varepsilon \left\{ Ab_1 \right\} \, \phi \, \left(\varepsilon \left\{ Ab_2 \right\} \ldots \varepsilon \left\{ Ab_n \right\} \right) \right) \right.$

$\left. \varepsilon \left\{ A \cap (b_1 b_2 \ldots b_n) \right\} \right) \urcorner$

S100. $\llcorner Ab_1 \ldots b_n \lrcorner \ulcorner \phi \left(\phi \left(\varepsilon \left\{ AA \right\} \, \phi \, \left(\varepsilon \left\{ Ab_1 \right\} \ldots \varepsilon \left\{ Ab_n \right\} \right) \right) \right.$

$\left. \varepsilon \left\{ A \cup (b_1 \ldots b_n) \right\} \right) \urcorner$

S101. $\llcorner Afb_1 \ldots b_n \lrcorner \ulcorner \phi \left(\varepsilon \left\{ A \sim (f(b_1 \ldots b_n)) \right\} \, \varepsilon \left\{ A \sim \underset{n}{[f]} (b_1 \ldots b_n) \right\} \right) \urcorner$

S102. $\llcorner Afhb_1 \ldots b_n \lrcorner \ulcorner \phi \left(\varepsilon \left\{ A \cap (f(b_1 \ldots b_n) \, h(b_1 \ldots b_n)) \right\} \right.$

$\left. \varepsilon \left\{ A \cap \underset{n}{[fh]} (b_1 \ldots b_n) \right\} \right) \urcorner$

S103. $\llcorner Afhb_1 \ldots b_n \lrcorner \ulcorner \phi \left(\varepsilon \left\{ A \cup (f(b_1 \ldots b_n) \, h(b_1 \ldots b_n)) \right\} \right.$

$\left. \varepsilon \left\{ A \cup \underset{n}{[fh]} (b_1 \ldots b_n) \right\} \right) \urcorner$

S104. $\llcorner Afb_1 \ldots b_n \lrcorner \phi \left(\phi \left(\varepsilon \left\{ AA \right\} \vdash \left(\llcorner C_1 \ldots C_n \lrcorner \ulcorner \vdash \left(\phi \, (\varepsilon \left\{ Af(C_1 \ldots C_n) \right\} \right. \right. \right. \right.$

$\left. \left. \left. \left. \varepsilon \left\{ C_1 b_1 \right\} \ldots \varepsilon \left\{ C_n b_n \right\} \right) \right) \urcorner \right) \right) \varepsilon \left\{ A \text{ "} \underset{n}{[f]} (b_1 \ldots b_n) \right\} \right)$

Suppose that D, being legitimate as nominative definition immediately after some thesis, is asserted as a thesis immediately
thereafter. Then, since the first word of the nucleus, not being
variable, is a coimplicator, the nucleus of definition D is a coimplication, whose coimplicate (resp. coimplicans) is identical with its

provisory coimplicate (resp. coimplicans) the provisory definiendum
(resp. definiens), which, since D is a definition, is simply the definiendum (resp. definiens) of D. Since the first word of the definiendum
(resp. definiens) of D is also non-variable, the definiendum of D is a
singular predication, whose provisory subject is the same individual
as its subject and is a variable of generalization D; and the definiens
of D, in order to guarantee its logical equivalence to the definiendum,
either is or has as conjunct a singular predication, of which predication the provisory subject is the same individual as its subject and is
a variable of generalization D related to the subject of the definiendum of D. Since any nominative definition is a universal generalization, its nucleus is the same individual as its quantificate. Finally,
the provisory predicate of the definiendum of D is the same individual as the predicate, and either (1) is a noun, identical with the
defined constant of D, which satisfies requirements LVI.14–.21
vacuously, or (2) is a nominal function, whose first word is the
defined constant of D, and which fulfills these last eight requirements regulating arguments and brackets of its one or more parenthemes.

So D is a nominative definition of this system of ontology if and
only if thesis D of this system of ontology fulfills the following
three sets of conditions, of which the first makes clear that D is a
universal generalization whose nucleus, identical with its quantificate, is a coimplication:

(1) The coimplicate of the quantificate (i.e., the provisory definiendum) of D is a singular predication, and the first word of its
predicate (i.e., the defined term) is a constant new in thesis D. The
coimplicans of the quantificate (i.e., the provisory definiens) of D,
if not itself a singular predication, is a conjunction of which at least
one conjunct is a singular predication; and (in either case) the
subject is a variable of generalization D related to the subject of the
provisory definiendum of D. Any word inside a quantifier itself in D
binds at least one variable of some ingredient of D; and any word
inside the universal quantifier of generalization D itself binds at
least one variable of D in the provisory definiens and exactly one in
the provisory definiendum of D. Any parentheme of the predicate
of the provisory definiendum of D, which predicate contains no

two terms of the same form nor two parenthemes of the same type, has at least one argument; and any such argument is a variable of generalization D related to one or more variables in the provisory definiens of D. (So the only non-variable terms in the provisory definiendum of D are its first word—i.e., its functor the singular predicator epsilon—and the first word of its predicate: i.e., the term to be defined. Furthermore, any generalization merely part of D is in the provisory definiens of D—not in the provisory definiendum, any parentheme in which is inside no parentheme and hence is a parentheme *of* the provisory definiendum of D.)

(2) The following additional conditions are fulfilled relative to the thesis of this system of ontology immediately preceding thesis D: Any term in the provisory definiens of D, if neither variable nor inside a quantifier, is an argument or functor of an ingredient of D and suited to be constant. All nonidentical convariables in the provisory definiens of D are arguments or functors of ingredients of D, and are quasihomosemes, eligible by analogy to the same semantic category.[84] Any generalization merely part of D is analogous, as argument of some ingredient of D, to a propositional argument of some ingredient of a thesis; its quantificate, if not a word, is a generating function with respect to some basic propositional phrase; and any function in the provisory definiens of D, if not the quantificate of some ingredient of D, is an argument or functor of an ingredient of A, and is eligible by analogy to the appropriate semantic category.

(3) Finally, the following conditions are fulfilled relative to thesis D itself, though not necessarily relative to any preceding thesis: Suppose P is the last parentheme of the predicate of the provisory definiendum of D. Then, if P′ is the last parentheme of any nominal function relative to the thesis of this system of ontology immediately preceding D, and every argument of P belongs to the same semantic category as the homologous argument of P′ (in which case arguments of P and of P′ are equinumerous), the initial brackets of P and P′ are of the same form (as are the symmetrical terminal brackets, so that P and P′ are of the same type); otherwise the brackets of P differ in form from those of any parentheme having the same number of arguments in any preceding thesis (so that P

is a parentheme of new type, no preceding thesis containing a parentheme of the same type). Suppose instead that parentheme P of the
predicate of the provisory definiendum of D immediately precedes
parentheme Q in D. Then, if parentheme P′ of any nominal function, relative to the thesis of this system of ontology immediately
preceding D, immediately precedes a parentheme Q′ of the same
function and of the same type as Q, and every argument of P belongs to the same semantic category as the homologous argument
of P′, the initial brackets of P and P′ are of the same form (so that
P and P′ are of the same type); otherwise the brackets of P differ
in form from those of any parentheme having the same number of
arguments in any preceding thesis (so that P is a parentheme of
new type, no preceding thesis containing a parentheme of the same
type).

An expression might be called legitimate as nominative definition
immediately after thesis B if and only if it *would* be a nominative
definition, fulfilling the three sets of conditions above, *were* it asserted
as a thesis immediately after thesis B. But Lesniewski's requirements have the advantage of being rigorously formulated without
use of subjunctive conditionals, so that they could later be reformulated in extensional language L itself. They are designed to
assure that the generalizations in the paragraph immediately preceding XLIV, above, hold not only for propositive but also for
nominative definitions, and so for all definitions in canonic language
L; and, in addition, that the predicate of the definiendum of any
nominative definition D be nominal, relative to D itself and to
any later thesis.

By virtue of the requirements regulating formation of brackets in
the definiendum of D, the following further generalizations hold,
relative to any one thesis specified as parameter, for any function
F in a proposition: Parentheme P of the predicate of the definiendum
of D is of the same type as parentheme P′ of F if and only if (1) F
too is a nominal function, (2) every argument of P belongs to the
same semantic category as the homologous argument of P′, and (3)
any parentheme immediately following P in D is of the same type
as the parentheme of F immediately following P′. So the predicate
of the definiendum of D belongs to the same genus as F if and only

if (1) F too is a nominal function, (2) all terminally homologous parenthemes of the two functions have the same number of arguments, and (3) all homologous arguments of such parenthemes belong to the same semantic category. The functors of such homogeneous and categoric functions are also homosemes.

Leśniewski's second directive for (nominative) theses of extensionality is based on explanation LVII° below, just as his first directive for (propositive) theses of extensionality is based on IL above, (§ 7.0) the prefatory remarks to which apply here too.

T.E. LVII°. A ε $_2$extnsnlo(B)   For every A and B:
A is *legitimate as nominative* (§ 7.0) *thesis of extensionality immediately after* (*thesis*) B (*of this system of ontology*) if and only if the following eleven conditions are fulfilled:

(1) For certain C and D, C and D are both words inside the universal quantifier of generalization A, and C precedes D.

(2) For every C and D, if C is a word inside D, and D is a universal quantifier in A, then, for certain E and F, E is in A, and F is a variable of generalization E bound by C and is (individual but) not an expression equiform to the first word in the nucleus of A.

(3) The first word in the provisory coimplicans of the nucleus of the provisory coimplicans of the nucleus of A is (individual but) not a variable of generalization A related to itself.

(4) For at least one C, the first word in the provisory predicate of the provisory coimplicans of the nucleus of the provisory coimplicans of the nucleus of A is a variable of generalization A related to the complex of the (at least one) expression that is a word itself inside C, and C is a parentheme of the provisory coimplicans of the nucleus of the provisory coimplicate of the nucleus of A.

(5) For at least one C, the first word in the provisory predicate of the provisory coimplicate of the nucleus of the provisory coimplicans of the nucleus of A is a variable of generalization A related to the complex of the (at least one) expression that is a word itself inside C, and C is a parentheme of the provisory coimplicate of the nucleus of the provisory coimplicate of the nucleus of A.

(6) For every C, if C is a function in A, then either (i) for at least one D, C is the nucleus of D, and D is a universal generalization in A; or (ii) for certain D and E, argument or functor C of an ingredient of A is eligible by analogy to the semantic category of its generate D and its analog E, relative to thesis B of this system of ontology.

(7) The provisory subject of the provisory coimplicans and that of the provisory coimplicate, respectively, of the nucleus of the provisory coimplicans of the nucleus of A are convariables of the provisory coimplicans of the nucleus of A.

(8) For every C, D, E, and F, if E is a parentheme of the provisory predicate of the provisory coimplicans of the nucleus of the provisory coimplicans of the nucleus of A, F is a parentheme of the provisory predicate of the provisory coimplicate of the nucleus of the provisory coimplicans of the nucleus of A, and argument C of E is analogous to argument D of F, then C and D are convariables of the provisory coimplicans of the nucleus of A.

(9) For every C, D, and E, if C is in A, and D and E are convariables of generalization C, then, for certain F and G, arguments or functors D and E of ingredients of A are quasihomosemes of their respective analogs F and G, relative to thesis B of this system of ontology.[84]

(10) For every C and D, if C and D are convariables of the provisory coimplicans of the nucleus of A then, for certain E and F, E and F are both in A, and argument C of parentheme E is analogous to argument D of parentheme F.

(11) For every C, D, and E, if C is the functor of function D, D is an argument of E, and E is a parentheme of the nucleus of the provisory coimplicate of the nucleus of A, then C is a variable of the provisory coimplicate of the nucleus of A bound by the complex of the (at least one) expression that is a word itself inside the universal quantifier of the provisory coimplicate of the nucleus of A.

So A is legitimate as nominative thesis of extensionality immediately after thesis B of this system of ontology if and only if the following eleven conditions are fulfilled: (1) At least one word inside precedes another word inside the universal quantifier of generalization A, which quantifier therefore encloses at least two different terms. (2) Any word inside a quantifier itself in A binds at least one variable of some ingredient of A which variable is not equiform to the first word in the nucleus of A. (3) The first word in the provisory coimplicans of the nucleus of the provisory coimplicans of the nucleus of A is (individual but) not a variable of generalization A. (4) The first word in the provisory predicate of the provisory coimplicans of the nucleus of the provisory coimplicans of the nucleus of A is a variable of generalization A related to the interior of some parentheme of the provisory coimplicans of the nucleus of the provisory coimplicate of the nucleus of A; and (5) the first word in the provisory predicate of the provisory coimplicate of the nucleus of the provisory coimplicans of the nucleus of A is a variable of generalization A related to the interior of some parentheme of the provisory coimplicate of the nucleus of the provisory coimplicate of the nucleus of A. (6) Any function in A, if not the quantificate of some ingredient of A, is an argument or functor of an ingredient of A, and is eligible by analogy to the appropriate semantic category, relative to thesis B of this system of ontology. (7) The provisory subject of the provisory coimplicans and that of the provisory coimplicate, respectively, of the nucleus of the provisory coimplicans of the nucleus of A are convariables of the provisory coimplicans of the nucleus of A; (8) all analogous arguments of parenthemes of the provisory predicates of the provisory coimplicans and of the provisory coimplicate, respectively, of the nucleus of the provisory coimplicans of the nucleus of A are convariables of the provisory coimplicans of the nucleus of A; (9) all convariables of any ingredient of A are arguments or functors of ingredients of A, and are quasi-homosemes, eligible by analogy to the same semantic category,[84] relative to thesis B of this system of ontology; and (10) all convariables of the provisory coimplicans of the nucleus of A are analogous arguments of respective ingredients of A. (11) The functor of any argument of any parentheme of the nucleus of the provisory coimplicate of the nucleus of A is a variable of the provisory coimplicate of the nucleus of A bound by the interior of the universal quantifier of the provisory coimplicate of the nucleus of A.

Since no term of the form ' ϕ ' of the first word in the nucleus of A is a variable of an ingredient of proposition A (relative to B), every term of this form in A is a coimplicator, and the provisory coimplicans (resp. coimplicate) of any ingredient of A is the same individual as the coimplicans (resp. coimplicate) of that ingredient coimplication. Since the first word (epsilon) in each coimplicant of the nucleus of the coimplicans of the nucleus of A is not a variable of an ingredient of A, every epsilon in proposition A (relative to B) is a singular predicator, and the provisory subject (resp. predicate) of any ingredient of A is the same individual as the subject (resp. predicate) of that ingredient singular predication. Since A and the coimplicants of its nucleus are all universal generalizations whose nuclei (i.e., quantificates) are coimplications, the canonic skeleton of A is schematically represented by the following diagram, wherein the blanks have yet to be filled according to further requirements:

$$\llcorner\lrcorner\ulcorner\phi\left(\llcorner\lrcorner\ulcorner\phi(\varepsilon\{\ \}\varepsilon\{\ \})\urcorner\llcorner\lrcorner\ulcorner\phi(\ )\urcorner\right)\urcorner.$$

So Λ is legitimate as nominative thesis of extensionality immediately after thesis B of this system of ontology if and only if the following *requirements for nominative theses of extensionality* are fulfilled: A and the coimplicants of its quantificate are all universal generalizations whose quantificates are coimplications. Calling the coimplicans of the quantificate of A *CnQA* for short, consider the two coimplicants of the quantificate of CnQA: They are singular predications whose subjects are convariables of CnQA and whose predicates, if not nominal terms, are nominal functions of whose one or more parenthemes the one or more arguments are all variables of CnQA, bound by their respective homomorphs inside the universal quantifier of CnQA. Indeed, only these two subjects and all analogous arguments of these parenthemes are convariables of CnQA. Calling the coimplicate of the quantificate of A *CtQA* for short, consider the two coimplicants of the quantificate of CtQA: They are simple monadic functions whose functors are convariables of CtQA, bound by the single homomorph that is the interior of the universal quantifier of CtQA. The sole term that is the interior of the sole parentheme of each coimplicant is a variable of A related to the first word in the predicate of the analogous coimplicant of the quantificate of CnQA, and is bound by the homomorph inside the universal quantifier of A, which quantifier thus encloses exactly two terms, each term binding both convariables of the equiform pair. So the representative diagram above may be schematically elaborated as follows, according to the conventions of IL:

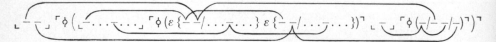

Finally, B is a thesis[85] of this system of ontology, relative to which are fulfilled the following *additional requirements to assure that any extensionality thesis A be a proposition*, relative to the latest thesis (either B or some preceding thesis) introducing a semantic category of expressions in A: Any word inside a quantifier itself in A binds at least one variable (of some ingredient of A) not of the form ' φ ' of the first word in the quantificate of A. All convariables of any ingredient of A are arguments or functors of ingredients of A, and are quasihomosemes, eligible by analogy to the same semantic category.[84] Any function in A, if not the quantificate of some ingre-

dient of A, is an argument or functor of an ingredient of A, and is
eligible by analogy to the appropriate semantic category.

I call *nominative thesis of extensionality* (*of this system of ontology*)
only any individual not only legitimate as nominative thesis of
extensionality, immediately after some thesis of this system of
ontology, but also actually asserted and subjoined to this system
of ontology as a new thesis immediately thereafter, according to
Lesniewski's second directive of extensionality. I call (*underived*) *thesis
of extensionality* (*of this system of logic*) only any propositive or
nominative thesis of extensionality of this system. Since the two
generalizations merely part of any nominative extensionality thesis
A are the coimplicants of the quantificate of generalization A, the
quantificate of every generalization itself in A is a coimplication,
and every term in A either is a variable of some ingredient of A,
is a word inside a quantifier itself in A and binds exactly two convariables of some ingredient of A, or is a coimplicator or singular
predicator not only suited to be but actually constant, relative to
the thesis introducing it (either Axiom AP or AO, respectively) and
hence to any later thesis. So A is a proposition, relative to the latest
thesis preceding A and introducing a semantic category of expressions in A. Proposition A (resp. B) below, for example, would be
legitimate and assertible as nominative extensionality thesis, immediately after Axiom AO (resp. a definition of an analog of functors 'f' in B), and would yield substitution instances such as A'
(resp. B'):

(A) $\llcorner bc \lrcorner \ulcorner \phi (\llcorner A \lrcorner \ulcorner \phi (\varepsilon \{A\ b\}\ \varepsilon \{A\ c\}) \urcorner \llcorner f \lrcorner \ulcorner \phi (f\{b\}f\{c\}) \urcorner) \urcorner$

(A') $\phi (\llcorner A \lrcorner \ulcorner \phi (\varepsilon \{A\ \Lambda\}\ \varepsilon \{A \sim (V)\}) \urcorner \llcorner f \lrcorner \ulcorner \phi (f\{\Lambda\}f\{ \sim (V)\}) \urcorner)$

$$[A: \Lambda/b; \sim (V)/c]$$

(B) $\llcorner hk \lrcorner \ulcorner \phi (\llcorner Ab \lrcorner \ulcorner \phi (\varepsilon \{A\ h(b)\}\ \varepsilon \{A\ k(b)\}) \urcorner \llcorner f \lrcorner \ulcorner \phi (f(h)f(k)) \urcorner) \urcorner$

(B') $\llcorner k \lrcorner \ulcorner \phi (\llcorner Ab \lrcorner \ulcorner \phi (\varepsilon \{A \sim (b)\}\ \varepsilon \{A\ k(b)\}) \urcorner \llcorner f \lrcorner \ulcorner \phi (f(\sim)f(k)) \urcorner) \urcorner$

$$[B: \sim /h]$$

All definitions in canonic language L being explicit and complete, nominative definitions and extensionality theses together make nominatively defined constants eliminable from any propositional context, in favor of constants in terms of which these are defined, in essentially the way already explained (in IL above) for propositively defined constants.

7.4 Final directives for this system of logic (§ 7.0)

The last two *directives for nominative definitions and theses of extensionality,* peculiar to ontology as distinguished from its effective protothetical basis, (§ 7.3) can now be formulated and incorporated in the following prescription of the complete directives for this system of logic:

Suppose that individual A is the last thesis actually subjoined to this system of ontology inclusive of protothetic; (§ 7.0) then expression B may be asserted and subjoined as a new thesis of this system of logic if and only if either at least one of the five conditions enumerated in § 7.2 above or one of the following two conditions is fulfilled:

(6) *Individual B is legitimate as nominative definition immediately after thesis A of this system of ontology.*

(7) *Individual B is legitimate as nominative thesis of extensionality immediately after thesis A of this system of ontology.*

8. PRINCIPLES OF LESNIEWSKI'S IDEOGRAPHIC NOTATION (§ 3.8)

The principles of notational correspondence characterizing Lesniewski's ideographic notation for constant connectors of propositional arguments depend only on basic outlines (not on numerical indices that may be added to distinguish between differently defined but logically equivalent constants, and that therefore do not affect the logical force of such a constant. *Ideographic* connectors in language L, like those named on p. 232 above, as distinguished from nonideographic connectors such as are suggested by S55–S67 on pp. 230–231, are supposed to be constant terms formed according to the principles explained in § 8 below, wherein for brevity 'connector' is to abbreviate 'ideographic constant connector in canonic language L'.). The basic outline of any singulary connector consists of a horizontal dash '—', to either end of which may be attached a vertical stroke as indicator, and hence has one of the following four forms: ⊣, ⊢, ⊢⊣, —. (See D3–D6 in XLIV of § 7.1 above.) The basic outline of any binary connector consists of a hub 'o', from which spokes may radiate rightward, downward, leftward, or upward, corresponding to four points of the compass or clock, and accordingly has one of the following sixteen forms: ⚲, ⚬, ⚲, ⚲, ⚲, ⚲, ⚬, ⚬, ⚬, ⚲, ⚲, ⚲, ⚲, ⚲, ⚲. (See Axiom AP in § 6.2.2 and D7–D21 in XLIV.) A vertical stroke occurs at left (resp. right) of a singulary connector if and only if, as that stroke indicates, the corresponding connection is true if its argument is false (resp. true). A spoke points right (resp. down, left, up) from the hub of a binary connector if and only if, as that spoke indicates, the corresponding connection is true if its antecedent and consequent are respectively false and true (resp. both true, true and false, both false).

Now let the value matrices for singulary and binary connectors be arranged as follows, strokes or spokes indicating truth and blanks (circled '0' in the "reference" positions for arguments) indicating falsehood. Then Lesniewski's ideographic connectors "embody" and graphically represent their own logical characteristics, their indicators indicating the "true" cases in their respective matrices in a self-contained semaphore code.

The characteristic matrix embodied in each singulary connector is represented below by (a homomorph of) that connector beneath the heading at top left. The two possible values for the single argument are represented in this heading, and the corresponding connection is named and verbally characterized below at right:

0—1 *Corresponding Connection of One Argument* (See D3–D6 in XLIV of § 7.1 above.)

⊣ *Affirmation:* true if and only if its argument is true, always having the same value as its argument.

⊢ *Negation:* true if and only if its argument is false, always having the opposite value.

⊢—⊣ *Tautologous connection of one argument:* tautologous (i.e., "logically true"),[47] whether its argument is true or false.

— *Contradictory connection of one argument:* contradictory (i.e., "logically false"), whether its argument is true or false.

The characteristic matrix embodied in each binary connector is represented below by (a homomorph of) that connector beneath the matrix outline. This outline is given in the form of a dial representing the four possible combinations of values for the two arguments— three (resp. six, nine, twelve) o'clock representing the combination false-true (resp. true-true, true-false, false-false). The dial may in imagination be translated downward and centered in the hub of each of the expressions beneath in turn, so that the spokes radiating outward indicate the "true" cases of the corresponding connection like pointers on a dial. Again this connection is named and verbally characterized at right:

Corresponding Connection of Two Arguments (See Axiom AP in § 6.2.2 and D7–D21 in XLIV of § 7.1 above.)
Coimplication: true if and only if its arguments have the same value, both being true or both false, and so coimply each other.

Disjunction: true if and only if its arguments are disjunctive, exactly (i.e., at least and at most) one being true, the other false.

Conjunction: true if and only if its arguments are conjointly true.

Exclusion: true if and only if at most one of its arguments is true, excluding the other, which is false.

Conegation: true if and only if each of its arguments is false, logically having the force of a conjunction of their negations.

Tautologous connection (of two arguments): tautologous (i.e., "logically true")[47] regardless of the values of its arguments.

Contradictory connection (of two arguments): contradictory (i.e., "logically false") regardless of the values of its arguments.

Distinction: true if and only if its antecedent is true, in distinction from its consequent, which is false.

Contradistinction: true if and only if its antecedent is false, in contradistinction to its consequent, which is true.

Implication: true if and only if its consequent is true if its antecedent is true, the antecedent implying the consequent; i.e., true if and only if either its antecedent is false or its consequent true; false if and only if its antecedent is true and its consequent false.

Counterimplication: true if and only if its antecedent is true if its consequent is true, its antecedent (conversely) being implied by its consequent.

Alternation: true if and only if at least one of its arguments is true, either one or alternatively the other or both.

Antecedent affirmation: true if and only if its antecedent is true, whether its consequent is true or false, logically having the force of an affirmation of its antecedent.

Consequent affirmation: true if and only if its consequent is true, whether its antecedent is true or false, logically having the force of an affirmation of its consequent.

Antecedent negation: true if and only if its antecedent is false, whether its consequent is true or false, logically having the force of a negation of its antecedent.

Consequent negation: true if and only if its consequent is false, whether its antecedent is true or false, logically having the force of a negation of its consequent.

So the logical characteristics and interrelations of such connections are reflected in their notational characteristics and interrelations, and can be inferred from the basic outlines of their connectors according to the following principles of notational correspondence:

(1) Any connector logically contains another of the same degree if and only if notationally it contains (the basic outline of) the other, having an indicator wherever the other has one, so that, super-imposed, it would completely cover the basic outline of the other. (For example, '⊢' contains '⊢' and '⊸'; '⊸' contains '⊸', '⊸', and '⊸'. See D24, D26, and S68 of XLIV in § 7.1 above.)

(2) Any connectors of the same degree logically are equivalent, having the same force and containing each other, if and only if notationally they are equiform (in basic outline, indices excepted), having the same basic outline and notationally containing each other. Examples: '—' and '—'; '⊸' and '⊸'. See D25, D27, and S69 of XLIV above.)

(3) Any connectors of the same degree logically are complemen-tary, each having the force of a "logical complement" (i.e., negation) of the other, if and only if notationally they are complementary, each having an indicator in only any indicator position where the other has none, indicators corresponding to blanks and blanks to indicators. (For example, '⊣' and '⊢' are complementary, as are '⊸' and '⊸'. See D29, D32, and S60 of XLIV above.)

(4) Any connector logically is equivalent to a "logical sum" or "union" (i.e., alternation) of two or more others of the same degree if and only if notationally (the basic outline of) the first is equiform to a sum or union of (the basic outlines of) the others—i.e., to what the latter, superimposed, would unite to form—, having an indi-cator only wherever at least one of the others has an indicator. (For example, '⊢⊣' is a union of '⊢' and '⊣'; '⊸', of '⊸' and '⊸', or of '⊸', '⊸', and '⊸'. See S56, S65, and S66 of XLIV above.)

(5) Any connector logically is equivalent to a "logical product" or "intersection" (i.e., conjunction) of two or more others of the same degree if and only if notationally (the basic outline of) the first is equiform to a product or intersection of (the basic outlines of) the others—i.e., to what the latter, superimposed, would have in com-mon and intersect to produce—, having an indicator only wherever each of the others has an indicator. (For example, '—' is an inter-section of '⊢' and '⊣'; '⊸', of '⊸' and '⊸'. See S55, S63, and S64 of XLIV above.)

The following principles also hold, though Lesniewski does not mention them in his publications:

(6) Any binary connectors logically are converse, each having the force of a converse of the other, if and only if notationally they are *converse*, each having an indicator 180° opposite only any indicator of the other with respect to a y-axis (i.e., vertical through its hub in its own plane), so that the basic outline of each is equiform to that of the other *converted* by 180° rotation around such an axis. (For example, ' ǫ ' and ' ǫ ' are converse, as are ' б ' and ' б '. See D34 of XLIV above.) Consequently (6a) any binary connector logically is *symmetrical with respect to conversion*, being equivalent to its own converse, if and only if notationally its basic outline is symmetrical with respect to such an axis and, being equiform to its own mirror reflection, is unaltered by such a conversion. In other words, the logical force of any connection of two arguments is not altered by reversing the order of its arguments if and only if the basic outline of its connector is not altered by reversal. (For example, ' б ' and ' б ' are thus symmetrical. See D37 of XLIV above.)

(7) Any binary connector logically is *intraverse* (resp. *contraverse*) to another, being equivalent to an *intraverse* (resp. *contraverse*) of the other, if and only if notationally the first is *intraverse* (resp. *contraverse*) to the other, having an indicator 90° clockwise (resp. counterclockwise) from only any indicator of the other with respect to a z-axis (i.e., perpendicular through its hub to its own plane), so that its basic outline is equiform to that of the other *intraverted* (resp. *contraverted*) by 90° rotation clockwise (resp. counterclockwise) around such an axis. (For example, ' б ' is intraverse to ' б '; ' б ' is contraverse to ' б '; ' ǫ ' is both intraverse to and contraverse to ' ǫ '. See D35 and D36 of XLIV above.)

Except for the supplementary remark about propositional constants, the following are corollaries of principles already stated:

(8) Any connectors of the same degree logically are *inverse*, each being equivalent to an *inverse* of the other, if and only if notationally they are *inverse*, each having an indicator 180° opposite only any indicator of the other with respect to a z-axis perpendicular through its hub to its own plane, so that its basic outline is equiform to that of the other *inverted* by 180° rotation around such an axis. (For

example, '⊢' is an inverse of '⊣'; '⊶' of '⊷'; '⊸' of '⊹'. See D28, D31, and S61 of XLIV.) This principle holds also for propositional constants (as "degenerate connectors" of degree zero) in the following form: Propositional constants are *inverse* in the sense that each has the force of a negation of the other if and only if notationally they are inverse, in that the basic outline of each is equiform to that of the other inverted. (For example, '∧' is an inverse of 'V'.) Consequently (8a) any connector is *symmetrical with respect to inversion*, being equivalent to its own inverse, if and only if notationally its basic outline, being symmetrical with respect to such a z-axis, is unaltered by such an inversion. In other words, the force of any connection is not logically altered by negating each of its arguments if and only if the basic outline of its connector is not altered by inversion with respect to such an axis. (Examples: '⊸'; '⊹'; '○'. See D38 and S70 of XLIV above.) Also (8b) connection C logically is equivalent to a connection the basic outline of whose connector is equiform to that of the connector of C, and whose antecedent and consequent are negations of homomorphs, respectively, of the consequent and antecedent of C, if and only if the basic outline of the connector of C notationally is symmetrical with respect to an x-axis horizontal through its hub in its plane. In other words, the force of any connection is not logically altered by interchanging and negating its two arguments if and only if the basic outline of its connector is not altered by rotating it 180° around such an axis. (Examples: ⊹ ; ⊹ ; ⊶; ○; ⊹.)

(9) Any connectors of the same degree logically are *dual*, each having the force of a *dual* (i.e., complement of an inverse, or vice versa) of the other, if and only if notationally they are *dual*, each being a notational complement of an inverse (or vice versa) of the other, obtainable from it by inversion and complementation, combined in either order, and having a blank 180° opposite only any indicator of the other with respect to a z-axis perpendicular through its center to its own plane. (Examples: '⊸' and '⊢⊣'; '⊢' and '⊢'; '⊷' and '⊹'; '⊹' and '⊹'. See D30, D33, and S62 in XLIV.)

(10) Any connection logically is tautologous, being true whatever the values of its arguments, and its connector is a *tautologous* or "universal" *connector*, if and only if the connector has all possible

indicators. (Examples: '⊢⁊⊣'; ' ⟡'. See D40, D42, and S71 of XLIV above.) Any connection logically is contradictory, being false whatever the values of its arguments, and its connector is a *contradictory* or "empty" *connector*, if and only if the connector has no indicator. (Examples: '——'; '○'. See D41, D43, and S72 of XLIV above.) Hence any connection logically is "stable", in the sense that the corresponding connection, being tautologous or contradictory, has a value independent of the order and values of its arguments, if and only if its connector has a maximal or minimal number of indicators.

In the familiar manner of speaking subjunctively about individual expressions in terms of their forms in abstraction from their occurrences, these ideographic principles can be loosely epitomized and extended as follows:

(1′) To obtain connections containing (resp. contained in) any connection, add to (resp. delete from) its connector *zero* or more indicators; and to obtain stronger (resp. weaker) connections, entailing (resp. being entailed by) it but not conversely, delete from (resp. add to) its connector *one* or more indicators.

(2′) To obtain a logical equivalent of any connection, simply delete from its connector any index added to differentiate it from logically equivalent but differently defined connectors, or change its index to that of some such connector.

(3′) To obtain a logical equivalent of any negation of connection C, delete the initial negator (together with the attendant brackets) and then notationally complement the connector of C by interchanging blanks and indicators in only all its indicator positions. Or conversely, to obtain a logical equivalent of any connection, notationally complement its connector and then negate the result.

(4′, resp. 5′) To obtain a logical equivalent of any alternation (resp. conjunction) of connections that all have the "same" argument sequence, connect the "same" arguments in the same order instead by a single notational union (resp. intersection) of the connectors of those connections, having an indicator in only any indicator position where at least one (resp. each) of those connectors has an indicator. Or conversely, to obtain a logical equivalent of any connection C, alternate (resp. conjoin) connections which all have the "same" argument sequence as C and whose connectors, superimposed, would unite (resp. intersect) to form the connector of C.

(6′) To obtain a logical equivalent of any connection of two arguments, reverse both its connector and the order of its arguments; i.e., interchange its antecedent and consequent, and convert its connector by 180° rotation around a y-axis vertical through its hub in its own plane (if the basic outline of the connector is alterable by such conversion).

(7′) To obtain another logical equivalent of any connection of two arguments, negate—or delete any negator (and the attendant brackets) of—its antecedent (resp. consequent), interchange the resulting arguments, and intravert (resp. contravert) its connector by 90° rotation clockwise (resp. counterclockwise) around a z-axis perpendicular through its hub to its own plane.

Intraversion and contraversion are "inverse" operations in the familiar mathematical sense that each undoes the other; and either conversion or inversion (in the sense, relevant here, of 180° rotation) is its own "inverse", in that its two-fold application leaves the original basic outline unchanged.

The following short-cuts yield the same results as combinations or successive applications of operations already mentioned:

(8′) To obtain a logical equivalent of any connection of two arguments, negate—or delete any negator (and the attendant brackets) of—each argument, and invert its connector by 180° rotation around a z-axis through its hub perpendicular to its own plane (if the basic outline of the connector is alterable by such inversion). To obtain a logical equivalent of any standard tautology 'V' or contradiction 'Λ', simply invert the constant itself and negate the result. To obtain a logical equivalent of any connection of two arguments the basic outline of whose connector is symmetrical with respect to an x-axis horizontal through its hub in its plane, interchange and negate—or delete any negator (and the attendant brackets) of—its antecedent and its consequent.

(9′) To obtain a logical equivalent of any connection of two arguments, negate—or delete any negator (and the attendant brackets) of—each argument, dualize (by notationally complementing the result of inverting) its connector, and then negate the result. Or conversely, to obtain a logical equivalent of any negation of a connection C of two arguments, negate—or delete the negator (and the attendant brackets) of—each argument of C, and then connect the resulting arguments instead by a dual connector (obtained by notationally complementing the result of inverting the connector of C, or vice versa).

(10′) To obtain a logical equivalent of any connection whose connector has all possible or no indicators, and so is respectively tautologous or contradictory, permute or negate its arguments at will, or replace it by any other tautology or contradiction, respectively.

Clearly, other connections may first be translated (in imagination or on paper) into logical equivalents expressed in terms of negation, alternation, or conjunction, and then transformed by means of operations already described. So, to obtain a logical equivalent of any conegation (resp. dyadic exclusion) of connections that all have the "same" argument sequence, simply perform the same operations as for an alternation (resp. conjunction) of such connections, and then notationally complement the connector of the result. To obtain a logical equivalent of any implication (resp. counterimplication) whose antecedent and consequent are connections having the "same" argument sequence, negate—or notationally complement the connector of—the antecedent (resp. consequent), and then perform the same operations as for an alternation of such connections. And to obtain a logical equivalent of any distinction (resp. contradistinction) whose antecedent and consequent are connections having the "same" argument sequence, negate—or notationally complement the connector of—the consequent (resp. antecedent), and then perform the same operations as for a conjunction of such connections. More explicitly—

To obtain a logical equivalent of any conjunction (resp. alternation, dyadic exclusion, conegation, disjunction, coimplication) of connections that all have the "same" argument sequence, connect the "same" arguments in the same order by a connector having an indicator in only any indicator position where the connector of each (resp. at least one, not each, none, just one, none or each) of those connections has an indicator.

To obtain a logical equivalent of any (dyadic) implication (resp. counterimplication) C whose antecedent and consequent are connections having the "same" argument sequence, connect the "same" arguments in the same order by a connector having an indicator in only any indicator position where the connector of the antecedent (resp. consequent) has a blank or the connector of the other argument of C has an indicator.

To obtain a logical equivalent of any distinction (resp. contradistinction) C whose antecedent and consequent are connections having the "same" argument sequence, connect the "same" arguments in the same order by a connector having an indicator in only any indicator position where the connector of the antecedent (resp. consequent) has an indicator and the connector of the other argument of C has a blank.

Other connections pose no problem: Any affirmation logically is equivalent to its own argument; any propositional phrase, to the negation of its negation; any antecedent or consequent affirmation (resp. negation), to an affirmation (resp. negation) of its own antecedent or consequent, respectively; any tautologous (resp. contradictory) connection, to any tautology (resp. contradiction); and any negation of a tautology (resp. contradiction) to any contradiction (resp. tautology).

As explained so far, these principles and operations can be applied only to connections having the "same" sequence of one or of two arguments. But Standley[38] devised a method of extending ideographic principles to connectors of any degree, by expressing arbitrary propositional phrases as connections having the "same" argument sequence, in order to solve problems involving connections of more than two arguments—a method analogous to that of replacing integers by fractions, and expressing fractions in terms of the least common denominator, in order to solve arithmetical problems in rational number theory.

For any connection of n arguments there are 2^n disjunctive (i.e., alternative, mutually exclusive) "possible cases", represented by rows in its characteristic value matrix or "truth table", or by alternants of a full normal form or Boolean expansion of a tautologous connection of n arguments. Therefore any ideographic connector of degree n should have 2^n corresponding positions for indicators or blanks, and any ideographic connection C should have some *simple* notational relation to any logically equivalent "degenerate" connection having additional arguments appended to "the" argument sequence of C. Now any affirmation (resp. negation) or tautologous (resp. contradictory) connection of one argument is logically equivalent, respectively, to any antecedent affirmation (resp. negation) or tautologous (resp. contradictory) connection whose antecedent is equiform to that argument. So a generalized ideographic notation for connectors of any degree *might* be based on and extended from Lesniewski's notation for singulary connectors. But the only singulary connector in continual use is the negator, as contrasted with the many commonly used binary connectors. And, as just mentioned, for every simple propositional phrase or connection of one argument there is a logically equivalent degenerate connection of two arguments. So it is more expedient to generalize Lesniewski's notation for binary connectors, instead, as follows.

Just as there are 2^n alternative "possible cases" for connections of n arguments, there are 2^{2^n} "possible values" for connectors of degree n. Now Lesniewski's ideographic notation for singulary and binary connectors has already been explained. And any connection of n + 1 arguments is logically equivalent to an alternative Boolean expansion developed according to scheme A below, wherein the 'F' and 'G' represent appropriate ideographic connectors of degree n (see S56 of XLIV in § 7.1 above):

(A) $\Rightarrow\!\Big(\wr\big(F(p_1\ldots p_n)\,p_{n+1}\big)\multimap\big(G(p_1\ldots p_n)\,p_{n+1}\big)\Big)$

(A') $FG(p_1\ldots p_np_{n+1})$

(B) $\Rightarrow\!\Big(\wr\big(F(pq)r\big)\multimap\big(G(pq)r\big)\Big)$

(B') $FG(pqr)$

(C) $\Rightarrow\!\Big(\wr\big(FG(pqr)s\big)\multimap\big(HI(pqr)s\big)\Big)$

(C') $FGHI(pqrs)$

(C") $\Rightarrow\!\Big(\wr\big(F(pq)\,\wr(rs)\big)\,\wr\big(G(pq)\,\multimap(rs)\big)\,\wr\big(H(pq)\multimap(rs)\big)$
        $\wr\big(I(pq)\,\delta\,(rs)\big)\Big)$

So the corresponding ideographic connection will accordingly be represented by the scheme A′, wherein 'FG' represents the concatenation of signs having the same basic outlines, respectively, as the ideographic connectors of degree n represented by the 'F' and the 'G' in scheme A, which concatenation is to be defined as the thus corresponding ideographic connector of degree n + 1. For example, the ideographic connection of three arguments logically equivalent to the alternative normal form represented by scheme B is accordingly represented by scheme B′; and the ideographic connection of four arguments logically equivalent to the alternative normal form represented by scheme C, which develops as represented by the scheme C″, is represented by scheme C′; and so on.

Observance of these ideographic principles leads, for example, to the illustrative equivalences indicated as follows (see S59 of XLIV):

$\llcorner$P$_1$P$_2$P$_3$P$_4\lrcorner$ $\ulcorner\phi\left(\text{p}_1 \dashv (\text{p}_1) \, \wp (\text{p}_1\text{p}_2) \, \wp\wp (\text{p}_1\text{p}_2\text{p}_3) \, \wp\wp\wp\wp (\text{p}_1\text{p}_2\text{p}_3\text{p}_4)\right)\urcorner$

$\llcorner$P$_1$P$_2$P$_3$P$_4\lrcorner$ $\ulcorner\phi\left(\; \vdash (\text{p}_1) \, \Diamond(\text{p}_1\text{p}_2) \, \Diamond\Diamond(\text{p}_1\text{p}_2\text{p}_3) \, \Diamond\Diamond\Diamond\Diamond(\text{p}_1\text{p}_2\text{p}_3\text{p}_4)\right)\urcorner$

$\llcorner$P$_1$P$_2$P$_3$P$_4\lrcorner$ $\ulcorner\phi\left(\; \vdash\dashv (\text{p}_1) \, \Diamond(\text{p}_1\text{p}_2) \, \Diamond\Diamond(\text{p}_1\text{p}_2\text{p}_3) \, \Diamond\Diamond\Diamond\Diamond(\text{p}_1\text{p}_2\text{p}_3\text{p}_4)\right)\urcorner$

$\llcorner$P$_1$P$_2$P$_3$P$_4\lrcorner$ $\ulcorner\phi\left(\; - (\text{p}_1) \, \circ(\text{p}_1\text{p}_2) \, \circ\circ(\text{p}_1\text{p}_2\text{p}_3) \; \circ\circ\circ\circ(\text{p}_1\text{p}_2\text{p}_3\text{p}_4)\right)\urcorner$

$\llcorner$P$_1$P$_2$P$_3$P$_4\lrcorner$ $\ulcorner\phi\left(\text{p}_2 \dashv (\text{p}_2) \, \wp(\text{p}_1\text{p}_2) \, \wp\wp(\text{p}_1\text{p}_2\text{p}_3) \, \wp\wp\wp\wp(\text{p}_1\text{p}_2\text{p}_3\text{p}_4)\right)\urcorner$

$\llcorner$P$_1$P$_2$P$_3$P$_4\lrcorner$ $\ulcorner\phi\left(\; \vdash (\text{p}_2) \, \Diamond(\text{p}_1\text{p}_2) \, \Diamond\Diamond (\text{p}_1\text{p}_2\text{p}_3) \, \Diamond\Diamond\Diamond\Diamond (\text{p}_1\text{p}_2\text{p}_3\text{p}_4)\right)\urcorner$

$\llcorner$P$_1$P$_2$P$_3$P$_4\lrcorner$ $\ulcorner\phi\left(\text{p}_3 \dashv (\text{p}_3) \qquad\qquad \Diamond\circ(\text{p}_1\text{p}_2\text{p}_3) \, \Diamond\circ\Diamond\circ(\text{p}_1\text{p}_2\text{p}_3\text{p}_4)\right)\urcorner$

$\llcorner$P$_1$P$_2$P$_3$P$_4\lrcorner$ $\ulcorner\phi\left(\; \vdash (\text{p}_3) \qquad\qquad \circ\Diamond(\text{p}_1\text{p}_2\text{p}_3) \, \circ\Diamond\circ\Diamond(\text{p}_1\text{p}_2\text{p}_3\text{p}_4)\right)\urcorner$

$\llcorner$P$_1$P$_2$P$_3$P$_4\lrcorner$ $\ulcorner\phi\left(\text{p}_4 \dashv (\text{p}_4) \qquad\qquad\qquad \Diamond\Diamond\circ\circ(\text{p}_1\text{p}_2\text{p}_3\text{p}_4)\right)\urcorner$

$\llcorner$P$_1$P$_2$P$_3$P$_4\lrcorner$ $\ulcorner\phi\left(\; \vdash (\text{p}_4) \qquad\qquad\qquad\; \circ\circ\Diamond\Diamond(\text{p}_1\text{p}_2\text{p}_3\text{p}_4)\right)\urcorner$

The general principles exemplified by the equivalences indicated above can be summed up as follows: The 2^n indicator positions of any connector of degree n, for n not less than two, are those filled by indicators in a tautologous connector of degree n, whose own basic outline is that of a concatenation of 2^{n-2} signs each having the basic outline of a tautologous binary connector. So the basic outline of any tautologous connector of degree n + 1 is formed by simply doubling the basic outline of a tautologous connector of degree n. For example, the basic outline of a tautologous ternary connector is of form '◇ ◇', and that of a tautologous quaternary connector is of form '◇ ◇ ◇'. And in general, when a degenerate connection of n + 1 arguments is logically equivalent to a connection C of respective homomorphs of its first n arguments in the same sequence, the basic outline of the degenerate connector of degree n + 1 is formed by simply doubling the basic outline of the n-ary connector of the logically equivalent connection C of n arguments. So, in order to translate propositional elements of a problem into connections which have the same argument sequence, and to which ideographic principles can be applied, any propositional phrase logically equivalent to a connection of two arguments, represented by the scheme '$F(p_1 p_2)$', may be replaced by a logically equivalent degenerate connection, of yet more arguments, represented by the scheme

'$FF(p_1 p_2 p_3)$', '$FFFF(p_1 p_2 p_3 p_4)$', '$FFFFFFFF(p_1 p_2 p_3 p_4 p_5)$',....,

or (schematically)

'$FF\ldots F(p_1 p_2 \ldots p_n)$' with 2^{n-2} 'F's.

For example 'p_1', being logically equivalent to '$\dashv(p_1)$' and hence to '$\triangledown(p_1 p_2)$', may be translated into the logically equivalent

'$\triangledown\ \triangledown(p_1 p_2 p_3)$', '$\triangledown\ \triangledown\ \triangledown\ \triangledown(p_1 p_2 p_3 p_4)$',
'$\triangledown\ \triangledown\ \triangledown\ \triangledown\ \triangledown\ \triangledown\ \triangledown\ \triangledown(p_1 p_2 p_3 p_4 p_5)$',....,

or (schematically)

'$\triangledown\underset{2^{n-2}}{\ldots}\triangledown(p_1 \ldots p_n)$',

wherein the exponent under the dots of ellipsis indicates the number of 'φ's. Similarly 'p_2', being logically equivalent to '$\dashv(p_2)$' and hence to '$\varphi(p_1 p_2)$', may be translated into the logically equivalent

$$\text{'}\varphi\,\varphi(p_1 p_2 p_3)\text{'}, \quad \text{'}\varphi\,\varphi\,\varphi\,\varphi(p_1 p_2 p_3 p_4)\text{'}, \quad \varphi \cdot;\cdot \varphi(p_1 p_2 p_3 p_4 p_5)\text{'}, \ldots,$$

or (schematically)

$$\text{'}\varphi\underset{2n-2}{\cdots}\varphi(p_1 \cdots p_n)\text{'}.$$

And in general, for every n greater then two, any propositional phrase is logically equivalent to, and so replaceable by, a connection of whose n arguments it is the last, and of whose ideographic connector the basic outline is a concatenation of 2^{n-3} basic outlines of a tautologous binary connector followed by the same number of basic outlines of a contradictory binary connector. For example, 'p_3' is logically equivalent to

$$\text{'}\diamondsuit\circ(p_1 p_2 p_3)\text{'},$$

and hence to

$$\text{'}\diamondsuit\circ\diamondsuit\circ(p_1 p_2 p_3 p_4)\text{'}, \quad \text{'}\diamondsuit\circ\diamondsuit\circ\diamondsuit\circ\diamondsuit\circ(p_1 p_2 p_3 p_4 p_5)\text{'}, \text{ etc.};$$

'p_4' is logically equivalent to

$$\text{'}\diamondsuit\,\diamondsuit\circ\circ(p_1 p_2 p_3 p_4)\text{'},$$

and hence to

$$\text{'}\diamondsuit\,\diamondsuit\circ\circ\diamondsuit\,\diamondsuit\circ\circ(p_1 p_2 p_3 p_4 p_5)\text{'}, \text{ etc.;}\ldots;$$

and 'p_n' is logically equivalent (schematically) to

$$\text{'}\diamondsuit\underset{2n-3}{\cdots}\diamondsuit\circ\underset{2n-3}{\cdots}\circ(p_1 \cdots p_n)\text{'}.$$

All the ideographic principles and operations already explained, except those of conversion, intraversion, and contraversion, can be generalized and extended from binary connectors to connectors of degree greater than two, simply by applying these familiar principles and operations consecutively to every sign in such connectors that has the basic outline of a binary connector. The generalization of the exceptions mentioned is simply this: To obtain a logical equivalent of any connection of two or more arguments, apply the familiar principles and operations of conversion, intraversion, or contraversion to its *first* two arguments and to every sign in its connector that has the basic outline of a binary connector. The following extension of inversion was called to my attention by Owen F. Herring: To obtain a logical equivalent of any connection, rotate the *entire* connector 180° around a z-axis perpendicular to its own plane and negate each argument of the connection.

Generalized in this way, Lesniewski's ideographic notation facilitates familiar combinatorial decision procedures, such as Boolean expansion or reduction to normal form, by making it possible to carry out expansions or reductions by simple, general, mechanical rules for rotation and transformation, without using special tables of truth-value analysis, since the connectors embody and take the place of their own matrices. For instance, the first (homomorph of an) implication below (corresponding to an example from Quine, *1959*, p.31) can be reduced to the simpler logical equivalent 'p' as follows:

$$\diamond\!\left(\diamond\!\left(\diamond\!\left(\diamond\!\left(\diamond(pq)\,\diamond(p \vdash (q))\right)\diamond(\vdash (p)q)\right)q\right)\diamond\!\left(\diamond(pr)\,\diamond(p \vdash (r))\right)\right)$$

$$\text{,, ,, ,, ,, ,, ,,}\ \ \diamond(qp))\qquad \multimap(qp)\Big)\qquad \text{,, ,, ,, ,,}\ \ \multimap(rp))\Big)$$

$$\text{,, ,, ,,}\ \ \diamond\!\left(\diamond(pq)\,\diamond(pq)\right)\qquad \multimap(pq)\Big)\qquad \text{,,}\ \ \diamond\!\left(\diamond(pr)\,\multimap(pr)\right)\Big)$$

$$\text{,, ,,}\ \ \diamond\!\left(\diamond(pq)\right)\qquad\qquad \multimap(pq))\qquad \text{,,}\ \ \diamond(pr)\Big)$$

$$\text{,,}\ \ \diamond\!\left(\diamond(pq)\right)\qquad\qquad\qquad \diamond(pq))\quad p\Big)\Big)$$

$$\diamond\!\left(\diamond(pq)\right)\qquad\qquad\qquad\qquad \diamond(pq))$$

$$\diamond(pq)$$

$$p$$

Similarly, the following (homomorph of an) implication (corresponding to an example from Quine, *1959*, p. 27) can be reduced to the simpler logical equivalent ' � (qr)':

$$\phi\left(\gamma\left(\varrho(p \qquad\qquad q)\,\varrho\,(\vdash (p) \qquad \vdash(r))\right)\ \phi(qr)\right)$$

,,   ,, $\varrho\left(\phi\circ(qrp)\,\gamma\gamma(qrp)\right)\,\varrho\left(\circ\phi(qrp)\,\lambda\lambda(qrp)\right)$,,   ,,

,, $\gamma\left(\varrho\circ(qrp) \qquad\qquad \circ\lambda(qrp)\right)$,,

$\phi\left(\varrho\lambda(qrp) \qquad\qquad\qquad\qquad \phi\phi(qrp)\right)$

$\phi\phi(qrp)$

$\phi(qr)$

Analogously, any tautologous connection can be reduced to a standard tautology; and its negation, or any other contradictory connection, to a standard contradiction.

In practice such transformations can be telescoped by omitting steps performed mentally; by omitting argument sequences from intermediate steps, but carrying them in mind, when they are the same throughout; by working toward whatever common argument sequence seems most expedient; by using a columnar arrangement of kind explained by Standley; and by exploiting whatever other expedients suggest themselves ad hoc. The ideographic operations already explained can be expedited, in particular, by short cuts or reductions based on the following principles, which are useful in the combinatorial decision procedure based upon case analysis[37] and axiomatized in protothetic as a method of proof. (§ 3.6) In what follows, names of connectors and connections are used as generalized (in T.E. XLIV of § 7.1 above) for any finite number of arguments, and replacement is supposed to accord with rules of logical syntax and consequently yield well-formed, propositional results.

Any alternation having a contradictory argument is "replaceable

by an alternation of the one or more remaining arguments"; i.e.,
is logically equivalent either to (a "degenerate alternation" consisting of) a propositional homomorph of the one remaining argument or to an alternation of homomorphs respectively of the two
or more remaining arguments. Any implication of whose three or
more arguments the first is contradictory or the last tautologous is
"replaceable by an implication of the two or more remaining arguments"; i.e., is logically equivalent to any implication of homomorphs respectively of the remaining arguments, taken in the same
order. Any conjunction or coimplication having a tautologous argument or implication having a tautologous first argument is "replaceable by a conjunction of the one or more remaining arguments";
i.e., is logically equivalent either to (a "degenerate conjunction"
consisting of) the one remaining argument or to a conjunction of
homomorphs respectively of the two or more remaining arguments.
Any disjunction or exclusion having a tautologous argument, conegation or coimplication having a contradictory argument, or implication having a contradictory last argument is "replaceable by a
conegation of the one or more remaining arguments"; i.e., is logically
equivalent either to a ("degenerate co-") negation of a homomorph
of the one remaining argument or to a conegation of homomorphs
respectively of the two or more remaining arguments. Any disjunction of whose arguments all but one are contradictory is logically
equivalent to, and so is replaceable by, the remaining argument.
Any alternation having a tautologous argument, conegation having
exclusively contradictory arguments, implication or coimplication
having exclusively tautologous or exclusively contradictory arguments, or conjunction having exclusively tautologous arguments is
logically equivalent to, and so is replaceable by, any tautology.
Any conjunction having a contradictory argument, conegation
having a tautologous argument, exclusion or disjunction having
more than one tautologous argument, or alternation having exclusively contradictory arguments is logically equivalent to, and
so is replaceable by, any contradiction.

9. NOTES

1. For information supplementing published sources I am indebted to three of Lesniewski's Warsaw associates: Dr. T. Kotarbinski; Dr. C. Lejewski, now of the University of Manchester; and Dr. B. Sobocinski, now of the University of Notre Dame. Dr. Kotarbinski and Dr. Lejewski read an earlier draft of this book and made numerous helpful comments, criticisms, and suggestions. I appreciate especially the interest Dr. Lejewski has long taken in my study of Lesniewski, and the kindness he has repeatedly shown in discussing it with me. I am grateful also to Arthur N. Prior and Michael Dummett, who read the earlier draft and asked questions pointing to flaws in my exposition; and to my wife, who assumed the burden of typing, took pains to detect ambiguous or awkward wording, and persuaded me to break certain sentences into paragraphs. Finally, I wish to express my thanks to Dr. E. W. Beth and to the North-Holland Publishing Company, particularly to Mr. L. Bauer.

2. Frege, *1893*, Introduction, p. 4, and *1903*, § 98. In connection with such examples as Chwistek's remarks about "classes" (§ 3.10) or Rosser's about "numbers", (§ 4.4) see Lesniewski, OM, *1927*, § 1; Dummett[13] on Frege; and Carnap, 1937, § 41, § 42, § 60a (p. 213), and § 68 (p. 249). See also Tarski, *1933* (or *1936*), § 1, in connection with § 3.4.0 above; Russell, *1956*, pp. 185, 331, 380–381; and Quine, *1951*, §§ 4–6, and *1953*, ch. 8.

3. See Lesniewski, *1929* (NS), § 11, esp. pp. 61, 76–77; Frege, *1903*, §§ 99–100; Russell, *1940*, pp. 23–25, 31–32, 36–38, 75–76, 86–87, 94–96, 241–242, 313, 328, 380–381, *1948*, pp. 62, 67, 250–251, 423–424, 474, *1959*, ch. 13, pp. 145–146; and Quine, *1960*, § 40, § 27 (pp. 129–132), and p. 215.

4. In reformulating Wajsberg's definition of Lesniewski's term 'organic' as applied to indicative sentences, I generalize for expressions of any semantic category in canonic language L. See Sobocinski, *1955–56*, III(c), p. 60; and Tarski, *1956*, p. 45, following Thm. 9.

5. Woodger, *1952* (BL), pt. 1; also *1951*. See too the ontological table presented in *1954* by Lejewski, who in *1957* treated names and related aspects of semantics from a similar point of view.

6. See Quine, *1960*, §§ 28–29, together with *1951*, § 12.

7. See Lesniewski, OM (*1931*), § 11, pp. 167–170; or, in English, Slupecki, *1955*, ch. 2, § 1, pp. 31–33, together with ch. 1, § 3. See also Woodger, *1951*, pp. 203–205; Prior, *1957*, together with the review by Martin in *1959;* and Quine, *1960*, § 36.

8. On the peculiarities in use of 'any', see Quine, *1960*, § 29, together with the more cursory accounts in Russell, *1908*, § 2, pp. 64–69; Rosser, *1953*, ch. 6, § 2, p. 99; Reichenbach, *1948*, §§ 20–21, esp. pp. 100–102, 105–106, 110–112; and Prior, *1955*, p. 149, n. 2.

9. See Aristotle, *Categories*, ch. 10, 13b; *On Interpretation*, ch. 7 (17b–18a), ch. 9 (18a), ch. 10 (19b–20b), ch. 12 (21), ch. 14 (24b); *Prior Analytics*, bk. 1, ch. 2 (25a), ch. 46 (51b–52a), ch. 15 (63b); and *Topics*, bk. 2, ch. 1 (109a), and bk. 3, ch. 6 (119a). See also Moody, *1953*, § 11, pp. 50–53, esp. the logical square of opposition characterizing medieval syllogistic as represented by Moody on p. 52.

10. Of course, Lesniewski's treatment of nouns in singular predication deviates from Russell's treatment of nouns as merely part of the verb (or "predicate" in the broader current sense). (§ 6.2.3) See Lejewski, *1960*, together with the following writings of Russell: *1905*. *1908*, esp. §§ 2–5, 8. *1910*, chs. 1, 2 (§ 6), 3; **14, 20–21; esp. pp. 23–33, 58–59, 67–68, 71–72, 76–84, 187, 198, 200, 204. *1918*, §§ 2, 5–9. *1919*, chs. 2, 13, 16–17, esp. pp. 12–14, 137–138, 181–187, 191–193. *1924*. *1925*, § 6, p. xxxix. *1937*, pp. v, x–xi, xiv. *1956*, pp. 81–83, 87, 89, 194, 230, 239, 253–254, 262, 265–274, 279–290, 326–331, 337–338. *1959*, chs. 6, 8, 14, esp. pp. 70, 82, 87–88, 158. See also Wittgenstein, *1922*, 6.031, together with 5.47321; Kotarbinski, *1920* and *1957*, ch. 28, § 3 and § 5, esp. pp. 182–184; Geach, *1950;* Quine, *1960*, §§ 19–25, 37–38, esp. pp. 92–93, 95–97, 99–102, 104, 118, 175; and the following writings of Carnap: *1928*, §§ 27, 33–40, 47, 50–52; *1937*, §§ 37–38, 71; *1956*, §§ 4–5, 26–27, 32 (Methods IV–V), 33–38, 45; *1954*, § 43b; *1958* (or *1954*), §§ 28c, 33–35 (esp. 34c, small type), 38.

11. Wittgenstein, *1956*, pt. I, App. II, § 1, p. 54. Cf. pt. 2, § 26, p. 77.

12. Russell, *1924*, p. 337. See also *1918*, esp. § 8, pp. 271, 279.

13. See Lesniewski, OM, § 2 (esp. pp. 183–184) and § 3. Lesniewski cited Kotarbinski, *1920*, pp. 7–11. See also Kotarbinski, *1929*, *1957* (esp. ch. 28, § 3), and *1958* (esp. the first part, 'Reizm Somatyczny'), *passim;* Wittgenstein, *1922*, 4.126–4.128, and *1956*, pt. IV, § 16, p. 142; Ryle, *1931–32* and *1938–39;* Carnap, *1937*, §§ 69–71, 74–81, together with *1950*, and *1958*, § 28c; Russell, *1925*, p. xxxix, *1946*, p. 691, and *1956*, pp. 185, 194, 230, 239, 267–269, 273–274, 334–337, and *1959*, pp. 69–70, 82, 158, 235–237; Dummett, *1955*, esp. pp. 96–97, 105 (n. 8), and *1956;* Quine, *1960*, § 56; and Hall, *1960*, chs. 1 and 2.

14. In *1958*, § 34, Carnap omits this existential requirement, and so by his definition "the null class is an equivalence class with respect to any relation whatever", as mentioned in § 37. Incidentally, his conditions of transitivity and symmetry in T34–1.c are logically redundant.

15. In *1951*, § 39, Quine omits the requirement of membership in the field, remarking that 'The practical advantage of this complication is not apparent.' So by his definition any individual is an ancestor of itself with respect to any relation whatever. I follow PM, vol. 1, § E, esp. *90 and *91, and vol. 2, *121, (informally explained by Russell in *1919*, ch. 3) except for adapting Frege's terminology for what Russell and Whitehead call the "proper ancestral". See Frege, *1879*, pp.

55–87, esp. pp. 58–62, 64, 71, 80; *1884*, §§ 79–81; and *1893*, §§ 45–46. Cf. Dedekind, *1888*, pp. 33–40.

16. At the time of Lesniewski's birth his father, a Polish engineer, was employed in constructing the trans-Siberian railroad. So, as suggested to me by Kotarbinski, who remembers that he and Lesniewski once verified that they were born in the same week, and who was himself born on 31 March 1886, I assume that the date (18 March 1886) given by Sobocinski in *1949–50* (n. 1) was recorded according to the Julian calendar used in pre-revolutionary Russia, and corresponds to 30 March 1886 according to the Gregorian calendar.

17. Lesniewski, OM, § 1; see also § 2 and § 11. Lesniewski contrasted the attitude expressed by Von Neumann in *1927*, pp. 3–5, with Frege's earlier critique of pure formalism in *1903*, §§ 86–137 (translated in *1952*, pp. 182–233), 145, and 156. Criticisms of similar ambiguities have been made by Carnap in *1937*, § 69, and *1943*, § 11, pp. 47–48; Quine in *1951*, § 5, pp. 31–33, and *1960*, § 41; and Lukasiewicz in *1957*, § 31.

18. See Lesniewski, OM, § 11; also § 2 and § 4, esp. pp. 187, 263 (n. 6), 264 (n. 2). See also Tarski, *1933*, Introduction and §§ 1–2, 6; *1936* (SS), opening pages; and *1944*, n. 7 and §§ 4, 6–8.

19. Jordan, p. 46 (n. 38).

20. The only exceptions were a proof that enabled Bochenski in 1947 to republish his study of the logic of Theophrastus; the surviving offprints of Lesniewski's first two papers (*1938*, EB and NS, § 12); and at least one review copy of Lukasiewicz, *1938*, later returned to Mme. Lukasiewicz by Professor Heinrich Scholz. After the war Sobocinski was able to reconstruct his axiomatization of the classical logic of conjunction and negation as 'Axiomatization of a conjunctive-negative calculus of propositions' in the *Journal of Computing Systems*, vol. 1 (1954), pp. 229–242; and to republish his investigations of prototethic in English in *1949*, with an introduction describing the misfortune and some of the contents of the destroyed volume.

21. The characterization that (A) only any general object representing certain individual objects has only any property common to them all entails that (B) any property of any general object representing certain individual objects is common to them all. For suppose that (1) X is general object representing objects (that are) b, (2) X is c, and (3) Y is b. Then characterization A and supposition 1 together entail that (4) for every c, X is c if and only if all b are c. It follows, by substitution and detachment on the basis of supposition 2, that (5) all b are c. And, together with an appropriate thesis (6—see below) of ontology, steps 5 and 3 entail that (7) Y is c. So, the deduction being completely general, it follows that (B) for every X, Y, b, and c, if X is general object representing objects b, X is c, and Y is b, then Y is c.

What Lesniewski demonstrated (as follows) was that the weaker characterization B, derivable (as above) from A, entails that (C') nothing is a general object representing more than one individual object. For suppose that (1, =B) if X is general object representing objects (that are) b, X is c, and Y is b, then Y is c; i.e., any general object representing objects b is c only if all b are c. Then it follows by substitution, for instance, that (2) if X is general object representing objects b, X is nonidentical with Z, and Z is b, then Z is nonidentical with Z; and (3) if X is general object representing objects b, X is identical with Z, and Y is b, then Y is identical with Z.

But, the consequent of step 2 being contradictory, it follows that (4) if X is general object representing objects b, and Z is b, then Y is identical with Z. So (5) if X is general object representing objects b, Z is b, and Y is b, then X is general object representing objects b, X is identical with Z, and Y is b. And steps 3 and 5 together entail that (6, =C) if X is general object representing objects b, Z is b, and Y is b, then Y is identical with Z. In other words, the deduction being completely general, it follows that (C′) for every b, if there are at least two b, then there is no "general object" representing objects b.

I add that, since no general object can thus represent more than one b, and any that represents b is itself b, it follows that (D) any general object represents itself but nothing else. For suppose that (1) X is general object representing objects (that are) b. Then, according to characterization A, it follows that (2) for every c, X is c if and only if all b are c. Now it is a thesis of ontology that (3) for every X and b, all b are b, and if X is anything at all then X is identical with X. Thesis 3 and supposition 1 together entail that (4) all b are b, and X is identical with X. Appropriate substitution instances of step 2, together with step 4, entail that (5) X is b, and any b is identical with X; i.e., that there is at most one b, and at least one—namely, X itself. In other words, according to the appropriate thesis of ontology that (6) for every X and b, if X is b, and any b is identical with X, then X is the sole b, it follows that (7) X is the sole b. Consequently, this deduction too being completely general, it follows that (D) for every b, any general object representing b is itself the sole b. Any such "Platonic Ideal Bed", for instance, is the sole bed in the universe; and therefore exists only if there is exactly one bed, namely itself, otherwise being nonexistent. (See Plato, *Republic*, bk. 10, 596–597, and *Parmenides*, 132–133; also Aristotle, *On Sophistical Refutations*, ch. 24, 179a, and *Metaphysics*, bk. 1, ch. 9, 990b.)

Lesniewski's technique of "natural deduction" by the suppositional method may be illustrated by recasting these sample deductions in the familiar symbolism, supplemented by counterparts of certain functors of ontology, that Lesniewski used in informal exposition. I presuppose truth-functional logic implicitly, and four theses of ontology explicitly.

Characterization A. [Xb] ∴ X ε repr(b) . ≡ : X ε X : [c] : X ε c . ≡ . b ⊂ c

Consequence B. [XYbc] : X ε repr(b) . X ε c . Y ε b . ⊃ . Y ε c

Derivation: [XYbc] ∴

(1)	X ε repr(b) .	
(2)	X ε c .	
(3)	Y ε b . ⊃ :	
(4)	[c] : X ε c . ≡ . b ⊂ c :	(consequence of A and 1)
(5)	b ⊂ c :	(4, 2)
(6)	[Ybc] : b ⊂ c . Y ε b . ⊃ . Y ε c :	(thesis of ontology)
(7)	Y ε c	(6, 5, 3)

C. [XYZb] : X ε repr(b) . Z ε b . Y ε b . ⊃ . Y ε Id(Z)
[XYZb] ∴

(1′)	X ε repr(b) .	
(2′)	Z ε b .	
(3′)	Y ε b . ⊃ :	
(4′)	X ε ∼ (Id(Z)) . ⊃ . Z ε ∼ (Id(Z)) :	(B, 1′, 2′)

(5′) $[XZac] : X \varepsilon a . (X \varepsilon \sim (c) . \supset . Z \varepsilon \sim (\mathrm{Id}(Z))) . \supset . X \varepsilon c :$

                                                       (thesis of ontology)

(6′) $X \varepsilon \mathrm{Id}(Z) .$ (5′, 1′, 4′)

(7′) $Y \varepsilon \mathrm{Id}(Z)$ (B, 1′, 6′, 3′)

C′. $[YZb] : Y \varepsilon b . Z \varepsilon b . \sim (Y \varepsilon \mathrm{Id}(Z)) . \supset . [X] . \sim (X \varepsilon \mathrm{repr}(b))$

$[YZb]$ ∴

(1) $Y \varepsilon b .$

(2) $Z \varepsilon b .$

(3) $\sim (Y \varepsilon \mathrm{Id}(Z)) . \supset :$

        $[X] :$

(4) $X \varepsilon \mathrm{repr}(b) . \supset . Y \varepsilon \mathrm{Id}(Z) :$ (C, 1, 2)

(5) $\sim (X \varepsilon \mathrm{repr}(b))$ (4, 3)

D. $[Xb] : X \varepsilon \mathrm{repr}(b) . \supset . X \varepsilon \mathrm{Id}(b)$ I.e.: $[b] . \mathrm{repr}(b) \subset \mathrm{Id}(b)$

$[Xb]$ ∴

(1) $X \varepsilon \mathrm{repr}(b) . \supset :$

(2) $[c] : X \varepsilon c . \equiv . b \subset c :$ (A, 1)

(3) $[Xab] : b \subset b : X \varepsilon a . \supset . X \varepsilon \mathrm{Id}(X) :$ (thesis of ontology)

(4) $b \subset b . X \varepsilon \mathrm{Id}(X) .$ (3, 1)

(5) $X \varepsilon b . b \subset \mathrm{Id}(X) :$ (2, 4)

(6) $[Xb] : X \varepsilon b . b \subset \mathrm{Id}(X) . \supset . X \varepsilon \mathrm{Id}(b) :$ (thesis of ontology)

(7) $X \varepsilon \mathrm{Id}(b)$ (6, 5)

22. Moody, § 7, p. 28 (note). See also Kotarbinski, *1929*, pt. 3, ch. 3, § 18, pp. 253–254; Lejewski, *1958* (LO), introductory paragraphs; Lesniewski, OM, § 11, pp. 162–163; Lukasiewicz, *1910*, pp. 9 ff.; Sobocinski, *1956*, § 8; Jordan, p. 24; Bochenski, *1961*, § 26.08; and Bense, pp. 186–188. Compare the views expressed by Wittgenstein in *1922;* by Carnap in *1950;* by Hall in *1960;* by Quine in *1953*, chs. 1, 2 (§ 6), 4 (§ 5), *1959*, Introduction, and *1960*, §§3, 33, 47, and pp. 221, 228–229, 275–276; and by Russell, Whitehead, Bergmann, and Goodman throughout their writings.

23. See Tarski, *1929*, as contrasted with the arithmetical models mentioned by Quine in *1951*, § 52, p. 279, and *1960*, § 52; and by Rosser in ch. 15, p. 519.

24. See also Woodger, *1949*, and Martin, *1949* and *1958*.

25. In addition to Lesniewski, OM, §§ 2–10, esp. § 2, see Sobocinski, *1949–50*, esp. §§ 6–8; and Kotarbinski, *1957*, ch. 18, § 3, pp. 121–122, ch. 28, § 2 and § 6, and ch. 29, §§ 3–4, pp. 189–192. Cf. also Frege, *1910*.

26. Examples of what Lesniewski avoided are to be found in PM, ch. 3, pp. 69–71, 80–83; *14; and *20. Quine's conventions in *1951*, *340 (n. 2), *512 (n. 1), and *540 (n. 1), though neater, are still ad hoc. Not even the auxiliary conventions of PM, *38, suffice to determine uniquely the intended resolution into constituents of amphibolous compounds (§ 3.10) like those of *38.3–.31, *40.7–.71, and *85.53, which accordingly are not univocal in significance, though one can guess what the authors intended. And Chwistek in *1924–25* demonstrated that what Russell and Whitehead supposed to be innocuous omission of their cumbersome indications of scope admits contradiction, so that their conventions cannot safely be thus relaxed. For further criticisms see Lejewski, *1960* (RD); Black, *1933*, pp. 73–74; Quine in

Whitehead, *1941*, § 8; Geach, *1950* (RT), pt. II; Carnap, *1956*, §§ 7–8 (esp. pp. 34–35) and 33; and Kalish, *1952*.

27. In *1912*, p. 7, Poincaré singled out "impredicative definitions of an object by a relation between it and *all* the individuals of a kind to which it (or something definable only by it) is itself supposed to belong." Various criteria of "impredicativity" are discussed by Hintikka in *1957*, pp. 245–249, as well as in *1956;* also by Gödel in the *1946* Russell volume edited by Schilpp; and by Fraenkel and Bar-Hillel in *1958*, ch. 3, § 10.

28. See in particular: Kotarbinski, *1929*, Preface, p. vii, and pt. 2, n. 17; *1957*, ch. 29, § 3, p. 191. Tarski, *1923*, § 3; *1933*, Introduction, §§ 1–2, 4, 6; *1936* (CF), § 7; *1936* (SS); *1944*, n. 7 and § 4, § 8; *1956*, pp. 8 (n. 1), 152–167 (esp. p. 155, n. 1), 215–217, 223 (n. 1), 263–285, 402. See also Carnap, *1942*, pp. v–vi, 29.

29. Tarski himself sought to formulate a purely structural[47] definition satisfying Lesniewski's criterion. (§ 4.6) In connection with Tarski's definition and his elimination of an empirical premiss from a liar paradox, see Buridan's discussion as summarized by Moody in ch. 4, § 13, p. 68, and ch. 5, §§ 16–17, pp. 101–110, together with Paul of Venice's discussion[52] of the third, seventh, and tenth to fourteenth medieval solutions, followed by Paul's exposition of his own, fifteenth solution, as summarized by Bochenski in *1961*, § 35. See too Lejewski's forthcoming analysis.

30. See Lesniewski, *1929* (NS), § 2, pp. 13–14. In connection with PM, esp. *12, Lesniewski cited Chwistek, *1924–25*, pp. 12–14, 26–33, 92–93, 97–100. He referred also to Husserl's conception of the *Bedeutungskategorien* of a general, purely logical grammar, as outlined by Husserl in *1913*, vol. 1, §§ 67–68; and in vol. 2, bk. 1, pt. 4, of which Lesniewski cited the introduction and §§ 5–7, 10, and 12ff. to the end of pt. 4, p. 342. Husserl's investigations are summarized by Farber in *1943*, ch. 11. See also Bar-Hillel, *1957*, together with *1950*, *1951*, both articles of *1953*, and ch. 3, § 9, of Fraenkel and Bar-Hillel, *1958*, in which Bar-Hillel develops the contributions of Ajdukiewicz in *1935* and Carnap in *1937*, § 27 and pt. 4, esp. §§ 46, 53–54. See also Aristotle, *Categories*, 5 (2a), *Prior Analytics*, ch. 1, ch. 36 (48b), ch. 37 (49a); Frege, *1891* (last five pages), *1892* (p. 201, translated in *1952*, pp. 50–51), *1893* (§§ 21–23, 26–33, esp. 23, 26, 28, 33.1); Russell, *1903* and *1908*, *passim*, and the passages cited in § 5.1[66] above; Chwistek's publications (i.e., *1921* and both articles of *1922*) leading up to the "theory of constructive types" presented in *1924–25;* Ramsey, *1925* and *1926;* Bochenski, *1949;* Curry, *1950*, § 5; Carnap, *1958* (or *1954*), §§ 16, 21b, 28, 29b, 33, 34c; Chomsky, *1953*, *1957*, *1958;* and Wundheiler, *1955*.

31. Russell discussed these difficulties at length in *1908* and in *1925*, §§ 6–7, pp. xxxix–xlv. But see Gödel's criticisms in Russell, *1946*.

32. Tarski, *1933*, § 4, esp. pp. 66–70, together with p. 61, n. 56 (translated in *1956*, ch. 8, § 4, pp. 215–219, and—except for omission of part of n. 56 of *1933*—in *1956*, p. 210, n. 2). But Tarski uses the material mode of expression or "hypostasis", which Lesniewski avoided; explains only certain underlying principles of Lesniewski's grammar, as informally adapted to unformalized languages or "calligraphically different" formalized languages; and superimposes his own conception of "orders", neither due to Lesniewski nor corresponding to Russellian orders. Furthermore, in carrying out metatheoretic investigations based on convenient postulates, (§ 4.6) Tarski[51] apparently found grammatical restrictions increasingly irksome. (§ 4.7)

In his postscript (*1936*, § 7) to the German version of *1933* (translated in *1956*, ch. 8, § 7, pp. 268, 270–271, except for truncation of n. 56 of the Polish original) Tarski added that he considered it interesting and important to investigate, also, formalized "languages" which do not conform to these basic grammatical principles but otherwise are structurally analogous to those which do; and recommended nearly grammarless set-theoretic calculi because of their formal simplicity. (§ 4.7) See also Tarski, *1956*, ch. 16, pp. 411–413.

33. See Quine, *1960*, § 33 and § 47, together with the other writings cited in n. 22 above.

34. See Frege, *1893*, §§ 26–33, esp. 28 and 33, supplemented by Frege's more informal general discussions in *1893*, pp. xiii–xiv (translated in *1952*, p. 145); *1903*, §§ 56–57, 137–144 (partially translated in *1952*, pp. 159–181); *1879*, pp. 7, 9, 11, 12, 36, 45–48, 56–58; *1896* (B), pp. 366, 369; *Geometry*, *1903*, pp. 319–320, 371, and *1906*, pp. 294, 302–303; *1884*, pp. i, vi, viii–x, and §§ 60–63, 67, 70, 74, 77, 80, 84–86, 88, 94–104, 106–107, 109; *1891*, pp. 3–4, 19 (translated in *1952*, pp. 22–23, 32); *1892*, pp. 201–205 (translated in *1952*, pp. 50–55); *1895*, *passim;* *1896;* and *1904*, p. 665 (translated in *1952*, p. 115). Frege's principles of definition are summarized by Jørgensen in vol. 1, pp. 153–156.

35. See Lesniewski, *1931* (UD), p. 292; or Theorem 9 of Lukasiewicz and Tarski's investigations, translated in Tarski, *1956*, ch. 4, § 2, p. 44.

36. In *1938* (EB, II) Lesniewski published the simplification of his deductions of *1929* (NS, § 3) by Lukasiewicz, who in his practically unobtainable[20] contribution of *1938* published his 1933 reduction of the logic of equivalence to the alternative short single axioms listed by Sobocinski in *1949*. In *1938* (NS, § 12) Lesniewski formally derived more than four hundred theorems from Axioms A1, A2, and A3. In these deductions he brought out the logical content of A3, just as Sobocinski in *1960* deductively develops the single axiom AP (§ 6.2.2) by which the axiom set consisting of A1, A2, and A3 can now be replaced.

37. See Tarski, *1923;* and *1933* (or *1936*), next to last footnote of § 5. Lesniewski's method is derived and used by Sobocinski in *1960;* and is explained in *1953* (chs. 5–14, esp. 10–12) by Slupecki, who (in chs. 13–14, Thms. 2–3, pp. 109–110) presents proofs of the completeness of protothetic that are based on this method, which is explained also by Prior in *1953* (ch. 3, § 2, pp. 52–61; see also § 4, pp. 65–68) as specialized for propositional expressions, and as used by Quine in *1938*. Cf. the related method of truth-value analysis explained by Quine in *1959*, §§ 5–6.

38. Standley's generalizations hold without the exceptions he mentions if adapted to Lesniewski's notation (explained in *1938*, EB, III) instead of that which Parry develops (in *1954*) on the basis of Lesniewski's notation and Peirce's still earlier notation of *1902*, and which embodies the same ideographic principles. (Peirce's basic diagram is reproduced by Bochenski in *1961*, § 42.20.) Parry's notation for any binary connector can be obtained from Lesniewski's, with which it corresponds one-to-one, simply by drawing one side of an inverted trapezoid in each position pointed to by an indicator in Lesniewski's notation, replacing Lesniewski's hub 'o' by an 'x' in case there is no indicator. (§ 8)

39. See for example Carnap, *1958* (or *1954*), §§ 21a, 27–28, 30, 31b, 32, 34, 36–38, 42e, together with the contrasted examples marked 'A' and 'C', respectively, in the following sections.

40. See Whitehead, *1919*, ch. 3, § 28, p. 102; also §§ 14, 16–21, 27–29. Although Whitehead expounded his theory only loosely and programmatically, as acknowledged in § 18.2, p. 76, he did in §§ 27–28 assert several fundamental theses and definitions, on which Lesniewski based the proofs published in OM, § 4, pp. 286–291.

41. Lesniewski's deductions are based on a translation into his ontology, not of Frege's revised principle V′ (§ 6.1.6) of "extensional abstraction" or "conversion", but rather of its corollary, theorem 1′, from p. 264 of Frege's *Nachwort* of *1903*. But (on the basis of definitions which Lesniewski would have regarded as faulty, and which violate his rule LVI.13° of nominative definition) (§ 7.3) Quine (in *1955*) and Geach (in *1956*) have since demonstrated that the paradoxical consequence that there is at most one individual object in the universe is provable in Frege's own system as revised in *1903*. Indeed, Geach generalizes Lesniewski's result, and shows that this unwelcome consequence is entailed by a yet weaker assumption.

42. See Slupecki, *1953*, pp. 44–45, and *1955*, pp. 8–9.

43. See Lesniewski, OM, Introduction (*1927*, translated into German as the introduction to NS, *1929*) and § 4, esp. pp. 261–262; *1929*, NS, § 11; and *1938*, EB, VI. Lesniewski cited the following writings: on antinomies, Grelling and Nelson, *1908*, p. 314; on the first edition of PM, Russell, *1925*, p. xiv, and Chwistek, *1924–25*, p. 22, n. 3; on rules of definition and deduction, Frege, *1893*, § 33 and § 48, together with PM, *1910*, pp. vi–vii, Russell, *1919*, p. 151, and Chwistek, *1924–25*, pp. 20–33, esp. p. 21; and, in his assessment of other systems, Frege's appendix of *1903* and Zermelo's *Untersuchungen* of *1908*.

44. Even in Whitehead's early mathematical work the search for maximum generality is combined with concern for meaning and truth, interpretation, extramathematical applications, and philosophical implications. See Quine, *1941*.

45. Contrast the attitude expressed by Rosser in *1953* (chs. 1 (§ 4), 5, 15, esp. pp. 10, 522), illustrated by several remarks quoted in § 4 above, and by Wittgenstein in *1956* (IV, § 52, p. 157, and V, § 16, p. 174). But in *1922* Wittgenstein had written that the solution of logical problems must set a standard of simplicity (*Einfachheit*), (§ 3.5.3) since they are not abstract but perhaps the most concrete problems of all, logic being a "transcendental", structural reflection of the world, whose propositions describe—or, rather, represent—its structural framework, and which should give *Jenes Einfachste*, not an image of the truth but the full truth itself. And even in his commentary of *1953*, §§ 77–98, he did not so much abandon this view as qualify it in the spirit of *1953*, § 81. Indeed, in *1956* (esp. V, § 40, § 46) he allows *mathematics* to set its own "norms" of construction, though he apparently does not allow the same right or privilege to "the" logic of an evolving historical language, which it seems we are to elucidate and then return to its "natural" state, just as we found it, or at least are to leave to the innovations, not of *living* logicians and philosophers, but only of the man on the job.

46. See Russell, *1919*, pp. 77, 117, 122, 124, 129–130, 131–143, 169–170, 190–205, esp. p. 203; *1937*, pp. vii–ix, xii, esp. p. viii; *1925*, p. xiv and §§ 6–7; *1910*, pp. 19–20, 481–482; *1912*, pp. 183, 203; *1913* (PM), pp. v, 234; *1956*, pp. 97–101, 240, 272, 326, 338–339, 352, 363; and *1959*, pp. 91–93.

47. Consider the problem of defining 'true' in the broad sense of "logically or extralogically true", in a philosophically clarifying way, on the basis of a prior

definition of some constant having the narrower sense of "logically true". How is one to avoid begging the question, by presupposing, at least implicitly, that theses of the system in question (which might be derived from "the" logic of some unformalized "natural" language) are "logically true" just because they are asserted as theses? The procedure, customary in metatheory, of taking as one's standard of "logical truth" in a formalized system the "intuitive logical truth" of translations or counterparts in an unformalized "natural" metalanguage does not avoid begging the question; it only conceals or shifts the presumption, by translating the question into another medium, in which—even apart from attendant questions as to accuracy of translation—to attain rigor and clarity is yet harder.

For example, Carnap (in *1937*, § 34b) demonstrates that 'the principles of induction and selection are analytic' according to his definition—but only by presupposing and using corresponding principles in his metalanguage. He concludes, quite candidly, that his demonstrations 'must not be interpreted as' proofs 'that the Principle of Induction and the Principle of Selection' are 'materially true. They only show that our definition of 'analytic' effects on this point what it is intended to effect, namely, the characterization of a sentence as analytic *if*, in material interpretation, *it is regarded as logically valid.*' (Italics mine.) Such definitions seem to me not so much philosophical clarifications as merely *formal criteria of adequacy of analysis*, like the formal, "translational" criterion which Tarski calls a "semantic definition of truth", but which makes it appear that the standard of truth of any proposition must be the truth of some correlated proposition. It is not *incorrect* to stipulate, for instance, that (an expression of the form) 'It is snowing here now' (resp. 'Es schneit jetzt hier') is a true proposition in English (resp. German) if and only if it is snowing here now; [29] (§ 4.6) indeed, any definition that yielded an incompatible consequence or failed to satisfy this criterion would be wrong or inadequate; but neither is it *illuminating*. It appears to lead to an indefinite (though only implicit) linguistic regress, without even making clear that there are extralinguistic as well as linguistic conditions for truth.

To me it seems clearer simply to apply the term 'thesis' to any proposition asserted in some (presumably) consistent axiomatic system that satisfies not only traditional formal standards of validity and rigor but also one's intuitive sense of significance, clarity, adequacy, etc. (perhaps derived from an unformalized language); and then call *true* only any proposition that either (1) is a thesis of the system, in this sense, or (2) fulfills *both* the logical and the extralogical, referential conditions for truth in an interpreted descriptive language based on that system. Without attempting to legislate for others, I myself use the expression 'thesis of (indicative) logic' in the technical sense of 'thesis of protothetic or ontology', thereby taking Lesniewski's system, subject to possible revision, as henceforth defining my own conception of "logical truth". At the same time I try to indicate the rationale of this conception (§ 6.0) and point to its historical continuity (§ 2.1) with the tradition of classical logic. (§ 6)

Here as elsewhere it seems to me vital to maintain balance midway between absolutistic theoretical dogmatism and pragmatic experimental vandalism. Provided the reaction does not carry too far, it may help counterbalance heedless pragmatism to regard even "tautologies" as extremal, limiting cases of true description; and to call, say, the law of excluded middle a "logical" or "logically true description of reality": for every p, either p or not p; for instance, either it is snowing here now or it is not. For this law at least excludes a third possibility—in a language based on the two-valued logic in question. And, although certain basic linguistic conventions may be arbitrary in detail, relative to the purpose in question, it is important to stress that, these conventions once being fixed, what follows is not. But I think the reaction would carry too far if it led to the assumption that there is, so to speak, just one true map of the world, regardless of cartographical aims, conventions, and chosen schemes of projection. For selected aspects of the world may be truly mapped according to diverse conventions and various projections, each suited to certain purposes. And, since all maps are selective, superficially different partial but true (*not* "partially true") maps need not conflict but may even supplement one another, each having its peculiar advantages and disadvantages. True, a constant cannot consistently be assigned different significances within the same language. Nor can, say, a three-valued system be obtained simply by introducing new constant connectors into a classical (extensional and two-valued) system, since any such constant therein would logically have one of the finite number of values possible for a connector of that degree in a classical system.[37] But the classical law of excluded middle need not be incompatible, say, with a law of excluded "fourth" in a three-valued system: for every p, *ither* p *ur nit* p *ur nat* p. For, in the case just imagined, 'ither...ur...ur' would evidently differ from 'either... or' in use, significance, and logical force, as 'nit' and 'nat' would differ from 'not'.

Consider for example the question how such a three-valued "logic" could be interpreted and used as basis for true description of reality in three-valued language. Although I fail to see how, I should hesitate to argue that what I cannot at present conceive is therefore impossible. Instead I should only raise the question, and ask for answers to objections such as the following: Two-valued languages seem to be more simple and practicable, since three-valued languages would not minimize but rather would multiply borderline cases, by laying down twice as many boundaries subject to dispute or indecision. (We users of a two-valued language have to decide whether it is the case that such-and-such or not; but users of a three-valued language, imagined above, would have to decide whether it is the case that such-and-such, *ur nit* such-and-such, *ur nat* such-and-such.) And no language can more than minimize borderline cases, together with the unavoidable vagueness of reference which they evidence and from which they arise, by successive approximation to an asymptotic, regulative ideal of exactness to be approached but never attained. In fact, English and other colloquial languages are not *strictly* n-valued for any n, being too plastic and flexible to be taken as norm for comparatively exact logic. But, to the extent to which we approach rigor in use, most of us seem, at least implicitly, to take the law of excluded middle as a regulative principle, not so much representative of our actual more-or-less careless usage as normative for ideally rigorous logical usage. As Frege pointed out (in *1903*, § 56), the law of excluded middle virtually amounts to an implicit form of the logical requirement that concepts be sharply and completely defined,[34] that vagueness and attendant borderline cases be reduced to a minimum, ideally vanishing with the metaphorical boundary, supposed in theory to be a Euclidean line but in practice inevitably smudged into a vague borderland. Nevertheless it is important to distinguish (so to speak) between thinking that certain cartographical conventions could hardly be bettered (for purposes one takes for granted) and thinking that there is or can be just one true map of the world, regardless of purposes and conventions, and that whatever is not represented on or built into this map cannot or ought not exist.

48. I single out Quine, not necessarily as source, but as a most vigorous champion and articulate spokesman of the "ontological pragmatism" that combines "nominalist" ideals with "platonist" practice, and perhaps uneasily attempts to make a virtue out of apparent necessity; and as a logician who has bravely faced philosophical issues, boldly grasped not a few philosophical nettles, and lucidly developed an explicit pragmatic rationale of tendencies at least verbally implicit in the material mode of expression traditional in mathematics and logic. (§ 1.8) Quine elaborates his pragmatic rationale in his contributions to Whitehead, *1941*, p. 153, and to the *1951* symposium; *1951* (ML), esp. Preface to the revised edition, Preface, and §§ 22–29, 36, 45–46, esp. 29, small type, pp. 163–166; *1953*, chs. 1, 2 (esp. §§ 2, 5–6), 4 (esp. § 5), 5 (pp. 82–83), and 8, together with the source essays mentioned on pp. 169–170; *1959*, Introduction and §§ 18, 24, 33–38, and 41, esp. pp. 94–96; *1960*, §§ 3–4, 6, 25, 39, 49–52, 55–56, esp. pp. 11–13, 22, 34, 119–120, 123–124, 131, 161, 182–183, 188–190, 228–232, 237, 241–243, 249–251, 253–254, 266–270, 274–276; and in the introductory manifesto of Goodman-Quine, *1947*, read as qualified by Quine in *1960*, § 49, n. 5 (p. 243).

49. Rosser, *1953*, ch. 1, §§ 3–4, pp. 7–10. See also ch. 6, § 2, p. 87, together with ch. 5, pp. 77–79, and ch. 15, p. 522, on conformity with current mathematical practice—which Frege found somewhat less worthy of emulation, in his discussion of definitions,[34] *1893* Preface and Introduction, *1895* critique of Schröder (esp. p. 449, translated in *1952*, p. 100), *1903* critique of pure formalism,[17] and *1904* conclusion.

50. Rosser, *1953*, ch. 3, pp. 50–53, in connection with which see the criticisms cited in notes 2 and 17 above, together with Frege, *1891*, *1892*, and *1904* (as translated in *1952*, esp. pp. 28, 46–47, 114–116), in the light of Dummett's[13] comments and Kleene, *1952*, § 10.

51. Tarski, *1933*, § 1, n. 5, pp. 5–6, and § 2, pp. 25–26, including n. 32. In *1956* see chs. 8 (§§ 1–2), 3, 5, 9, 16, esp. pp. 31 (n. 3), 63–64, 156 (n. 1), 173 (n. 3), 174–175, 282 (n. 2), 411–413.

52. Frege, *1903*, § 124 and § 92 (as translated in *1952*, esp. p. 219 and p. 187). See also *1903*, §§ 123–132 (translated in *1952*, pp. 218–228), together with Quine, *1960*, § 40, pp. 194–195, and *1953*, pp. 128–129; and Goodman-Quine, *1947*, § 2. For a case illustrating the philosophical importance of such details, see Paul of Venice's discussion of a liar paradox.[29] See too Lejewski's forthcoming analysis.

53. Quine, *1960*, § 47, p. 230, § 50, p. 244, § 53, pp. 257–258, 260–262. On the issue of falsity v. meaninglessness, contrast p. 177 with p. 229.

54. Russell, *1937*, p. vi. See also *1959*, p. 110, together with Frege's *1903* critique of pure formalism,[17] and Ramsey, *1925* (p. 18) and *1926* (pp. 68–73).

55. Cf. Russell, *1919*, ch. 13, esp. pp. 134–137, and ch. 17, pp. 190–193. See also PM, p. 53; *1908;* and *1940*, p. 43, note.

56. In addition to Quine,[48] see for example Rosser, *1953*, ch. 9, §§ 1–2, pp. 197–213, esp. 202–206, and ch. 11, § 1, pp. 346–348, in connection with which see also Bernays-Fraenkel, *1958*, pt. 1, § 7, and pt. 2, ch. 5, § 1, pp. 117–118.

57. See for example the following writings: Bolzano, *1837*, § 86. Frege, *1884*, §§ 7–9, 22–23, 28, 39, 41, 45, 54; Introduction of *1893; 1894*, § 3; *1905*, § 120; and *1910*. Russell, *1903*, §§ 21, 48, 68–75, 79, 130, 133–137, 140, 148, 328, 330, 482–489,

together with the provisos Russell added in *1937; 1914*, pp. 210–212; *1919*, p. 183. As for later writings, see the works cited in n. 10 and n. 25 above, together with Weyl, *1949*, p. 12; Quine, *1951*, § 22, p. 120, and *1953*, ch. 4, esp. § 3, pp. 72–74; Goodman, *1951*, ch. 2, §§ 4–5, esp. pp. 42–43, 46, 51–52, 55, and ch. 4, § 1, pp. 93–95; and Dummett, *1956*, 'Nominalism'.

58. Cantor, *1887*, p. 83: 'Jede Menge wohlunterschiedener Dinge kann *als ein einheitliches Ding für sich* angesehen werden, in welchen jene Dinge Bestandteile oder constitutive Elemente sind.'

59. Cantor, *1888*, pp. 242–243.

60. Cantor, *1883*, p. 43: 'jedes Viele, welches sich als Eines denken lässt, d.h. jeden Inbegriff bestimmter Elemente, welcher durch ein Gesetz zu einem Ganzen verbunden werden kann'.

61. Cantor, *1895*, p. 481: 'jede Zusammenfassung M von bestimmten wohlunter- schiedenen Objekten m unsrer Anschauung oder unseres Denkens (welche die 'Elemente' von M genannt werden) zu einem Ganzen'.

62. In addition to Frege,[52] see Chwistek, *1948*, ch. 8, § 6, pp. 207–208.

63. Lesniewski cited Bolzano, *1837*, p. 257, together with Bolzano's quotation, on p. 79, from Savonarola. See also Quine, *1960*, pp. 103, 107, 132–133, 138.

64. See Lejewski, *1954* and *1958* (LO), together with § 1.7 and §§ 6.1.1–6.1.3 above.

65. Bernays-Fraenkel, *1958*, pt. 2, Introduction, pp. 41–43. See also ch. 1, §§ 1, 3–4; ch. 2, §§ 3–4; ch. 5, § 1, § 3; ch. 6, §§ 1, 3, 5; ch. 7, § 1, § 5; ch. 8, § 2; esp. pp. 45, 56–57, 59, 63, 72–74, 76, 117–118, 124, 131–132, 139, 141, 147–148, 155, 161–162, 189, 200–208. See also Fraenkel's preceding historical introduction, pt. 1, §§ 3, 4, 7, esp. pp. 11–13, 18, 24–26, 31–34. Accounts of recent trends in set theory are given also by Quine in *1951*, § 29, pp. 163–166; by Fraenkel and Bar-Hillel in *1958;* by Wang in *1954;* and by Wang and McNaughton, *1953*.

66. See Russell, *1903*, § 492, p. 518, together with p. 522, Note; *1908*, opening paragraph; *1910*, Introduction, ch. 2, esp. opening paragraph on p. 37, p. 53, and §§ 6–7, pp. 55–70; *1918*, § 8; *1919*[55]; *1924; 1937*, pp. xiii–xiv; *1940*, chs. 1, 4, 12–13, and 22, esp. pp. 26, 62–63, 166–167, 170–174, 177, 182–183, 190, 194–195, 202; *1946*, pp. 691–692; *1959*, pp. 79–80, 131–132, 157–158, 165–166, 187–189, 235. In the *1956* reprinting, see pp. 59, 267–269, 333–334, 370–371.

67. For example, in most of the writings cited in n. 30, above, and published since Carnap and Morris popularized "logical syntax" or "syntactics" in the 1930s, the term 'syntactical' is used instead of 'semantical'.

68. See Quine, *1936*; also *1955*, together with Quine's acknowledgment, in *1960*, § 31, n. 4, of an error pointed out by Church.

69. See Russell's writings, *passim*, esp. *1940*, ch. 17; *1910*, ch. 2, § 3, § 8; *1914* (as reprinted in *1956*, esp. p. 156); *1918; 1919*, ch. 6; *1924; 1925*, App. C; *1948*, pt. 2, ch. 10, pt. 4, ch. 3, and pt. 6, chs. 1, 4, 6, 10; *1950; 1959*, pp. 113–114, 125, 196. See also Leibniz's 'Dialog concerning the connection between things and words'; Hertz on dynamic models in his introduction of *1894;* Frege, *1919;* Wittgenstein, *1922;* Ramsey, *1926*, esp. pp. 69–71; Schlick, *1932;* Storer, *1950, 1951* analysis of logical positivism, and *1952;* Anscombe, *1959;* Stenius, *1960*; and Hall, *1961*.

70. Quine, *1960*, § 33, p. 158. Cf. PM, *1910*, Preface; Whitehead, *1911*, ch. 5;

Wittgenstein, *1922*, 4.1213 as illustrated by 4.0411; and Anscombe, *1959*, ch. 11, pp. 138–141.

71. See Frege, *1879*, § 11, p. 19 (translated in *1952*, p. 16), and *1903*, § 65; and Russell, *1903*, § 83, and 1908, pt. III.

72. See for example Rosser, *1953*, ch. 6, § 8; and Carnap, *1958* (or *1954*), § 17c, and *1937*, §§ 16, 38b, 55.

73. See Frege, *1884*, final note of § 68 (p. 80), § 77 (p. 90), § 107 (p. 117); 1892 (BG); *1893*, §§ 10, 20, 25, 31; and *1894*, pt. II, last paragraph, in connection with *1884*, § 74, p. 88, and the appendix of *1903*.

74. Lesniewski's attitude, as expressed in *1929* (NS, § 4, p. 30), in discussing prototethic, may reflect the fact that in 1922 Tarski proved a thesis of extensionality to be inferentially equivalent, in prototethic, to various other theses concerning which Lesniewski had no doubts. See Tarski, *1923*, and Slupecki, *1953*. In connection with the development of extensional language, see also the following investigations: Russell, *1925*, p. xiv and App. C; *1940*, chs. 12ff; and *1959*, ch. 13 and p. 185, together with the earlier writings there cited. Carnap, *1928*, §§ 43–45; *1937*, §§ 18, 31, 60a, 63–71, 74–78, 85–86; *1942*, § 39, pp. 249–250; *1956*, §§ 2, 11–17, 32 (Methods IV–VI), 33–38, 42–45, and Supplements C–E. Lewis, *1944* and *1946*, chs. 3–4. Reichenbach, *1948*, ch. 8, and *1954*. Olds, *1956*. Quine, *1960*, ch. 6, esp. §§ 41, 43–44, together with the further references given by Quine.

75. Lesniewski, *1931* (UD), p. 295, n. 3.

76. See Hermes, *1939;* Woodger, *1952* (BM, p. 11) and *1937* (p. 42); and Carnap, *1958* (or *1954*), § 53b.

77. See for example Myhill; Slupecki, *1955*, ch. 4, § 1, pp. 61–66, esp. Thm. VII; Weyl, pt. 1, ch. 1, § 2, esp. pp. 10–13; and Suppes (§ 8.2), whose footnote to p. 153 seems difficult to reconcile with the theorem just mentioned.

78. In addition to Frege on definitions,[34] esp. *1884*, §§ 55–56, and the writings cited in n. 71 above, see Hilbert-Bernays, *1934*, pp. 25–27, § 7, esp. pp. 293–301, and *1939*, Supplement IV.G; Carnap, *1937*, § 8, § 29; Kleene, §§ 6, 43–44, 53; Tarski, *1956*, p. 177, n. 1; Kalmar, *1940;* Fraenkel, *1953*, ch. 3, § 10, pp. 249–253; Rosser, *1953*, chs. 8 (§ 2), 11 (§ 3), 12 (§ 2), esp. pp. 189–191, 405–417, 462–466, and 519; and Suppes, *1957*, ch. 8. In contrast to Frege's and Lesniewski's respectful treatment of definitions, see the prevalent view expressed, after the fashion of Russell, *1903* (§ 63, p. 63, and § 412, p. 429) and *1910* (pp. 11–12), by Quine in 'Definition and the double life' (*1960*, § 39, pp. 188–190, as illustrated by Quine's remarks on myth in § 51, p. 250) and in *1951* (pp. 47, 75, 103, 126, 142–143) and *1953* (ch. 2, § 2, pp. 24–27, and ch. 5, pp. 82–83, 91), and by Church in *1956* (§ 11, pp. 75–77).

79. See Lejewski, *1960* (BA); Tarski, *1935* (as translated in *1956*, esp. p. 333, n. 1, and p. 341); and Grzegorczyk, (§ 6.5) *1955*, esp. § 4.

80. In addition to the geometries of Lesniewski and Tarski (*1929*), projects of the various kinds mentioned have been sketched or undertaken by, among others, (1) Whitehead, Russell, Chwistek, Reichenbach, Carnap, Robb, Mehlberg, Schnell, and Los; (2) Carnap and Goodman; (3) Woodger; (4) Lesniewski, Tarski, Lejewski, Quine, Goodman, Martin, and Woodger. For partial references see Carnap, *1958* (or *1954*), pt. 2, esp. §§ 39, 46–57.

81. See Slupecki (*1955*, p. 66, Thm. VIII), who attributes this interpretation of ontology in protothetic to Kruszewski. By using defined constants of level two it is possible to interpret mereology in ontology at a lower level than Lesniewski's unpublished interpretation in real-number theory, mentioned by Sobocinski (in *1954–55*, p. 36), who has recently proved that ontology (in effect) contains and is consistent relative to an unbounded classical functional logic like PM constructed according to a simple type grammar.

82. See the opening page of *1940*, in which Leonard and Goodman acknowledge Lesniewski's 1921 axiomatization of mereology (see OM, § 10) as their model. But Grzegorczyk may have relied instead on Goodman's statement in *1951* (ch. 2, § 4, p. 42, n. 8): 'The calculus of individuals was first published by Lesniewski ...A version of the calculus developed independently by Lesniewski by Henry S. Leonard and Nelson Goodman was included in Leonard's thesis *Singular Terms* (1930), typescript, Widener Library'.

83. My use in T.E. XV of the stylistic variant 'related variable' is suggested by Frege's phrase 'verwandte Argumentstellen'. See Frege, *1893*, § 8, p. 13; also *1897*, § 11 (translated in *1952*, pp. 16–18); and, more recently, Carnap, *1937*, §§ 54–55; and Quine, *1951*, § 14, p. 76, illustrated by the quantificational diagram in § 12, p. 70.

84. See Frege's logical grammar of *1893*,[30] together with § 6.1.6 and my commentary on T.E. XXXIX'.5 in § 7.1 above.

85. Although any one requirement that might appear to entail that B is a thesis can be satisfied vacuously, by an expression not meeting the antecedent condition, (§ 1.7) in conjunction Lesniewski's requirements do entail this consequence. (In XLIV, the first of several similar cases, this is shown by the following argument: Suppose A contains a generalization. Then, according to XLIV.6, some individual is propositional relative to thesis B. Hence B is a thesis, unless this generalization is the same individual as A, in which case according to XLIV.9 the nucleus of A, being a coimplication, is a generating function with respect to some basic propositional phrase relative to thesis B, so that B even then is a thesis. So B is a thesis if A contains a generalization. But suppose A does not. Then there is no word inside a quantifier in A, and therefore no variable in A. It follows, according to XLIV.4, that any term in the provisory coimplicans of the nucleus of A is an ingredient of A suited to be constant relative to thesis B. And there is such a term. For XLIV.2 entails the existence of the provisory coimplicate of the nucleus of A, and hence that of its provisory coimplicans, which, being an argument of the parentheme of the nucleus of A, contains at least one term. So in this case too B is a thesis. It follows that B is a thesis, whether A contains a generalization or not.)

86. 'Contributions to mereology' (from the Notre Dame doctoral thesis) by Robert E. Clay is to appear, together with results due to Sobocinski and Lejewski, in the *Notre Dame Journal of Formal Logic*, beginning in vol. 3, 1962.

87. For any directive satisfying Lesniewski's canons would have to be prescribed constructively, and not ad hoc for the special case of particular quantification but with complete generality, to provide for introduction of any kind of quantifier admissible in language L. (See Sobocinski, *1960*, p. 68, n. 3; also Lejewski, *1956*.)

10. BIBLIOGRAPHY (§ 1.0)

10.0 Primary sources:
Kotarbinski, Lejewski, Lesniewski, Slupecki, Sobocinski, Tarski

Kotarbinski, Tadeusz

1920. 'Sprawa istnienia przedmiotow idealnych'. PF, (§ 1.0) vol. 28, as reprinted in *1958*, pp. 7–39. (Question of existence of ideal objects. Contains summary of Lesniewski's arguments and views.)

1929. Elementy Teorji Poznania, Logiki Formalnej i Metodologji Nauk. Lwow. (Elements of theory of knowledge, formal logic, and methodology of science. Preface acknowledges Lesniewski's pervasive influence. Characterization of Lesniewski's ontology in pt. 3, ch. 3, contains illustrative theses of elementary ontology, and was for more than two decades the only elementary published account. Ed. 2, revised, 1961, Warsaw.)

1957. Wyklady z Dziejow Logiki. Lodz. (Lectures from history of logic. Contains personal recollections of Lesniewski's unpublished treatments of certain topics in semantics, together with brief informal accounts of his theories.)

1958. Wybor Pism, vol. 2. Warsaw. (Selected writings.)

Lejewski, Czeslaw

1954. 'Logic and existence'. *British Journal for the Philosophy of Science*, vol. 5, pp. 1–16.

1954–55. 'A contribution to Lesniewski's mereology'. *Rocznik V Polskiego Towarzystwa Naukowego na Obczyznie* (*Yearbook V of the Polish Society of Arts and Sciences Abroad*, London), pp. 43–50.

1955–56. 'A new axiom of mereology'. *Ibid., Rocznik VI*, pp. 65–70.

1956. Review of Slupecki, *1955*. JSL, (§ 1.0) vol. 21, pp. 188–191.

1957. 'Symposium: proper names. II.' *Aristotelian Society, Supplementary Vol.* XXXI, pp. 229–256.

1958 (ID). 'On implicational definitions'. *Studia Logica*, vol. 8, pp. 189–205.

1958 (LO). 'On Lesniewski's ontology'. *Ratio*, vol. 1, pp. 150–176.

1960 (RD). 'A re-examination of the Russellian theory of descriptions'. *Philosophy*, vol. 35, pp. 14–29.

1960 (BA). 'Studies in the axiomatic foundations of Boolean algebra'. *Notre Dame Journal of Formal Logic*, vol. 1, pp. 23–47, 91–106, and vol. 2 (1961) pp. 79–93.

1961. 'Aristotle's syllogistic and its extensions'.

Forthcoming (1962 ?) 'The Liar and the concept of truth'.

Lesniewski, Stanislaw

Early writings, later repudiated: (§ 2.1, § 2.3)

1911. 'Przyczynek do analizy zdan egzystencjalnych'. PF, (§ 1.0) vol. 14. (Contribution to analysis of existential propositions. See *1913* below.)

1912. 'Proba dowodu ontologicznej zasady sprzecznosci'. PF, vol. 15. (Attempt to prove ontological principle of contradiction. See *1913* below.)

1913. Logiceskia razsuzdenia. (Transliterated Russian title.) St. Petersburg. (Contains Russian versions of *1911* and *1912*.)

1913. 'Czy prawda jest tylko wieczna czy tez wieczna i odwieczna?' *Nowe Tory*, vol. 18. (Is truth only eternal or both eternal and sempiternal?)

1913. 'Krytyka logicznej zasady wylaczonego srodku'. PF, (§ 1.0) vol. 16. (Critique of logical principle of excluded middle. Misprint 'srodku' in title should be 'srodka'.)

1914. 'Czy klasa klas, nie podporzadkowanych sobie, jest podporzadkowana sobie?' PF, vol. 17, pp. 63–75. (Is the class of classes not subordinate to themselves subordinate to itself?)

1916. Podstawy ogolnej teoryi mnogosci. I. Moscow. (Foundations of general theory of manifolds, or collective sets. Pt. II never appeared in print, and even pt. I became a 'bibliographical rarity', whose results Lesniewski reformulated in OM (*1928*), § 4, and developed in §§ 5–10.) (§ 2.1, § 2.3)

Mature publications: (§ 2.1, § 2.3, § 3.10)

OM (*1927–31*). 'O podstawach matematyki'. PF, (§ 1.0) vols. 30–34. (On foundations of mathematics. Apportioned as follows:)

1927 (Introduction). 'Wstep'. Vol. 30, pp. 164–169. (Translated into German as Introduction to NS, *1929*. Lesniewski's brief characterization of his as compared with other systems of logic and foundations of mathematics, esp. in treatment of antinomies and of definitions.)

1927. § 1. 'O pewnych kwestjach, dotyczacych sensu tez "logistycznych"'. Vol. 30, pp. 169–181. (On certain questions concerning sense of "logistic" theses. Lesniewski's account of initial difficulties with mathematical logic. Detailed criticism of ambiguities in PM.)

1927. § 2. 'O "antynomji" p. Russella, dotyczacej "klasy klas, nie bedacych wlasnemi elementami"'. Vol. 30, pp. 182–189. (On Russell's "antinomy" concerning "the class of classes not elements of themselves". Recapitulation of initial analysis. Refutation of "representative general objects" appended.)

1927. § 3. 'O roznych sposobach rozumienia wyrazow "klasa" i "zbior"'. Vol. 30, pp. 190–206. (On various ways of understanding expressions "class" and "set". Collective conception characterized and compared with other interpretations, which are subjected to critique.)

1928. § 4. 'O "Podstawach ogolnej teoryi mnogosci. I"'. Vol. 31, pp. 261–291. (On "Foundations of general theory of manifolds", or "collective sets", later renamed mereology (§ 2.1)—originally developed in *1916* treatise recapitulated here. Contains appended historical footnotes, and critique of Whitehead's theory of events.)

1929. § 5. 'Dalsze twierdzenia i definicje "ogolnej teorji mnogosci", pochodzace z okresu do r. 1920 wlacznie'. Vol. 32, pp. 60–101. (Further theorems and definitions of mereology from the period up to and including 1920. Historical footnotes appended.)

1930. § 6. 'Aksjomatyka "ogolnej teorji mnogosci", pochodzaca z r. 1918'. Vol. 33, pp. 77–81. (1918 axiomatization of mereology.)

1930. § 7. 'Aksjomatyka "ogolnej teorji mnogosci", pochodzaca z r. 1920'. Vol. 33, pp. 82–86. (1920 axiomatization of mereology.)

1930. § 8. 'O pewnych ustalonych przez pp. Kuratowskiego i Tarskiego warunkach, wystarczajacych i koniecznych do tego, by P bylo klasa p-tow *a*'. Vol. 33, pp. 87–90. (On certain conditions established by Kuratowski and Tarski as sufficient and necessary for P to be (the collective) class of *a*.)

1930. § 9. 'Dalsze twierdzenia "ogolnej teorji mnogosci", pochodzace z lat 1921–1923'. Vol. 33, pp. 90–105. (Further theorems of mereology from 1921–1923.)

1931. § 10. 'Aksjomatyka "ogolnej teorji mnogosci", pochodzaca z r. 1921'. Vol. 34, pp. 142–153. (1921 axiomatization of mereology.)

1931. § 11. 'O zdaniach "jednostkowych" typu "A ε b"'. Vol. 34, pp. 153–170. (On "singular" propositions of the kind "A ε b", as treated in Lesniewski's ontology, the origin and character of which is briefly discussed.)

1929. (G). 'Über Funktionen, deren Felder Gruppen mit Rücksicht auf diese Funktionen sind'. *Fundamenta Mathematicae*, vol. 13, pp. 319–332. (Contents of both 1929 articles on groups indicated in § 3.6 above.)

1929 (AG). Über Funktionen, deren Felder Abelsche Gruppen in bezug auf diese Funktionen sind'. *Ibid.*, vol. 14, pp. 242–251.

1929 (NS, §§ 1–11). 'Grundzüge eines neuen Systems der Grundlagen der Mathematik'. *Ibid.*, vol. 14, pp. 1–81. (§ 11 contains the terminological explanations and directives for prototethic translated in § 7 above, followed by proofs of contradiction in Chwistek, *1924–25*, and Von Neumann, *1927*. Other contents indicated in § 2.3, § 3.6, and § 3.10 above.)

1930 (GO). '*Über die Grundlagen der Ontologie*'. *Comptes Rendus des séances de la Société des Sciences et des Lettres de Varsovie*, Classe III (sometimes listed as *Sprawozdania z posiedzen Towarzystwa Naukowego Warszawskiego*, Wydzial III), vol. 23, pp. 111–132. (Contains the terminological explanations for ontology translated in § 7 and described in § 2.3 and § 3.10 above, followed by brief remarks concerning alternative axiomatizations.)

1931 (UD). 'Über Definitionen in der sogenannten Theorie der Deduktion'. *Ibid.*, vol. 24, pp. 289–309. (Contents indicated in § 3.5.1 above. Contains the appended explanation translated as T.E. XXXIX' in § 7.1 above, together with examples illustrating mutual independence of requirements of the kind mentioned in § 7.0. To be included in the selection by McCall.)

1938 (NS, § 12). 'Grundzüge eines neuen Systems der Grundlagen der Mathematik', § 12. *Collectanea Logica*, vol. 1, pp. 61–144. (Journal and inaugural volume destroyed with its Warsaw printing house during the war. (§ 2.3) Offprints of both *1938* articles survive in Harvard College Library—NS, § 12, indexed 'Math. 69.2.5', EB indexed 'Math. 69.2.7'—and in the logical library of the University of Münster in Westphalia. In NS, § 12, more than four hundred theses of prototethic are derived from axioms A1, A2, and A3 of NS, *1929*. (§ 3.6)

1938 (EB). 'Einleitende Bemerkungen zur Fortsetzung meiner Mitteilung u.d.T. "*Grundzüge eines neuen Systems der Grundlagen der Mathematik*"'. *Ibid.* (see

1938 above), pp. 1–60. (Résumé of §§ 1–10 of NS, *1929*, followed by supplementary remarks on aspects of protothetic: axiomatization of alternative "computative" systems; Lukasiewicz's simplification of NS, § 3; reduction to progressively shorter single axioms; key to principles of ideographic notation; (§ 3.8, § 8) further criticisms of defective formalization of rules for introducing new expressions, substantiated by additional proofs of contradiction in Von Neumann's revision of *1931*. (§ 3.10) To be included in the forthcoming selection edited by McCall.)

Slupecki, Jerzy

1953. 'St. Lesniewski's protothetics'. *Studia Logica*, vol. 1, pp. 44–111. (Slupecki's two surveys of unpublished results are largely based on students' notes collected after wartime destruction of Lesniewski's own lecture notes, (§ 2.3, § 3.10) mainly concern systems other than those formalized in *1929* (NS) and *1930* (GO) and dealt with in this book, and follow Slupecki's own conventions.)

1955. 'S. Lesniewski's calculus of names'. *Ibid.*, vol. 3, pp. 7–70. (See *1953* above. Reviewed by Lejewski in *1956*.)

Sobocinski, Boleslaw

1934. 'O kolejnych uproszczeniach aksjomatyki "ontologji" prof. St. Lesniewskiego', in *Ksiega Pamiatkowa ku uczczeniu 15-lecia pracy nauczycielskiej w Uniwersytecie Warszawskim Prof. Tadeusza Kotarbinskiego—Fragmenty Filozoficzne*, pp. 143–160. (On successive simplifications of the axiomatization of Lesniewski's "ontology".)

1949. An Investigation of Protothetic. Cahiers de l'Institut d'Etudes Polonaises en Belgique, No. 5. Brussels. (Translation of Polish contribution to destroyed volume of *Collectanea Logica*, preceded by introductory recapitulation of related results and account of *Collectanea Logica*, listing and describing its contents, including contributions not listed here because of their destruction.) (§ 2.3, § 3.10)

1949–50. 'L'analyse de l'antinomie Russellienne par Lesniewski'. *Methodos*, vol. 1, pp. 94–107, 220–228, 308–316, and vol. 2, pp. 237–257. (Detailed presentation of Lesniewski's hitherto unpublished later analysis, related investigation of Frege's revised foundations, and demonstration that Frege's revision of *1903* is unsatisfactory. Contains account of origins of Lesniewski's theories.) (§ 3.3, § 3.9)

1953–54. 'Z badan nad aksjomatyka prototetyki Stanislawa Lesniewskiego'. *Rocznik IV Polskiego Towarzystwa Naukowego na Obczyznie* (Yearbook IV of the Polish Society of Arts and Sciences Abroad, London), pp. 18–20. (From investigations of axiomatization of Lesniewski's protothetic.)

1954–55. 'Studies in Lesniewski's mereology'. *Ibid.*, *Rocznik V*, pp. 34–43.

1955–56. 'On well constructed axiom systems'. *Ibid.*, *Rocznik VI*, pp. 54–65. (Explains and illustrates Lesniewski's hitherto unpublished canons of axiomatization.)

1956. 'In Memoriam Jan Lukasiewicz'. *Philosophical Studies* (Maynooth, Ireland), vol. 6, pp. 3–49. (§§ 1–3 and 8 contain background information about Lesniewski's outlook and research in Warsaw.)

1960. 'On the single axioms of protothetic.' *Notre Dame Journal of Formal*

Logic, vol. 1, pp. 52–73; vol. 2 (*1961*), pp. 111–126, 129–148 (to be contd.). (Derivation of standard basis for classical propositional logic from Axiom AP.) (§ 6.2.2)

Tarski, Alfred

1923. 'On the primitive term of logistic', in *1956*, pp. 1–23. (English translation based on 'O wyrazie pierwotnym logistyki', PF, vol. 26, pp. 65–89, and on the modified French version in two parts: 'Sur le terme primitif de la logistique', *Fundamenta Mathematicae*, vol. 4, pp. 196–200; and 'Sur les *truth-functions* au sens de MM. Russell et Whitehead', *ibid.*, vol. 5, pp. 59–74. Represents Tarski's doctoral research under Lesniewski, fundamental for construction of prototothetic.)

1929. 'Foundations of the geometry of solids', in *1956*, pp. 24–29. (English translation of 'Les fondements de la géométrie des corps', *Ksiega Pamiatkowa Pierwszego Polskiego Zjazdu Matematycznego*, supplement to *Annales de la Société Polonaise de Mathématique*, Krakow, with later additions. Axiomatization based on Tarski's reformulation of Lesniewski's mereology. Lesniewski's distinction between ingredient and part is translated into the terms 'part' and 'proper part', respectively, throughout *1956*.)

1933. *Pojecie Prawdy w Jezykach Nauk Dedukcyjnych*. Warsaw. (Concept of truth in languages of deductive sciences. Mentions related aspects of Lesniewski's research, contains summary of Lesniewski's conclusions concerning semantic antinomies, and presents an informal account of certain underlying principles of Lesniewski's grammar of semantic categories.[32])

1935. 'On the foundations of Boolean algebra', in *1956*, pp. 320–341. (English translation of 'Zur Grundlegung der Booleschen Algebra. I.', *Fundamenta Mathematicae*, vol. 24, pp. 177–198. Contains characterizations of Boolean algebras, extended by rules like Lesniewski's, and mentions their relations to mereology.)

1936 (CF). 'The concept of truth in formalized languages', in *1956*, pp. 152–278. (Translation of 'Der Wahrheitsbegriff in den formalisierten Sprachen', *Studia Philosophica*, vol. 1, pp. 261–405, itself a modified version of the *1933* Polish original, with significant omissions and additions.)

1936 (SS). 'The establishment of scientific semantics', in *1956*, pp. 401–408. (Translation of 'O ugruntowania naukowej semantyki', PF, vol. 39, pp. 50–57, which appeared in German as 'Grundlegung der wissentschaftlichen Semantik', *Actes du Congrès International de Philosophie Scientifique*, vol. 3, of Actualités Scientifiques et Industrielles, vol. 390, Paris. Mentions certain of Lesniewski's fundamental insights.)

1944. 'The semantic conception of truth'. *Philosophy and Phenomenological Research*, vol. 4, pp. 341–375. (Reprinted in Feigl-Sellars, *1949*, and Linsky, *1952*. In n. 7 of this summary Tarski adds to his remarks in *1933* and *1936*, CF.)

1956. *Logic, Semantics, Metamathematics: Papers from 1923 to 1938*, translated by J. H. Woodger. Oxford.

10.1 Other publications cited

Anscombe, G. E. M. *1959*. *An Introduction to Wittgenstein's Tractatus*. London.

Ajdukiewicz, Kazimierz.

1935. 'Die syntaktische Konnexität'. *Studia Philosophica* (Lwow), vol. 1, pp.

1–27. (Translated and mimeographed as *Syntactic Connection* at the College of the University of Chicago in 1951. To be included in the selection by McCall.)

1935–36. 'Der logistische Antiirrationalismus in Polen'. *Erkenntnis*, vol. 5, pp. 151–161.

1951. 'On the notion of existence'. *Studia Philosophica* (Poznan), pp. 8 ff.

Bar-Hillel, Yehoshua (See also Fraenkel and Bar-Hillel.)

1950. 'On syntactical categories'. JSL, vol. 15, pp. 1–16.

1951. 'Comments on logical form'. *Philosophical Studies* (Minneapolis), vol. 2, pp. 26–29.

1953. 'A quasi-arithmetical notation for syntactic description'. *Language*, vol. 29, pp. 47–58.

1953. 'Some linguistic problems connected with machine translation'. *Philosophy of Science*, vol. 20, pp. 217–225.

1957. 'Husserl's conception of a purely logical grammar'. *Philosophy and Phenomenological Research*, vol. 17, pp. 362–369.

Bense, Max. *1951.* (*Zwischen den beiden Kriegen*, vol. 1:) *Die Philosophie*. Frankfurt am Main.

Bergmann, Gustav

1954. *The Metaphysics of Logical Positivism*. New York, London, Toronto.
1958. *Philosophy of Science*. Madison, Wisconsin.
1960. *Meaning and Existence*. Madison, Wisconsin.

Bernays, Paul, and *Fraenkel*, Abraham A. *1958.* *Axiomatic Set Theory*. Amsterdam.

Beth, Evert W. *1959.* *The Foundations of Mathematics*. Amsterdam.

Black, Max. *1933.* *The Nature of Mathematics*. London.

Bochenski, I. M.

1949. 'On the syntactical categories'. *New Scholasticism*, vol. 23, pp. 257–280.
1956. *Formale Logik*. Freiburg and Munich. (See *1961* below.)
1961. *A History of Formal Logic*. Notre Dame and Oxford. (Transl. and ed. of *1956* by Ivo Thomas. All cited section numbers the same.)

Bolzano, Bernard. *1837.* *Wissenschaftslehre*, vol. 1, as reprinted in 1914 in Leipzig. (Also reprinted in 1929, Leipzig.)

Cantor, Georg

1883. *Grundlagen einer allgemeinen Mannichfaltigkeitslehre. Ein mathematisch-philosophischer Versuch in der Lehre des Unendlichen.* Leipzig. (Also in *Mathematische Annalen*, vols. 15, 17, 20, 21.)

1887. 'Mitteilungen zur Lehre vom Transfiniten. I.' *Zeitschrift für Philosophie und philosophische Kritik*, n.s. vol. 91, pp. 81–125, 252–270. (*1887* and *1888* also in *Zur Lehre vom Transfiniten*, 1890, Halle.)

1888. 'Mitteilungen zur Lehre vom Transfiniten. II.' *Ibid.*, vol. 92, pp. 240–265. (See *1887* above.)

1894. 'Beiträge zur Begründung der transfiniten Mengenlehre. I.' *Mathematische Annalen*, vol. 46, pp. 481–512. (Translated and edited by Jourdain, in *Contri*-

butions to the Founding of the Theory of Transfinite Numbers, 1915, Chicago, recently reprinted by Dover in New York, pp. 85–136.)

Carnap, Rudolf

1928. Der logische Aufbau der Welt. Berlin.

1937. The Logical Syntax of Language. London. (Expanded translation of *Logische Syntax der Sprache*, 1934, Vienna.)

1942. Introduction to Semantics. Cambridge, Mass.

1943. Formalization of Logic. Cambridge, Mass.

1950. 'Empiricism, semantics, and ontology'. *Revue internationale de Philosophie*, vol. 4, pp. 20–40. (Reprinted by Linsky in *1952* and, with minor changes, by Carnap in *1956* as Supplement A.)

1954. Einführung in die symbolische Logik. Vienna. (See *1958* below.)

1956. Meaning and Necessity, enlarged edition. Chicago. (1947 edition differs only in lacking the supplementary appendices.)

1958. Introduction to Symbolic Logic and its Applications. New York. (Slightly revised English translation of *1954.* Cited section numbers the same.)

Chomsky, Noam

1953. 'Systems of syntactic analysis'. JSL, vol. 18, pp. 242–256.

1957. Syntactic Structures. The Hague.

1958. 'Linguistics, logic, psychology, and computers', in *Computer Programming and Artificial Intelligence*, compiled and edited by John W. Carr, III, Chapel Hill, N. C., pp. 429–454.

Church, Alonzo

1954. Review in JSL, vol. 19, pp. 143–144.

1956. Introduction to Mathematical Logic, vol. 1. Princeton, N. J.

Chwistek, Leon.

1921. 'Antinomje logiki formalnej'. PF, (§ 1.0) vol. 24, pp. 164–171.

1922 (A). 'Über die Antinomien der Prinzipien der Mathematik'. *Mathematische Zeitschrift*, vol. 14, pp. 236–243.

1922 (T). 'Zasady czystej teorji typow', PF, vol. 25, pp. 359–391. (Principles of pure theory of types.)

1924–25. 'The theory of constructive types (Principles of logic and mathematics)'. *Rocznik Polskiego Towarzystwa Matematycznego (Annales de la Société Polonaise de Mathématique)*, vol. 2, pp. 9–48, and vol. 3, pp. 92–141.

1948. The Limits of Science. London. (Revised and enlarged translation of *Granice Nauki*, 1935, Lwow and Warsaw.)

Curry, Haskell B. *A Theory of Formal Deducibility.* Notre Dame, Ind.

Dedekind, Richard. *1888. Was sind und was sollen die Zahlen?* Braunschweig. (English translation in *Essays on the Theory of Numbers*, 1901, Chicago and London, pp. 31–115.)

Dummett, Michael

1955. 'Frege on functions: a reply'. *Philosophical Review*, vol. 64, pp. 96–107.

1956. 'Note: Frege on functions'. *Philosophical Review*, vol. 65, pp. 229–230.

1956. 'Nominalism'. *Philosophical Review*, vol. 65, pp. 491–505.

Farber, Marvin. *1943. The Foundation of Phenomenology*. Cambridge, Mass.

Feigl, Herbert, and *Sellars*, Wilfrid, eds. *1949. Readings in Philosophical Analysis*. New York.

Flew, Antony G. N., ed.

   1951. Essays on Logic and Language, first series. Oxford.
   1953. Essays on Logic and Language, second series. Oxford.

Fraenkel, Abraham A. (See also Bernays-Fraenkel above.)

   1923. Einleitung in die Mengenlehre, ed. 2. Berlin. (Ed. 3, 1928, Berlin, reprinted in 1946, New York.)
   1953. Abstract Set Theory. Amsterdam. (Ed. 2, revised, 1961.)

Fraenkel, Abraham A., and *Bar-Hillel*, Yehoshua. *1958. Foundations of Set Theory*. Amsterdam.

Frege, Gottlob

   1879. Begriffsschrift. Halle. (Ch. 1, §§ 1–12, translated in *1952*, pp. 1–20.)
   1884. Die Grundlagen der Arithmetik. Breslau. (Reprinted with original pagination, and with parallel translation, as *The Foundations of Arithmetic*, 1950, Oxford.)
   1891. Funktion und Begriff. Jena. (Translated in *1952*, pp. 21–41, and in *Mind*, vol. 60 (1951), pp. 168–180.)
   1892 (BG). 'Über Begriff und Gegenstand'. *Vierteljahrsschrift für wissentschaftliche Philosophie*, vol. 16, pp. 192–205. (Translated in *1952*, pp. 42–55, and in *Mind*, vol. 60 (1951), pp. 169–180.)
   1892 (SB). 'Über Sinn und Bedeutung'. *Zeitschrift für Philosophie und philosophische Kritik*, n.s. vol. 100, pp. 25–50. (Translated in *1952*, pp. 56–78, and in *Philosophical Review*, vol. 57 (1948), pp. 209–230; also in Feigl-Sellars, *1949*.)
   1893. Grundgesetze der Arithmetik, vol. 1. Jena. (Selections from foreword, introduction, and §§ 1–7 are translated in *1952*, pp. 137–158, and in the *Monist*, vols. 25–27.)
   1894. Extracts from Frege's review of Husserl in *Zeitschrift für Philosophie und philosophische Kritik*, n.s. vol. 103, pp. 313–332, as translated in *1952*, pp. 79–85.
   1895. 'Kritische Beleuchtung einiger Punkte in E. Schröder's Vorlesungen über die Algebra der Logik'. *Archiv für systematische Philosophie*, vol. 1, pp. 433–456. (Translated in *1952*, pp. 86–106.)
   1896. Lettera del sig. G. Frege all'Editore (dated Jena, 29 Sept.) in *Revue de mathématiques* (*Rivista di matematica*), vol. 6, pp. 53–59.
   1896 (B). 'Über die Begriffsschrift des Herrn Peano und meine eigene'. *Berichte über die Verhandlungen der Königlichen Sächsischen Gesellschaft der Wissenschaften zu Leipzig, Mathematisch-physische Klasse*, vol. 48, pp. 361–378.
   (*Geometry*), *1903*. 'Über die Grundlagen der Geometrie'. *Jahresbericht der Deutschen Mathematiker-Vereinigung*, XII, pp. 319–324, 368–375 (transl. by Szabo as 'The foundations of geometry', *Philosophical Review*, vol. 69 (1960), pp. 3–17); also *1906*, XV, pp. 293–309, 377–403, 423–430.
   1903. Grundgesetze der Arithmetik, vol. 2. Jena. (Selections from §§ 56–57, 86–137, 139–144, 146–147, and *Nachwort* are translated in *1952*, pp. 159–244; see also *Philosophical Review*, vol. 59 (1950) pp. 77–93, 202–220, 332–345.)

1904. 'Was ist eine Funktion?' (*Festschrift Ludwig Boltzmann gewidmet zum sechzigsten Geburtstage 20. Februar 1904*, Leipzig) as translated in *1952*, pp. 107–116.

1910. Discussion with Jourdain as quoted by Bochenski in *1956* or *1961*, § 45.02.

1918. 'Der Gedanke. Eine logische Untersuchung.' *Beiträge zur Philosophie des Deutschen Idealismus*, vol. 1, pp. 57–77. (Transl. by Quinton as 'The thought: a logical inquiry', *Mind*, vol. 65 (1956), pp. 289–311.)

1919. 'Die Verneinung. Eine logische Untersuchung.' *Beiträge zur Philosophie des Deutschen Idealismus*, vol. 1, pp. 143–157, as translated in *1952*, pp. 117–135.

1923. 'Logische Untersuchungen. III: Gedankengefüge'. *Beiträge zur Philosophie des Deutschen Idealismus*, III, pp. 36–51.

1952. *Translations from the Philosophical Writings of Gottlob Frege*, eds. P. T. Geach and Max Black. Oxford. (Revised ed., 1960.)

Geach, Peter T.

1950 (RT). 'Russell's theory of descriptions'. *Analysis*, vol. 10, pp. 84–88. (Reprinted by Macdonald in *1954*.)

1950 (SP). 'Subject and predicate'. *Mind*, vol. 59, pp. 461–482.

1956. 'On Frege's way out'. *Mind*, vol. 65, pp. 408–409.

Goodman, Nelson. *1951. The Structure of Appearance.* Cambridge, Mass. (See also Leonard-Goodman.)

Goodman, Nelson, and *Quine*, W. V. O. *1947.* 'Steps toward a constructive nominalism'. JSL, vol. 12, pp. 105–122.

Grelling, Kurt, and *Nelson*, Leonard. *1908.* 'Bemerkungen zu den Paradoxien von Russell und Burali-Forti'. *Abhandlungen der Fries'schen Schule*, n.s. vol. 2, pp. 301–334.

Grzegorczyk, Andrzej. *1955.* 'The systems of Lesniewski in relation to contemporary logical research'. *Studia Logica*, vol. 3, pp. 77–95.

Hall, Everett W.

1960. Philosophical Systems: A Categorial Analysis. Chicago.

1961. Our Knowledge of Fact and Value. Chapel Hill, N. C.

Hausdorff, Felix. *1927. Mengenlehre.* Berlin and Leipzig. (Ed. 3, enlarged, translated as *Set Theory*, 1957, New York.)

Hermes, Hans. *1939. Semiotik: Eine Theorie der Zeichengestalten als Grundlage für Untersuchungen von formalisierten Sprachen.* (*Forschungen zur Logik und zur Grundlegung der exakten Wissenschaften*, 5, ed. Scholz). Leipzig.

Hertz, Heinrich. *1894. Die Prinzipien der Mechanik.* Leipzig. (English translation *The Principles of Mechanics*, 1956, New York.)

Hilbert, David, and *Bernays*, Paul

1934. Grundlagen der Mathematik, vol. 1. Berlin.

1939. Grundlagen der Mathematik, vol. 2. Berlin.

Hintikka, K. J. J.

1956. 'Identity, variables, and impredicative definitions'. JSL, vol. 21, pp. 225–245.

1957. 'Vicious circle principle and the paradoxes'. JSL, vol. 22, pp. 245–249.

Husserl, Edmund. *1913. Logische Untersuchungen*, ed. 2, revised. Halle.

Jordan, Z. *1945. The Development of Mathematical Logic and of Logical Positivism in Poland between the two Wars.* London.

Jørgensen, Jørgen. *1931. A Treatise of Formal Logic.* London and Copenhagen.

Kalish, Donald. *1952.* 'Logical form'. *Mind*, vol. 66, pp. 57–71.

Kalmar, Lazlo. *1940.* 'On the possibility of definition by recursion'. *Acta Scientiarum Mathematicarum (Szeged)*, vol. 9, pp. 227–232.

Kleene, Stephen C. *1952. Introduction to Metamathematics.* New York and Amsterdam.

Lemmon, E. J. *1958.* 'Quantifiers and modal operators'. *Proceedings of the Aristotelian Society*, vol. 58, pp. 245–268.

Leonard, Henry S., and *Goodman*, Nelson. *1940.* 'The calculus of individuals and its uses'. JSL, vol. 5, pp. 45–55.

Lewis, Clarence I.
   1955. 'The modes of meaning'. *Philosophy and Phenomenological Research*, vol. 4, pp. 236–249. (Reprinted by Linsky in *1952.*)
   1946. An Analysis of Knowledge and Valuation. La Salle, Ill.

Lindenbaum, Adolf. *1931.* 'Bemerkungen zu den vorhergehenden "Bemerkungen..." des Herrn J. v. Neumann'. *Fundamenta Mathematicae*, vol. 17, pp. 335–336.

Linsky, Leonard, ed. *1952. Semantics and the Philosophy of Language.* Urbana, Ill.

Lukasiewicz, Jan
   1910. O Zasadzie Sprzecznosci u Arystotelesa: Studyum krytyczna. Krakow. (On the principle of contradiction in Aristotle: a critical study.)
   1938. 'Der Äquivalenzenkalkül'.[20] *Collectanea Logica*, (§ 2.3) vol. 1.
   1951. 'On variable functors of propositional arguments'. *Proceedings of the Royal Irish Academy*, 54A2 (vol. 54, § A, no. 2), pp. 25–35.
   1953. 'The principle of individuation'. *Aristotelian Society Supplementary Vol.* XXVII, pp. 69–82.
   1957. Aristotle's Syllogistic, ed. 2, enlarged. Oxford. (Ed. 1, 1951, Oxford.)

Macdonald, Margaret, ed. *1954. Philosophy and Analysis.* Oxford.

Martin, R. M.
   1949. 'A note on nominalistic syntax'. JSL, vol. 14, pp. 226–227.
   1958. Truth and Denotation. London.
   1959. Review of Prior, *1957. Mind*, vol. 68, pp. 271–275.

Martin, R. M., and *Woodger*, J. H. *1951.* 'Toward an inscriptional semantics' JSL, vol. 16, pp. 191–203.

McCall, Storrs, ed. Forthcoming. *Polish Logic.* (Selection in translation.)

Moody, Ernest A. *1953. Truth and Consequence in Mediaeval Logic.* Amsterdam.

Myhill, John R. *1953.* 'Arithmetic with creative definitions by induction'. JSL, vol. 18, pp. 115–118.

Neumann, J. von

   1927. 'Zur Hilbertschen Beweistheorie'. *Mathematische Zeitschrift*, vol. 26, pp. 1–46.

   1931. 'Bemerkungen zu den Ausführungen von Herrn St. Lesniewski über meine Arbeit "Zur Hilbertschen Beweistheorie"'. *Fundamenta Mathematicae*, vol. 17, pp. 331–334.

Olds, M. E. *1956*. 'Synonymity: extensional isomorphism'. *Mind*, vol. 65, pp. 473–488.

Parry, William T. *1954*. 'A new symbolism for the propositional calculus'. JSL, vol. 19, pp. 161–168.

Peirce, Charles S. *1902*. 'The simplest mathematics', as printed in *Collected Papers of Charles Sanders Peirce* (eds. Hartshorne and Weiss, 1933, Cambridge, Mass.), vol. 4, paragraphs 227–323, pp. 189–262.

Poincaré, Henri. *1912*. 'La logique de l'infini'. *Scientia*, vol. 12, pp. 1–11.

Prior, Arthur N.

   1955. *Formal Logic*. Oxford. (Revised ed., 1962.)

   1956. 'Definitions, rules and axioms'. *Proceedings of the Aristotelian Society*, n.s. vol. 56, pp. 199–216. (See corrections in same volume.)

   1957. *Time and Modality*. Oxford.

Quine, W. V. O. (See also Goodman-Quine.)

   1936. 'The axiom of reducibility'. *Mind*, vol. 45, pp. 498–500.

   1937. 'New foundations for mathematical logic' (*American Mathematical Monthly*, vol. 44, pp. 70–80) as reprinted, with modifications, in *1953*, pp. 80–101.

   1938. 'Completeness of the propositional calculus'. JSL, vol. 3, pp. 37–40.

   1940. Review in JSL, vol. 5, p. 83. (See also *1951* below.)

   1941. 'Whitehead and the rise of modern logic', in Whitehead, *1941*, pp. 127–163.

   1951. 'Symposium: on what there is. III.' *Aristotelian Society Supplementary Vol.* XXV, pp. 149–160.

   1951 (ML). *Mathematical Logic*, revised ed. of 1940 original. Cambridge, Mass.

   1952. 'The problem of simplifying truth functions'. *American Mathematical Monthly*, vol. 59, pp. 521–531.

   1953. *From a Logical Point of View*. Cambridge, Mass.

   1955. 'On Frege's way out'. *Mind*, vol. 64, pp. 145–159.

   1959. *Methods of Logic*, revised ed. New York. (Ed. 1, 1950, New York.)

   1960. *Word and Object*. New York.

Ramsey, Frank P.

   1925. 'The foundations of mathematics' (*Proceedings of the London Mathematical Society*, ser. 2, vol. 25, pt. 5, pp. 338–384), reprinted as title essay in *1931*, pp. 1–61.

   1926. 'Mathematical logic' (*Encyclopaedia Britannica*, second of the supplementary volumes constituting ed. 13, pp. 830–832) as reprinted in *1931*, pp. 62–81.

   1931. *The Foundations of Mathematics and other Logical Essays*. London.

Reichenbach, Hans

   1948. *Elements of Symbolic Logic*. New York.

   1954. *Nomological Statements and Admissible Operations*. Amsterdam.

Rosenbloom, Paul C. *1950. The Elements of Mathematical Logic.* New York.

Rosser, J. Barkley. *1953. Logic for Mathematicians.* New York, Toronto, London.

Russell, Bertrand (See also Whitehead-Russell.)

    1903. The Principles of Mathematics. London.

    1905. 'On denoting' (*Mind*, n.s. vol. 14, pp. 479–493) as reprinted in *1956*, pp. 41–56. (Also reprinted by Feigl-Sellars in *1949*.)

    1908. 'Mathematical logic as based on the theory of types' (*American Journal of Mathematics*, vol. 30, pp. 222–262) as reprinted in *1956*, pp. 59–102.

    1910. Russell's Introduction to PM, ed. 1, vol. 1.

    1912. The Problems of Philosophy. London.

    1914 (A). 'On the nature of acquaintance' (*Monist*) as reprinted in *1956*, pp. 127–174.

    1914 (K). *Our Knowledge of the External World.* London.

    1918. 'The philosophy of logical atomism' (*Monist*, vols. 28–29) as reprinted in *1956*, pp. 177–281.

    1919. Introduction to Mathematical Philosophy. London. (Ch. 16, 'Descriptions', reprinted by Linsky in *1952*.)

    1924. 'Logical atomism' (*Contemporary British Philosophy*, first series, ed. Muirhead, London) as reprinted in *1956*, pp. 323–343.

    1925. Russell's Introduction and appendices to the second edition of PM, vol. 1.

    1937. Introduction to the second edition of *1903*. London.

    1940. An Inquiry into Meaning and Truth. London.

    1946. The Philosophy of Bertrand Russell, ed. Schilpp. Evanston, Ill.

    1948. Human Knowledge: Its Scope and Limits. New York.

    1950. 'Logical positivism' (*Revue internationale de Philosophie*, vol. 4) as reprinted in *1956*, pp. 367–382.

    1956. Logic and Knowledge: Essays, 1901–1950. London.

    1959. My Philosophical Development. London.

Ryle, Gilbert

    1931. 'Systematically misleading expressions'. *Proceedings of the Aristotelian Society*, vol. 32, pp. 139–170. (Reprinted by Flew in *1951*.)

    1938. 'Categories'. *Proceedings of the Aristotelian Society*, vol. 38, pp. 189–206. (Reprinted by Flew in *1953*.)

Schlick, Moritz. *1932.* 'Form and content, an introduction to philosophical thinking', as printed in *Gesammelte Aufsätze, 1926–1936*, ed. Waismann, 1938, Vienna, pp. 151–249.

Schröder, Ernst. *1891. Vorlesungen über die Algebra der Logik* (*exakte Logik*), vol. 2, pt. 1. Leipzig.

Sierpinski, Waclaw. *1923. Zarys teorji mnogosci*, I., ed. 2, revised. Warsaw. (Outline of theory of sets.)

Standley, Gerald B. *1954.* 'Ideographic computation in the propositional calculus'. JSL, vol. 19, pp. 169–171.

Stenius, Erik. *1960. Wittgenstein's 'Tractatus', a Critical Exposition.* Oxford.

Storer, Thomas F.

   1950. 'On communication'. *Philosophical Studies* (Minneapolis), vol. 1, pp. 33–40.
   1951. 'An analysis of logical positivism'. *Methodos*, vol. 3, pp. 245–272.
   1951. 'On defining 'soluble''. *Analysis*, vol. 11, pp. 134–137.
   1952. 'Linguistic isomorphisms'. *Philosophy of Science*, vol. 19, pp. 77–85.
   1954. 'On defining 'soluble'—reply to Bergmann'. *Analysis*, vol. 14, pp.123–126.

Suppes, Patrick. *1957. Introduction to Logic.* Princeton, N.J.; New York, London, Toronto.

Thomas, Ivo. *1951.* 'Farrago logica'. *Dominican Studies*, vol. 4, pp. 69–79.

Wang, Hao. *1954.* 'The formalization of mathematics'. JSL, vol. 19, pp. 241–266.

Wang, Hao, and *McNaughton*, R. *1953. Les systèmes axiomatiques de la théorie des ensembles.* Paris and Louvain.

Weyl, Hermann. *1949. Philosophy of Mathematics and Natural Science.* Princeton. (Revised and expanded translation of 1927 German original.)

Whitehead, Alfred N.

   1911. An Introduction to Mathematics. London, New York, Toronto.
   1919. An Enquiry concerning the Principles of Natural Knowledge. Cambridge.
   1929. Process and Reality. New York.
   1941. The Philosophy of Alfred North Whitehead, ed. Schilpp. Evanston, Ill.

Whitehead, Alfred N., and *Russell*, Bertrand

   PM *(1910–1913). Principia Mathematica*, ed. 2, 1925, vols. 1–3. Cambridge. (Listed under the original dates of publication, since ed. 2 differs from ed. 1 only in correction of minor errors and Russell's additional introduction and appendices.) (§ 1.0)
   1910. PM, vol. 1.
   1912. PM, vol. 2.
   1913. PM, vol. 3.

Wittgenstein, Ludwig

   1922. Logisch-philosophische Abhandlung. (Annalen der Naturphilosophie, vol. 14, 1921, pp. 185–262) as reprinted in *Tractatus Logico-Philosophicus*, with Introduction by Bertrand Russell. London. (Reprinted with index and new English translation by Pears and McGuinness in 1961.)
   1953. Philosophische Untersuchungen, with parallel translation by Anscombe, in *Philosophical Investigations.* Oxford.
   1956. Bemerkungen über die Grundlagen der Mathematik, eds. von Wright, Rhees, and Anscombe, with parallel translation by Anscombe, in *Remarks on the Foundations of Mathematics.* Oxford.

Woodger, J. H. (See also Martin-Woodger.)

   1937. The Axiomatic Method in Biology. Cambridge. (App. E contains a reformulation of Lesniewski's mereology due to Tarski.)
   1951. 'Science without properties'. *British Journal for the Philosophy of Science*, vol. 2, pp. 193–216.

1952 (BM). 'From biology to mathematics'. *British Journal for the Philosophy of Science*, vol. 3, pp. 1–21.

1952 (BL). *Biology and Language*. Cambridge.

Wundheiler, Luitgard and Alex. *1955*. 'Some logical concepts for syntax', in *Machine Translation of Languages* (eds. W. N. Locke and A. D. Booth, London), pp. 194–207.

Zermelo, Ernst

1908. 'Neuer Beweis für die Möglichkeit einer Wohlordnung'. *Mathematische Annalen*, vol. 65, pp. 107–128.

1908. 'Untersuchungen über die Grundlagen der Mengenlehre. I.' *Ibid.*, vol. 65, pp. 261–268.

11. INDEX

In what follows numerals without prefix refer to pages. Boldface type indicates not only the more important page numbers but also related headings, as if '*q.v.*' were tacitly appended to each boldface expression. For brevity 'see' is used in the sense of 'see also'. To facilitate alphabetization and cross reference, hyphens and numerical indices are disregarded, and the usual conventions of quotation waived, so that an expression may be used autonymously (like Falstaffian honor) to refer to itself or any other *expression* of the same form.

See also the table of contents (vff) and the bibliography (§ 11, 320ff), which is not indexed here. Technical symbols are indexed in § 11.1 below only if represented also outside pages 226–231 and 277–279. Authors named in the bibliography are indexed only when cited on some topic; and notes (§ 9, 306ff) only when self-explanatory out of context, since others can be traced through the numerical references in the text.

11.1 Unalphabetized technical symbols

Ideographic constants of protothetic

φ, Λ, V, ⊣, ⊢, ⊢⊣, —, -o-, φ, -ờ-, ờ, -ờ-, o, -o, o-, φ, φ, -φ, φ-, φ-, ờ-, -ờ 41f, **143** (AP), **226ff** (D1–D21), **232ff**, **289ff**

Constants of ontology

ε **9f**, **12f**, 72ff, **145ff**, 267ff

△, ⊂, =, ≡, ▢ **10ff,** 72ff, 145ff
Λ **10ff**, 47, 115f, 255f, **277** (D76)

~, ∩, ∪ **10**, 233, **277ff** (D74, D77, D79, D83–D85, S99–S103)

∞, ∽ 11

Punctuators: brackets, corners

( ) **143** (AP), 197ff, **226** (D3), **230** (S55)
{ } 10f, **145** (AO), 173, 267–270
⟨ ⟩ 10f, **173**, **274** (D74, D77), **279** (S99)
[ ] In **parenthemes**: 277 (D82, D84), 279 (D98) In **quantifiers**: 39, 112, 114, **143**, 145, **309f** In **meta-linguistic indexes**: 132, 256ff, 266
⌞ ⌟ ⌜ ⌝ **143**, 174, **176ff**, 183ff
⊥ ⊥ **183**ff

11.2 Authors and subjects

-al isomorph v. equi-significant 122

-ality 3, 5, **15**, 30, 33f, 87, 92, **96**, 105, **118ff**, **125ff**, 153, 159, **167f**, **258–266**, **283–289**, **315**, n. 74 See classical, eliminable defined constants.

-ality directives 30, 38, 40, 92, **118ff**, **140ff**, **144f**, 154, 158f, **169f**, 258, 263, 265f, 283, **288**

-ality directives formulated 265f, 288

-ality theses 118, 127, **132**, **139–142**, **144f**, 159, 167, **169f**, **258–266**, **283–288**, n. 74

-ality theses, expressions legitimate as **propositive** or **nominative** 169f, **258ff**, **283ff** See **schemes**.

-ality theses, underived (v. **derivable**) **propositive** or **nominative** 262, 287

-al v. nonextensional **3**, **33f**, 87, 92, **96**, **105**, **118**ff, **121**ff, 315 See **attitude**, **modal**, **conditional**.

coextensive or **equivalent**: of same **extent**, **value**, or — 234f

or **class** as **platonist object 5**, 15, 75, 78, **81**, **119ff**, 131

exter-ior, -nal: outside 11

extralinguistic reference 120 See **names**.

ext–ralogical constant, **postulate**, or application of **mathematics** in **language L** 11, 21, 24f, **28f**, 45, **50–53**, **59–63**, 72ff, 78, 87, **91ff**, 97, 100f, 105f, **108ff**, 112f, 116, **121–126**, 133ff, **136f**, **148ff**, **156**, 160ff, **164–166**, 314f See **counting**, **mereology**, **meta-**, **names**, **semantics**, **spatiotemporal**.

extraneous: outside 11 See **paradox**.

false 9, **100** See **bivalence**, **contradiction**, **nonsense**, **semantic liar paradox**.

family of (**fam**) 104, **278**(D96)

Farber, Marvin n. 30

fewer in **number** 11

fiction See **creative**, **myth**, **nonentity**.

field member of (**mem**) 278(D91)

finite definable 17 See **infinite number** following

expression 174, **177**

logically 247 See **consequence**.

force: **extension** or **value** 235

form 4f, **15f**, 98

-**alization** 4, 24, 36ff, **50**, **89ff**, 96, **106**, 118, **126**, 155f, **167f**, n. 87 See **axiomatization**, **decision**, **grammar**, **interpretation**, **language**.

-**ally impredicative defined** 101

-**al** or **categorial** expression 14

-**al** (v. **material**) mode of **expression** 14, 101, **126**, 167

homomorphs: **equiform expressions** of same — 2, **4**, **15f**, **173**, 176

of **expression** 2f, **4f**, **15f**, 36f, **58ff**, 86, **91**, **96ff**, **105**, 114, 118, 120, **126f**, **128ff**, 162, **167**, **175ff**, 217, 219, 248, 255f, 295, 334 See **alphabetic**, **brackets**, **homonymous**, **ideographic**, **normal**, **platonism**, **systematic ambiguity**.

pure -alism, -**alist** 14, **19**, **24**, **45–66** (*passim*), 71, **74–80**, 84ff, **91**, **93**, 98, 101, 105, **108**, 110, 135, 155f, **158–162**, **165f**, n. 17 See **calculus**, **interpretation**.

-**s** of **constants** and **variables** not predetermined **36f**, 41, **96f**, **118**, **127ff** See **contextual**, **revision**.

founded by, **category introduced** and 214

Fraenkel, Abraham A. **58**, **66**, **71**, **76ff**, 148, nn. 27, 65, 78

free See **creative**, **variables**.

Frege, Gottlob 3, 19, **29f**, **36f**, 39, **43**, 45ff, 49, 51, **55f**, 61, 63, **69**, 71, **73–79**, **81f**, **85**, **91ff**, **119ff**, **128**, **130–133**, **136f**, 142, **146**, 149, 157, 162, 166, **207f**, **223**, 245, 252, 275, **315**, nn. 15, **17**, **30**, **34**, **41**, **43**, **49**, **78**, 83f

frontal language L 107 See **punctuation**.

function 3, **5ff**, 13, **32ff**, 61, 63, 87, 89, 92, **94ff**, 99, 101, **107**, 119ff, **125ff**, 131f, 137, **143ff**, 149, 163, 168, **173**, **188–202**, 210f, **215**, 217ff, 221f,